GREAT ENGINEERS

GREAT
ENGINEERS

By

PROF. C. MATSCHOSS

Translated by

DR. H. STAFFORD HATFIELD

LONDON
G. BELL AND SONS LTD
1939

Printed in Great Britain by The Camelot Press Ltd.
London and Southampton

CONTENTS

v

LIST OF ILLUSTRATIONS

PREFACE

In this volume an attempt is made to give an account of men especially representative of the engineering profession over a space of time of 5,000 years. Since the size of the book was determined in advance by considerations of price, the number of engineers dealt with had to be limited. The selection was the harder because the importance of many engineers not treated of in the book was nevertheless clearly visible in the history of technology. This is particularly true of the great civil engineers, who built roads, canals, bridges, and tunnels. It is to be hoped that this large group of engineers will be described in a special volume from a competent pen, but in any case it will be easy to make a long list of distinguished men whose names are not to be found in these pages. The space allotted is the explanation of this, but it is hoped that if this book is well received, the more obvious omissions in it may later be rectified.

The choice of great engineers is by no means evenly distributed over the various historical ages. We know very little concerning the personalities of the engineers of antiquity, but the works still in existence prove to us that they achieved great things. The nearer we come to our own time, the larger the amount of material at our disposal, and the harder the selection from it, but even in modern times we often find to our regret that engineers have hitherto concerned themselves very little with their eminent predecessors. Only too often, carefully written biographies are still wanting.

'By their works ye shall know them.' That is also true of

great engineers, the content of whose lives is mainly determined by the creative work of their profession. But here much limitation is inevitable, for a full description of the technical work of these men would involve the writing of a history of technology in many volumes. The present task is to describe the man and his personal fate, as far as we have data, and to recognize that no great work is imaginable without a man as its creator.

The reader who desires to go more deeply into the subject may be referred to the bibliography at the end of the book which, however, makes no claim to be exhaustive. In the course of forty years' work in the field of technical history I have already dealt with many of these men from a biographical point of view, and in a few places I have made use of this material.

Technology is not confined within frontiers, and there is nothing in it that anyone can do entirely alone. The threads run from nation to nation and from generation to generation. Much of our engineering work of the present day may be traced to roots at the beginning of history. We Germans have done great pioneering work all over the world, and we are indebted to other nations as much as they are indebted to us.

Generals have never been able to fight their battles alone. Every leader has need of the rank and file. The greatest engineers knew, and willingly recognized, how much of their success they owed to those who co-operated with them. Thousands of unknown engineers and workers spend industrious lives in the service of the work of great men. These unknown workers, whose names are not written down in the book of history, are always to be remembered with gratitude when we celebrate the deeds of the great.

This book is addressed to lovers of technical achievement, and of the men responsible for it, who show by their lives that great deeds are brought about by ideals which are far beyond the mere material valuation of technical work.

Goethe says: 'The best of history's gifts to us is the enthusiasm which it inspires,' and we may hope that this will be
true also of the present work. Enthusiasm for engineering
is more than ever needed to-day, in view of the great tasks
which our times lay upon us.

PREFACE TO THE ENGLISH EDITION

Great Engineers, which had so kind a reception in Germany,
now makes its appearance in English dress. I owe my best
thanks to the energetic publishers and to the able translator
for thus enabling me to lay the book before my many English-
speaking friends as a thank-offering for all the many and
various ways in which they have helped and stimulated me in
the course of my labours in the field of technical history.

My debt to English technical literature is a great one.
Samuel Smiles, in his *Lives of the Engineers*, gave us many
decades ago a wonderful series of descriptive essays. And
for more than thirty years I have been availing myself of
that treasure-house of scientific history, the Science Museum
in South Kensington.

In England and America, a growing recognition of the
cultural value of engineering activity has led to a close study
of technical history. I hope that this book too, in its English
form, may contribute to our admiration of the great engineers
of all nations, for their technical achievements are an essential
part of human history.

THE AUTHOR

Berlin
February 6th, 1939

THE GREAT ENGINEERS OF ANTIQUITY

CONCERNING THE UNKNOWN ENGINEER

TECHNOLOGY, the art of applying in the service of man forces and materials suited to a given task, accompanies humanity in the whole course of its development. It is much older than any history which has come down to us, for it stretches far back into the hundreds of millenniums of pre-history. The line of succession of the engineers working in the technical field goes back no less far. Their achievements are attested by their works even in cases when their names, and everything else connected with their personalities as men, have long ago disappeared into oblivion. This is true of the long aeons of pre-history. How wonderfully did the engineers of the Stone Age manage their brittle material flint, forming it into weapons, tools and all sorts of instruments; how greatly did they develop metallurgy after they had succeeded in taming fire and making of it their most valuable domestic ally! Again and again we are surprised to see how well they managed, long before the dawn of history, the casting in bronze of works of high artistic value. They raised mighty monuments in stone, concerning the purpose of which we are still in doubt. We talk of the graves of the giants, Stonehenge in the South of England, and Menhir in the North of France. We are scarcely able even to-day to explain how works of this sort could be carried out with the primitive appliances of those times. Primitive man created the first weapons acting at a distance, bows and blowpipes; he crossed rivers and seas in his ships, using the wind in their sails as motive power. He irrigated his land, tamed men and animals, invented spinning and weaving, and created these fundamental elements of technology upon which later ages, counted as part of history, were able to build, and so bring great works to fruition.

The first great civilized empires arose in China and India, in Mesopotamia and Egypt, in the regions drained by great rivers, which fertilized with their water and mud the land through which they flowed. It was thus that the foundations of a culture were laid. In such regions, food was obtainable in quantities sufficient to feed, in addition to the producers, great numbers devoting themselves to other tasks than the mere struggle for daily bread. In these old civilizations of China and India, and of Sumeria, Babylonia, Assyria, and Egypt, offspring of the Nile, the engineers of historical times were given their first great task. The problem was to irrigate large stretches of country, a matter of keeping great water-courses in their beds, and learning how to make canals and regulate rivers. Water transport called for efficient ships, and safe and spacious harbours. The growing towns had to be safeguarded from enemy attack by strong fortifications. They had to be supplied with fresh water, and their sewage had to be disposed of. Rulers demanded in their lifetime wonderful palaces, and after their death great monuments, which reached their highest development in Egypt with the building of the Pyramids. In addition to these living rulers, there were the gods to be honoured by great temples, which again gave rise to extensive organizations, presenting in their turn new problems for the engineer.

War, as old as humanity, called upon the engineer to create more and more effective weapons, some of which soon took the form of powerful machines. Trade developed increasingly, and here again much depended upon invention and progress. Another great field of work was opened up to the engineer. If we were to discuss all the directions in which engineering was essential, we should be writing a history of technology.

In ancient times there was as yet no division of engineering into those numerous special branches with which we are familiar to-day. The names attached to the different callings have also changed through the centuries. The old Greek word 'architect' signifies a person having the direction of building, but the title was by no means limited to the business of erecting buildings in the narrower sense. The architect of antiquity was concerned with all branches of the technology of his time. At one time he was erecting a building, at another developing irrigation, at another building ships and machines; indeed, as we shall see shortly, Vitruvius reckons fine mechanism as part of an architect's business. We are thus justified in applying the present-day notion of engineer to all these fields of activity.

The engineers of antiquity relied chiefly on the force of human muscles for their power, and the mighty monuments of those ages could not have been erected without big armies of workers obedient to a single will. The engineer was the commander of an army, an organizer of human power, who had to think out things in advance for many thousands of persons, collecting at the decisive moment all their forces, and directing them according to his will. Here he becomes comparable to the general of an army, and it was not uncommon, as in Roman times, for the chief of an army to be also a great military engineer. The Egyptian temples were not only places of worship, but formed great economic units, like the estates of the German emperors of the Middle Ages, where also a great majority of technical works had to be carried out. The priests built, tilled the soil, and in addition, developed the arts to their highest point. These temples had in their service many engineers, in fact they were recruited among the priesthood; we may actually speak of engineer priests.

The distinction was made very early between the engineer

who directed the work, and the skilled worker, just as indispensable in the carrying out of special work in which he had the necessary training. It was already common in antiquity to talk of mechanics and machine builders, and a distinction was made between those who built the machine and those who worked it. The latter were called 'organists,' where we to-day use the term 'machinists.' The education of engineers was accomplished by apprenticeship, present in the Middle Ages in a highly developed form. Care was also taken that experience should be written down and collected, and here and there—as in ancient Egypt—these written experiences were stereotyped to a dogma, which hindered further development. A technical literature came into being, forming an essential contribution to the transmission of experience from one generation to the next.

While the engineers of prehistoric times naturally remain anonymous, we yet find even in antiquity very few names to remind us that the innumerable great engineering works were created by living men. The history of all ages teaches us that great deeds are unimaginable without great men. But what the names of these men were, how they lived, what were their ideas about their work, all this is almost entirely outside our knowledge. Civilization could not have been developed without the work of engineers, but it was not considered necessary to enter their names in the book of history along with those of princes and kings, statesmen and generals. Hence the little that we know of those engineers of long past times will never be more than a few scraps here and there. But we will be thankful for the little that the industry of the learned has dug out of old writings, monuments, and documents, even if it is of no great help in enabling us to add anything of importance to the great works themselves.

THE GREAT YU (2283 B.C.)

One of the old Chinese classics tells us how China suffered under a widespread deluge 4,200 years ago. This deluge was certainly not the first, and as we know to-day, not the last. The Emperor Yau had his engineer build great waterworks, dykes, and dams. But the water was not mastered in this way. The Emperor then determined to call in the hydraulic engineer Yu, and he carried out the work with great success in eight years. He studied the peculiarities of the rivers, and showed a genius for turning the force of the water to his purpose; his method of working is still used in the control of rivers. But the people acclaimed the engineer Yu as 'the Great Yu'; in those days the work of an engineer was evidently appreciated. After the death of the Emperor Shun, Yu became Emperor of China, because he had saved lost land from the water. Even at the present day, we see everywhere on the rivers temples in which prayers may be said to this great hydraulic engineer of China. The old chronicles tell us a good deal more about water regulation, which could only have been performed by first-rate engineers. There were already in those ancient times great waterways for ships, which rendered possible a sufficient volume of trade in this densely populated country.

ABOUT THE GREAT EGYPTIAN ENGINEERS

Egypt with its mighty buildings was for thousands of years a technical country of the first rank. Engineers were already highly esteemed in the time of the first dynasty. Imhotep, a small statue of whom is to be seen in the Berlin Egyptological Museum, was the son of an architect. He chose the career of his fathers and built, almost 5,000 years ago under the Pharaoh Zoser, the famous great step pyramid of Sakarra.

He was considered to be the actual inventor of building in stone, he was master of the 'eternal stones,' which the ancient Egyptians, with their sense of eternity, well understood how to use in their vast buildings. In those days there was a great enthusiasm for building. Even royal princes were proud to call themselves overseers of the king's works, that is to say master builders. But these Egyptian engineers were much concerned about their reputation with posterity; they desired like their rulers to live on in the memory of men, so they set great store by high and magnificent titles, which, inscribed on their monuments, were to tell the living, but more especially posterity, how great was the work which they had accomplished. Imhotep calls himself Chancellor of the Kings of Lower Egypt, Keeper of the Great House, Hereditary High Priest. He was a carpenter, he knew how to manage wood and stone, but he also understood the irrigation of land and saved Egypt from famine. Besides all this, he was an astronomer and a physician. He lived on in the memory of men as a clever and ever helpful man, and temples were built to him for centuries later. Divine honours were paid to him as a great healer of the sick, and so an engineer became the God of Healing. The Greeks recognized in him their own physician-god Aesculapius, and paid divine honours to both.

ENENE

Twelve hundred years later, under the Pharaoh Amenophis I (1557–1501 B.C.) we have the work of the engineer and architect Enene. He was still living under the reign of Thutmosis III (1501–1447 B.C.) and the famous Queen Hatshepsut. Enene had hewn two great obelisks out of the vast granite quarries at Assuan, transported them on big cargo ships, and erected these immense masses successfully in front of the palace temple. This was a great feat, and we readily understand the pride with which he points out expressly that he carried out this task without a single accident. But the Egyptians' love of titles comes out very clearly on their tombs. The longing to live on in man's memory in a way desired by themselves overcomes every restraint of modesty. Long rows of titles are especially popular; one man has on his monument more than forty offices, having put down all which he held throughout his life. All these great men had as subordinates numbers of craftsmen and workmen, organized like soldiers in platoons. Headed by their standard bearers these march past their master. As leader of each we have the 'over-workmen.' Our Enene calls himself Pasha, Count, Chief of all the Works at Karnak, overseer of the double houses of silver and gold; he seals all contracts. He is the chief manager of the double granary: 'I was the highest director of every work, all workshops were under my orders, the overseers acted for me, I made up the accounts.' He was fed from the king's own table, and at the end of this epitaph composed by himself, he says: 'I was great beyond all conception, I was always powerful in peace, and had no misfortunes. My years were passed in happiness. I was no traitor and no shirker, and I never did wrong. I was the overseer of all overseers and made no mistakes. I always obeyed the orders of those above me, and I never blasphemed against holy things.'

SENEMUT AND BEKENCHONS

The first of these also lived around 1500 B.C. under Queen Hatshepsut, who was so fond of him that she even entrusted the education of her daughter to him. His monument is to be found to-day in the Berlin Museum. He too combined in himself every imaginable title: 'I was the greatest of the great in the whole land. One who was admitted alone to audience in the High Council. I was the overseer of overseers. I was one to whom all occurrences in Egypt were reported, I was a nobleman who was obeyed; more still: I had access to all the writings of the prophets. There was nothing I did not

know of what was written from the beginning of things.'
Senemut was also a great artist. But at his time only the
patron was named, and not the creator of the work. But
Senemut thought out a way of getting round this edict, and
he was successful. He had to build for the queen a temple
with two great courts. From these courts one could enter
single small rooms, the doors of which opened inward, so
that the opened door covered a large surface of the stone.
The High Priest, according to tradition, was the first to enter
and the last to leave these rooms. The doors were then
closed and so no one ever had an opportunity to see the part
of the wall covered by the door. It was on this that Senemut
based his plan. He put on the wall a bas-relief of himself
kneeling with his face towards the altar and an inscription
with his name and titles. This was blasphemy, since only the
king, himself a God, had the right to place his likeness in the
temple. When the queen, his friend and protectress, died, she
was succeeded by her brother. He was suspicious of all of
whom the queen had been fond. The secret of Senemut was
betrayed, and all his images were demolished by the pick-
axe. Only in one small dark room was his image overlooked
by the destroyer, and in this way his desire was fulfilled after
all when the temple was excavated. We know his likeness
and his deeds.

The statue of another great Egyptian engineer, Bekenchons, is in the Glyptothek in Munich. He also acted in
accordance with the song of the harpist of the Hyksos age:
'Forget not to praise yourself with joyful heart, and follow
your heart as long as you live.' He lived under Rameses II
(1293–1225 B.C.). He was educated at a sort of military
school, and early displayed the qualities of leadership. He
rose higher and higher in his career and became a priest in the
temple of Aman, the richest god. He also erected wonderful
granite obelisks, 'the beauty of which comes near to heaven.'
But he too has for his chief desire that his name should go
down to posterity for ever. All who live upon earth after

1. THE GREAT YU
From a Chinese drawing

2. BEKENCHONS
Glyptothek, Munich

3. ARCHIMEDES of SYRACUSE, *c*.287–212 B.C.

4. APOLLODORUS, A.D. 98–117
Glyptothek, Munich

him for millions of years, and who are capable of understanding true worth, are to know what a valuable servant of his master he was, discreet and just ! 'I loved the truth and hated lies, I was a good father to those set under me, I had both hands on the tiller of the State, I was the helmsman. I am to-day happier than yesterday, and to-morrow the God may increase my happiness still more.'

This insistent wish of the great Egyptian engineers to secure a reputation with posterity seems to us rather curious in the form chosen by them, but these high-flown words which they chose and used according to the custom of the time were less important than their deeds, which we still admire to-day.

GREAT ENGINEERS OF CLASSICAL ANTIQUITY

Egypt had already passed the zenith of her development, when the Greeks were fighting for Troy. Homer created out of an historical event the great epic known to the whole of the western civilized world. The mist of early poetic mythology soon clears to show Greek history with its migrations, great feats of colonization, incessant wars and political struggles. But at the same time great technical achievements came into being. The clear critical understanding of the Greeks led them to the sources of science. Their profound spirit made of them world-famous philosophers; mathematics and science are indebted to them for their foundations. Great works throughout the whole range in space and time of Greek civilization are clear evidence of the powers of their engineers. But of the men who were their creators, we rarely know even the names. Frequently we are able to learn only from the work a little of their lives, their training, and method of working, of their joys and cares. Let us put together a few of the things which investigators in this field are able to report. The name, a shadow often hardly recognizable, distorted in the course of centuries of tradition, may at least remind us that here also the great work had to be created by a living man.

Thales, the engineer from Miletus, one of the seven wise men of the East, lived around 585, in the sixth century before Christ. Legend represents him, so Diels tells us, sometimes as an absent-minded student, and at others as an adroit business man who speculated successfully in oil. He was at any rate at home in astronomy, for he is said by the chroniclers to have correctly foretold an eclipse of the sun. As a man immersed in practical affairs, he certainly also worked successfully at the technical problems of his time, particularly those of hydraulic engineering.

The famous bridge of boats over which the king of Persia brought great armies from Asia to Europe across the Hellespont, is connected with the name of notable engineers. Herodotus tells us that on his great journey to Samos he saw a picture representing the bridge of boats over which Darius (521–486 B.C.) led his soldiers across the Bosphorus into Scythia. Mandrocles, the constructor of the bridge, gave as a votive offering to the famous temple of Hera in Samos a picture with the inscription:

'Mandrocles, who lately built the bridge over the waters of the Bosphorus, dedicated this picture to the honour of Hera. He won for himself a laurel crown, for the Samians world renown, and the completed work was also praised by the king.'

The king sees from his throne the troops entering the enemy's country by way of this technical masterpiece. Herodotus saw in this temple of Hera in Samos one of the finest buildings of the world known to him, and the latest German excavations give us some idea of its beauty.

At a later time, Harpalos built for the Persian King Xerxes the famous bridge of boats over which the mighty Persian armies marched into Greece. A further master work of technology was also created on Samos. The engineer Eupalinos drove a tunnel over 3,000 feet long through the mountain of Kastro, for the purpose of bringing water from the springs into the town. The tunnel was driven simultaneously from the two ends. This tells us how far even at that time the foundations of science had been created, for such a success to be possible here in the middle of the sixth century B.C. Here also, German archaeology has enabled us fully to appreciate the great achievement of this engineer.

Pythagoras also grew up in Samos, and became one of the great founders of mathematics. One of the great builders of classical cities was Hippodamos. He came from Miletus and lived around 450 B.C. Pericles gave him the work of planning the suburb of Athens, Piraeus. The streets crossed one another at right angles, dividing up the whole site in equal blocks. One spoke in classical times of the system of Hippodamos. It was applied in Miletus, Alexandria, and Priene. Later, the plans of Roman camps and many Roman towns remind us of it. Aristophanes describes in his *Birds* how he planned the town correctly with ruler and compass. In the middle was the market place, with straight streets radiating in all directions from it. This plan was revived at the beginning of the eighteenth century in Karlsruhe. Hippodamos is taken by Diels as a representative of that school of Greek thought according to which even the life of man is finally nothing but a problem in calculation. They would have no more to do with anything irrational, and men were to be governed by reason, *ratio*. They puzzled their heads over the problem of squaring the circle; everything had to be rationalized. Thus the problems of a time much nearer to us had their beginnings far more than 2,000 years ago.

Great work in the art of war was accomplished by classical engineers. The tyrant of Syracuse, Dionysius, was only able to defend himself from the Carthaginians by the aid of great technical achievement. He called together from all sides engineers to his town, and he gave them the problem of building new forms of weapons for hurling projectiles, and so at that time the ancient simple bow was already developed into great catapults, depending for their power on bundles of cords twisted together. Dionysius was also wise enough to reward his engineers adequately for this achievement, for it was finally the success of their machines that prevented Sicily and Italy from being conquered by the Carthaginians. These new weapons are said to have been used for the first time in 397 B.C. with great effect in a siege on the west coast of Sicily. One hundred and eighty-five years later, in the year 212 B.C., Syracuse again drew into the service of the city the famous mathematician and engineer Archimedes, who applied his great knowledge to the construction of powerful military machines of all sorts.

Plutarch tells us how the war machines of Archimedes hurled massive stone projectiles at the advancing Romans, putting the legions in disorder and forcing them to flee. On the sea coast, the mighty power of the machines was used to sink the Roman ships. Other machines again, furnished with iron hands or hooks like a crane's beak, lifted the fore-part of the ship out of water, while others again even twisted the ships round, and finally threw them on the rocks. But the most dreadful sight was to see a whole ship lifted right out of the water by the machines, shaken to and fro, and finally thrown back into the sea. The Roman general Marcellus would have brought up great siege catapults, but these were completely destroyed by Archimedes' machines. The Romans believed that the new machines would certainly fire over their heads if they ran right up to the walls. But the great engineer had also provided for this by setting up short-range weapons behind the wall, and these defeated the attack irresistibly. The Romans are said finally to have been thrown into a state of panic by the mere sight of a bit of rope or wood appearing over the wall. They took even this for a new machine of Archimedes, and had no

appetite for a closer acquaintance with it. Marcellus therefore determined, for fear of the machines, to stop all attacks
and attempt to enclose the enemy and reduce him by
hunger.

We know how, after years of siege, the town fell into the
hands of the Romans, and how a soldier, disobeying his
general's orders, struck down the savant, who did not wish
to be disturbed in his calculations. Later, Cicero brought
the grave of Archimedes to light on a visit to the town,
and the Roman is said to have ordered a cylinder and a
sphere to be placed upon his grave, for he was the first
to calculate the cubic contents of these two solids. We are
comparatively well informed about these old machines, the
great one-armed siege weapons, the ballistae, and the two-
armed catapults, for here the engineer was in the front ranks
of the general fighting for power. His achievements had a
large share in deciding the fate of the nation, so it is just
to these achievements that great attention has been paid.
Reconstruction in modern times of the old Greek and Roman
weapons has shown how efficient they were compared with
the great clumsy weapons worked by gravity, which were the
only ones known in the early Middle Ages before the coming
of gunpowder. Firearms had already been terrifying
nations at war for a century, when these ancient torsion
weapons were rediscovered, and regarded for a long time
as more effective than the cannon of their day.

Ctesibios of Alexandria is called by Diels the king of
classical engineers. He lived under Ptolemy Philadelphos
(285–227 B.C.). He invented the water organ and many
other forms of apparatus operated by air pressure. He constructed efficient projective machines, which are also said to
have been operated by air pressure. He was the inventor
of the fire syringe. But there is now said to have been a
later Ctesibios, surnamed the Bather, who lived about a
hundred years after, and the learned are not yet certain
which of the two invented this or that. In any case, later

writers have given us much information concerning the works of Ctesibios.

Philo of Byzantium, who lived around 260–200 B.C. may also be reckoned among the great inventors and engineers of his time. He made use of the scientific knowledge which he possessed to design a number of interesting devices, and constructed those automatic toys which were so widely popular in his day. The contemporary engineer may note that, according to Beck, Philo already knew the Cardan suspension and used it in his machines. We should not forget that Philo made a machine gun—a magazine weapon— in which after every shot of the arrow a new arrow was automatically brought into the groove; this machine was invented by Dionysius of Alexandria.

In our day the names of seven famous engineers were found by chance written on a bit of papyrus. These seven were far-famed as engineers two centuries before our era. Of four of them we know nothing to-day, and very little of the three others. Among them was Diades. He built great siege machines for the Macedonian king Philip, and went to the war with Alexander the Great. Diels shows us in his *Antiken Technik* how this Diades conducted the famous siege of Tyre. He, a literary writer of history, is surprised that the historians have given such full reports of the siege itself. They go into all the details. The name of the soldier who was the first to climb the wall has been transmitted to us by history, 'but the historians know nothing of the engineer who conducted this and all other sieges in Alexander's campaigns, who wrote a textbook of his art, describing his inventions: the siege tower on wheels, new forms of ram, drawbridges, and other war machines. They in fact despised, as did the rest of the ancient world, the technical man.'

What is the reason for the fact that the ancient world concerned itself so little with even the successful engineer ? This want of respect extended to the artist as well. 'While men worship images of the gods, they despise those who make them,' says Seneca. It has been said of the Greeks that they invented not only science, but scientific arrogance. Plato, in his ideal state will not hear of the citizens whose occupation is of a practical description taking any part in the education of the ruling classes. Even great artists such as Phidias were looked upon as mere craftsmen. It was not considered gentlemanly to work with one's hands; speech-making, thinking, writing, and ruling were the only dignified occupations for a free man. This contempt for practical work was increased by the fact that slaves were put to it in ever-increasing numbers, and the contempt for a slave was carried over to the sort of work which he did. Even in Germany the time is not so long past when it was thought necessary to couple respect for intellectual work with contempt for first-rate technical work. Martial's advice: 'make the fool of the family an architect,' was considered by many teachers to be applicable quite generally to all technical occupations.

The development of the Roman Empire set the engineers great tasks. We still admire to-day those ancient buildings which have been preserved. But the greatest achievement of Roman technical work was the making of roads. Rome's military leaders covered the empire with a network of highways. A country was with good reason only considered to be conquered when the building of good roads throughout it had created the possibility of making quick changes in military dispositions. These Roman military engineers built over 47,000 miles of roads and many of the great Roman generals may with justice be accounted also great civil engineers. In the time of the Caesars, when Rome's empire over the known world reached its highest development, we find renowned engineers.

Apollodorus of Damascus, the Emperor Trajan's architect (A.D. 98–117), was one of the most distinguished engineers of antiquity. He built roads on a large scale, constructed the stone bridge over the Danube at the Iron Gate, and also did great things in the way of harbour building. Trajan's reign is regarded as one of the greatest periods of ancient engineering art. Trajan's successor Hadrian, like Trajan himself, was imbued with a passion for building, and built his own Mausoleum in Rome, now known as Castel S. Angelo. It is said that he murdered his architect in anger, because he incautiously showed his conceit by criticising his imperial master's design.

VITRUVIUS AND HERO

All that is known to us of Vitruvius is that he was an engineer concerned with the construction and use of the catapults and ballistae in the army of the Emperor Augustus. He was also actively concerned with the construction of the water supply of Rome in about 20 B.C. His famous ten books on architecture—which in fact are a small book with ten divisions—were written some time between 40–28 B.C. Vitruvius was a contemporary of Cicero, and an old man in the year 28 B.C., receiving a pension from the State for his services. His book shows us how comprehensive the conception of architecture still was in those days. For Vitruvius includes in it not only building, but also the construction of machines, more particularly war machines, and small mechanisms—instruments, as we should say. He repeatedly emphasizes the fact that he had gone to Greek sources for material, and much of the knowledge of ancient times has come to us through him alone. But Vitruvius had a great deal of experience of his own, being by profession an engineer, and his descriptions bear the stamp of the practical man.

But he does not write only for the engineer; his importance lies rather in his endeavour to give the layman a notion of the engineer's field of work. Anyone wishing to enter technical work as a professional architect must, according to Vitruvius, 'possess not only natural gifts, but also keenness to learn, for neither genius without knowledge, nor knowledge without genius suffices for the complete artist. He must be ready with a pen, skilled in drawing, trained in geometry, not ignorant of optics, acquainted with arithmetic, learned in history, diligent in listening to philosophers, understand music, have some knowledge of medicine and of law, and must have studied the stars and the courses of the heavenly bodies.'

We see how great a value was placed by this engineer nearly 2,000 years ago on a wide range in engineering education. He also goes on to give good reasons for the necessity of his requirements in practical work. Furthermore, he does not forget to demand in the engineer high ethical standard and nobility of character. The engineer is not to be impertinent, but obliging, he is to be conscientious, and not avaricious; he is not to be over-eager for contracts, but must maintain his dignity tactfully. Philosophy makes these demands upon him, 'for no work can in fact flourish without conscientiousness and honesty of mind.'

The need for some knowledge of music arises according to Vitruvius out of work with torsion machines. The twisted cords were tuned by ear, and the sound amplifiers which were put in theatres under the rows of seats had also to be tuned by the ear. The whole of architecture is divided by the author into three parts: building, clock making, and machine construction. Practical hints concerning all that has to be taken into consideration, follow in the next chapters. Then we have a treatise on building materials, the different forms of masonry are described at length, and then the actual forms and styles of building are fully treated. Not only the architect in the narrower sense finds in this book important data for his profession; the building engineer, the machine constructor, and the mechanic are not forgotten.

In the preface to the ninth chapter Vitruvius expresses his surprise that the ancient Greeks showered the highest

CE

distinctions upon victors in the Olympic Games, while no one thought of the writers whose work was of the greatest value for all times, and for all nations. Those who have handed on valuable knowledge should not only be decorated with palm branches and wreaths, but also accorded triumphs; indeed, those with especial achievements to their credit should be given a place among the gods.

Among the machines he describes are all sorts of lifting appliances, water elevators, and the first prime mover—a water-wheel for driving corn mills. He gives especial attention, with good reason, to the pump invented by Ctesibios, an excellent two-cylinder piston pump frequently used by the Romans in his time. A pump of this sort dating from Roman times and used as a fire engine, has been found in Trèves. Even the water organ is not forgotten. The taximeter itself is also described by Vitruvius as a long-known invention. The revolutions of the carriage wheel measure the distance, and a device allows small stones or balls to fall into a box after a certain distance has been passed over, so that at the end of the journey it is only necessary to count the balls in order to know how far one has travelled. Also, he does not omit to mention that the balls may be allowed to fall into a bronze vessel, so that one hears the passage of every mile. The fact that Vitruvius gives a detailed account of war machines is very natural in view of the importance of artillery in war.

We learn at one point something which is hardly unfamiliar to us, namely that the architects of antiquity did not always keep within their own estimates, and he praises the Greek town of Ephesus, which made a law that an architect, before carrying out an order for the State, had to hand in an estimate which he had to guarantee by his own fortune. If the actual cost exceeded the estimate by not more than 25 per cent., the State covered it by a grant. But if the actual costs were further in excess, the architect had to pay the excess out of his own pocket. If he did not exceed his estimate at all, he received a special distinction. Vitruvius adds to this account the wish: 'if only the immortal gods had decreed that such a law existed also for the Roman people, and not only in respect of national, but also of private construction !' He believed that many persons who knew nothing at all about the business, would then be afraid of it, and that the architects would be compelled to calculate the costs more carefully beforehand. This also gives us a little insight into the troubles of patrons and their architects, troubles which do not seem to have changed very much with the passage of the centuries.

A second technical writer, Hero of Alexandria, emerges for us along with Vitruvius out of the shadowy figures of the engineers of antiquity. Neither, probably, was an engineer of the first rank, and their contemporaries would be surprised at our paying so much attention to them as compared with many other and greater scientific and technical men who were their predecessors or contemporaries. The reason is that they were not only engaged in practice, but have given us full accounts of the thoughts and deeds of others, as well as of their own experience, and that we are still able to study their writings to-day. When the ancient world was rediscovered a few centuries ago, the works of these men played a great part; they were studied in as much detail as the Bible, and all that was preserved in them of the knowledge of long past times, was greatly admired. They were re-published, and commentated again and again; now and then, this very commentary only made them more obscure. The literature on Vitruvius and Hero kept on growing into our own times, and attempts will continue at a solution of the riddles which they still present to us. But as far as their actual lives are concerned, both of them remain no more than shadows.

We have a choice of five centuries in dating Hero's life on earth. Some maintain that he must have lived in the third century B.C., others in the second century A.D. The present position of this scientific investigation puts him in the first century A.D. Hero in his writings has always an eye to practical applications. He has no great interest in pure science, and even believes that philosophy, so highly esteemed in his day, is less essential than the construction of guns to a quiet life, the highest aim of earthly wisdom; guns are more important than all the chatter of philosophers. Hero had himself experience of the art of war.

His writings naturally contain not only the results of his own technical work, but are, like those of Vitruvius, a collection of what others had thought and done for centuries before. Apart from Hero's strictly mathematical writings, we find in his work on surveying a description of measuring instruments, even at this early date. He tells us how levelling is carried out, describes the construction of shafts, adits and tunnels, and ways of measuring distances over land and sea. One of his works which has attracted most attention is the chapter on pressure apparatus and on puppet theatres. But he also writes about water clocks, cranes, and many other subjects as well. An especially great part is played by the theory of the lever, which he also uses everywhere with great skill. Many technical and physical devices described by him in detail serve the purpose of producing surprise and amusement. The ancients were very fond of such mechanical toys, as were also the Middle Ages, and later the seventeenth and eighteenth centuries, where automatic operation, now so familiar to us, gave the greatest pleasure. What seemed like miracles were worked with water, heated air, and even with steam. Hero built little mechanical theatres and astonished the people in the courts of the temples. Tables which moved of themselves towards the beholder, and on which he saw played scenes from the life of Bacchus or Hercules, delighted visitors. A bronze god is supplied, unseen by the visitor, with steam from a small boiler in the cellar; this comes out of an opening in his mouth, and the god is seen to be breathing. The steam is then turned off by the priest, it condenses, a vacuum is formed, and the god drinks with pleasure the wine or other liquid oblation from a bowl held to his lips. The priests will have taken care that this wine was not wasted—'what the idol eats, the priest digests.' The expansive force of heated air was used for the mysterious opening and closing of temple doors.

Most famous of all Hero's inventions is his aeolipile, a hollow metal ball pivoted about a vertical axis, with two short pipes bent at right angles coming out of opposite sides. A flame under it boils water in it, the steam rushes out through the pipes, and turns the ball by its reaction. This was the first steam reaction turbine. Anyone discussing these latest and mightiest of heat engines, which generate electric current in our central stations at many millions of horse-power, or drive our greatest ships over the sea, cannot but call Hero to mind. Fountains of the most varied description were a joy to the great nobles in the gardens of Alexandria and in other places in the ancient world. The princes of the Renaissance also learned from Hero. Men such as Leonardo da Vinci, Albrecht Dürer and Galileo paid the greatest attention to his writings. A favourite entertainment was given by using water and air pressure to make models of birds sing, or to sound trumpets. More practical appliances were fire engines, and we even find coin-in-slot machines like those of the present day. Priests, who thought not only of eternity but of making money here and now, made use of holy water machines, which gave the faithful his ration of the water only when he had paid his obolus. The mechanical theatre was not an invention of Hero. It was already giving pleasure in the third century B.C. We may at any rate see from these remarks the level to which knowledge of physics and mechanics had attained. If this knowledge was frequently used for trivial purposes, it yet contained the seed of many applications on a large scale in later times, and so Hero, though we know little of his life, is still living for us in our own times.

II

FROM THE FALL OF THE ROMAN EMPIRE TO THE DEVELOPMENT OF MODERN TECHNOLOGY IN THE EIGHTEENTH CENTURY

WAR AND CHURCH AS CLIENTS

THE Roman Empire at its height seemed built for eternity. It fell apart when its fund of great ideas which had held it together was exhausted, and the smouldering fire of patriotism, the source of the greatness of ancient Rome, finally died out in a welter of races. New and powerful peoples destroyed and built up again. A new world power, the Christian Church, came into being. There was war of all against all. This terrible and warlike time is given the all-too-peaceful name of the migration of the nations. Destruction did not stop at the work of the engineers. Buildings and whole towns were annihilated. Roads and bridges fell into ruin. Much of the higher arts of industry were forgotten, but war itself had need of technology.

The smith was held in high honour by the northern races. An old English document tells us that he 'ate at the table of the king.' The product of his art—the sword—was celebrated in Saga and legend as greatly as the hero who bore it. These warriors set a higher value on a good sword than on gold and jewels. We think of Weyland the Smith, of the warrior Siegfried, when we call to mind how highly this side of the engineer's work, born out of struggle and working for war, was valued by the nations. Offensive and defensive weapons of the most varied sort had to be developed and constructed.

But not only were the knight and his horse protected by iron armour, his house was surrounded by stone walls and high towers, and became a stronghold. And the great towns, now growing rapidly, learned to protect themselves in the same way. The art of fortification was developed more and more. Wherever we look, we already find examples of high engineering art in the early Middle Ages, though it is only rarely that we are able to name a great man. We are again among the unknown soldiers of technology.

Another great originator and patron of high engineering achievement in the Middle Ages was the Church. Great buildings were put up in monasteries and towns to the honour of God and as a witness to that faith in God and his Saints which permeated the whole of existence. But what was an honour to God, was also an honour to one's own town, and so also an honour to the builders, the patron, and the architect. In this way there came into being, in the early Middle Ages, the wonderful churches, minsters and cathedrals in North France, England, and the old German towns, buildings which excite to-day our wonder and admiration for their artistic expressiveness, and also on account of their sovereign mastery of material and their high technical achievement. Long before the word 'engineer' was invented, engineering works of the highest class were in existence, and though the professional term 'architect' rarely or never appears in mediaeval documents, it would be a mistake to conclude from this that architects did not exist.

Certain romantically minded persons, who do not think it necessary to make themselves acquainted with the nature of great technical creative work, would actually have us believe that these wonders of architecture are a sort of collective product, stone having been added to stone only by the eager faith of the many. These structures suddenly grew up everywhere, it is said, upon the soil of faith, like the trees of the forests and the flowers of the fields. Nothing could be more wrong-headed than this view. Great deeds always

imply great men. True, the life of a single man was too short
to begin and complete such works. Whole generations of
men built these cathedrals, which often give us the clearest
signs in their history of changing times and architects. The
fact that we do not know any names would be no proof, even
if it were true, that the architects themselves did not live. It
is, furthermore, false. Careful historical investigation has
made us acquainted with the names of a great number of
mediaeval architects, but they were not architects in our
sense, but simple stonemasons, members on an equal footing
of the building undertaking, which was organized on the
guild system. Just as almost into our own times the designers
of machines were recruited from the mechanics working at
the bench, so a training in the stonemason's craft was the
foundation for the career of the great architect, who, when
he had the talent in him for great works, acquired, from his
apprenticeship and from travels to great buildings, the
knowledge necessary for his art. The building guild was
also a treasure-house of important technical experience,
which was there collected and preserved. Those mystery-
loving times also laid special stress upon the preservation of
trade and professional secrets, but it may also be that in those
days before the coming of American publicity, many a pious
architect—monks and priests were sometimes among these
builders—may have found it suffice to work only for God and
his Church, and may have cared little for our being able
to-day to tell the story of his life's work.

THE GREAT ARCHITECTS

We will, however, give a short account of one of these
men, taking him as a representative example of the mediaeval
master-builders, for his name is inseparably linked with the
architectural history of one of the most wonderful German
churches, the Strasbourg Minster.

ERWIN VON STEINBACH

'Magister Erwinus' is the name written on his tombstone. The 'von Steinbach' was added much later, no doubt as a description of his birthplace, but there are a great number of places of this name. The only date known as connected with him, is that of his death, which took place in Strasbourg on February 16th, 1318. It is supposed that he was born around 1244. The building of the Minster was begun long before his time, for we know that it was already seriously damaged, about 1200, by five fires, those terrible scourges of mediaeval towns. Master-builders Rudolf von Strasbourg, father and son, are named as great architects and predecessors of Erwin. In Strasbourg we are still able to study great drawings and plans going back to those times. These are structural outlines drawn on parchment, one of them being 7 ft. high. This is a wonderful design of Erwin's, and is accounted one of the most beautiful produced by the highest period of the Gothic.

Though it did not fall to him to finish the Minster—mediaeval churches were in fact never finished—he nevertheless is famed, long after his time, as a great master-builder who was not only a great artist, but an excellent engineer with a mastery of statics. His fundamental creative ideas are repeated for over a century in many German buildings. The history of architecture takes us to Mainz and Cologne, to Magdeburg and Chorin, to Prenzlau, to Suabia, and to South Tirol.

'What use to you is a monument? You have made for yourself one most magnificent!' was said of Erwin by Goethe, for whom the Strasbourg Minster became a lifelong experience. Erwin's sons went on building in the spirit of their father; his family can be traced in Strasbourg up to 1386. Other great architects followed. We find the famous Suabian architect Ulrich von Einsingen in Strasbourg from 1399 to his death in 1419. His son Matthias left the town, for he was unable to agree with the Council.

The new man was master Johann Hültz from Cologne, who, in the years 1419 to 1439, crowned the Octagonal Tower built by Einsingen by the uncommonly bold spire. This gave Strasbourg, for a very long time, Germany's highest tower, 468 ft. Only in the last century was this over-shadowed by Cologne, 510 ft., and Ulm, 540 ft.

Strasbourg Minster was spoken of in the times gone by as the eighth wonder of the world; this supreme masterpiece produced the strongest impression on all who were able to behold it. The fame of this structure extended to the Guild. The West- and South-German stonemasons, meeting in 1459 in Regensburg, saw in the Strasbourg Guild 'the court of highest instance for stonemasonry.' The Duke of Milan, in 1481–2, applied to Strasbourg for an architect to build the dome of his cathedral. Thus it was that architects and engineers gained fame for their employers.

GERMAN GUNSMITHS

THE GUILD OF GUNSMITHS

In the first third of the fourteenth century, the earliest firearms saluted the new era. Since then six centuries have passed, but a short space in the history of man, and how great has been the influence upon the fate of nations of this invention, itself a great technical achievement developed by generations of engineers. Firearms first broke the strong-holds of the knights, who were unwilling to make themselves members of a greater community. Gunpowder energetically put an end to those small and very small independent powers which had become unendurably arbitrary in their behaviour. We are thus unable to imagine history without the effects of these weapons, and are hardly able to lay too great a stress on their significance.

5. MASTER-BUILDER HIERONYMUS, *d.* 1318
From a drawing by Albrecht Dürer

6. GUNSMITH'S SHOP
From an engraving after Stradanus (1536-1605)

7. MARTIN MERCZ, *d.* 1501

Tombstone in the Martinskirche, Amberg

Photo: Bayer. Landesamt für Denkmalpflege

8. KONRAD KYESER
VON EICHSTÄDT,
1366–1405

From a miniature

Photo:
Deutsche Museum

But who was the discoverer of gunpowder ? Here, again, we know neither name, place, nor date. The story of the monk Berthold the Black, who sought the philosopher's stone and found gunpowder, is but a legend.

The mixture of carbon, sulphur, and saltpetre had long been known to the Chinese and the Tartars, and had been used by them for rockets. The Arabs and Byzantines had produced thunder-like reports by means of fireworks, and had even hurled these out of thin wooden tubes now and then at their enemies. But the use of gunpowder for hurling projectiles from metal tubes was the pioneer invention from which the history of firearms and their revolutionary effect on all human relations is to be dated. The start was no doubt made with small tubes of copper or bronze furnished with a stock. This was a form intermediate between a gun and a small cannon. Development always takes place from that which is already known, and hence the projectile first used was the bolt of the crossbow, but lead bullets very quickly came into use. The terror produced by these fire-spitting weapons, which went off with a noise like thunder, was at first, no doubt, their chief effect of military value. The first firearms could have done little bodily damage to the enemy.

Bernhard Rathgen, an eminent artillerist of the German Army, has given us a great work on the development of firearms in the first century of their history, in which he has critically investigated the latest sources of information, derived chiefly from the account books of German towns. According to him, the first appearance of firearms was in the years 1321–31. Although Germany is not yet able to bring forward documentary proof of being their originator, the facts seem to speak very plainly. Firearms were made in Germany shortly after 1320, and were in wide use there ten years later. The cradle of their development was on the upper or middle Rhine. Of the countries on the lower Rhine, Flanders, then in close cultural connection with Germany, was especially concerned with the further development of firearms. In foreign countries, their invention has been ascribed to Germany from the earliest times. The great Italian poet Ariosto (1516) tells us that the Devil gave Roland a firearm, but this knight '*sans peur et sans reproche*' consigned this unworthy weapon in the deepest depths of the sea. But after many years, this infernal machine was pulled up again out of the sea by the power of a magician, and then first taken to the Germans. By the aid of the evil spirit, who sharpens the wits, the use of it was learned, and very soon other countries also began to make use of it. Then follows the condemnation of it, which in all history has been applied to every new and unknown weapon:

> Thou hast taken away honour from the soldier's service.
> The glory of war will be shattered by thee.
> Through thee—so far have power and courage sunk—
> The coward seems to overcome the brave.
> Through thee strength and heroism are taken from us,
> And the chance to prove oneself in the field.
> Through thee have perished, and will continue to perish
> Noble gentlemen and knights in great number.

The desire to reduce the strongholds of rebellious knights and shorten the siege of towns protected by walls, led to the development of greater cannon of extraordinary dimensions. Enormous stone balls were used as projectiles, and hence these weapons were spoken of as stone-guns. The huge tubes lay on great masses of oak, the recoil being taken by a structure of piles driven into the earth, and beams. When the shot was fired, the recoil brought this arrangement into disorder which took some time to rectify; hence people were at first satisfied if they were able to fire one shot in three days with such a weapon. When an artillerist actually succeeded in firing one shot a day with his gun, and even 'in any direction he pleased,' it was believed that he was in league with the Devil, and his penalty for this technical improvement was to make a pilgrimage to Rome.

These great cannon were made of wrought iron, iron staves being held together like a cask by strong iron rings. But soon after cast bronze was used. The technique came from the bellfounder. There was in fact a considerable resemblance between the bell and the cannon, which in the early days sometimes had a funnel-shaped mouth for loading the balls. This art made use of a number of different craftsmen of the time. In addition to the bellfounder, there was the smith, who had to make the iron tubes. And carpenters and joiners also could not be dispensed with. Whenever a new field for technical work is conquered, there is a shortage of skilled labour. The existing trades then supply those of their men who are sufficiently enterprising to throw in their lot with the new development. We saw this happen when the first steam engine came into existence, and when electrical engineering made entirely fresh demands on the knowledge and ability of its exponents.

There was also the case in the fourteenth century. Anyone who was an expert in firearms was also required, above all, to be able to make his own gunpowder. But this was a dangerous art. When the gun was ready loaded, it had to be fired, and firing these huge guns was sometimes more dangerous for the artilleryman than for the enemy he was firing at. The men whom we have to thank for the development of firearms were called 'gunmasters,' and this designation of their calling appears early in old documents. Also, the earlier trade of the master is frequently given in the accounts, thus we hear of the 'bellfounder–gunmaster.' He frequently continued in his earlier business. Every gunmaster had his assistants, and needed above all men who were familiar with the service of the gun. Thus were developed the gunfirers who became the artillerists of our day. The gunmasters belonged for the most part, since they had to do with fire, to the guild of smiths, but by virtue of the novelty of their art, they felt themselves with good reason greatly superior in their powers to the single handicraft guilds. For they had not only to make guns, but were also leaders of the artillery in war, directing the attack or defence of towns. They were surrounded by a peculiar glory. These fire craftsmen belonged to the highest class of the men of knowledge. They were also at pains to maintain this belief in their art by keeping their knowledge as secret as possible. In rich towns they formed impressive brotherhoods. The German emperors gave them rich privileges. In 1446, for example, they were promised in advance all bells in the enemy's country, and in conquered towns the armaments and arsenals, the guns and powder. The gunmasters were often free-lances, negotiating on a purely private commercial basis with those carrying on war. If the promises made to them were not kept, a clause in their agreement stipulated that they were absolved from their duty and might leave the field of war. We find it a little hard to imagine how, in the middle of war, they might go 'to friends and enemies, without injury to their honour.'

However, we also find gunmasters in the service of a town. They are then employees getting a fixed wage, with a special bonus when they are fortunate in their shooting. The towns lent their famous gunmasters to the princes and to other towns when it suited their politics, and so we often find them on their travels. At first, the casting of such a great bronze cannon was an event. A special foundry was erected for the purpose at a suitable point in the town. When a gun was needed anywhere, it was often easier, in view of the difficulty of transport, to cast it on the spot—even in the field behind the front—rather than to produce it in a proper foundry and then transport it along the worst imaginable roads. We know that around 1450, 200 strong men and seventy oxen were needed to move cannon of this size.

A gunmaster here and there began quite early on to write down his experience and his art, adding with great pleasure any information he could collect from others. So it was that in those days the beginnings of technical literature were made in the form of the famous books of marvels, books of the fire arts, and so on. They are a curious form of technical literature. They are permeated by a love of secrecy and adventure; there is no trace of that training in criticism so much cultivated in antiquity. It often appears as if that which is not understood by the writer himself seems to him specially valuable and peculiar. These old books are therefore a curious mixture of truth, genuine experience, and unfettered imagination. The more fantastic they were, the more willingly were they read. But we are able to discover the knowledge of the time, even in this forest of weeds. Everyone who possessed a book of marvels of this sort looked upon it as very valuable. It was kept secret, and many an author excuses himself to his colleagues for having written it, and so made it more difficult to preserve the secrets of the art. It passed as a rule from father to son, and the town, in so far as it had all its experience written down, was also careful to see to it that others were not able to make use of its experience. This secrecy naturally put a brake on technical progress, and frequently made it very difficult. Many a good idea was forgotten again completely, turning up again centuries later as an entirely new invention.

But these great German gunmasters to whom we owe almost the whole technical development in the first century of firearms, and who were at home in almost all countries, these great predecessors of our present-day engineers in this important and extensive field of work, are worthy of having at least some of their names and deeds put on record here. We will attempt in a few lines to do honour to German gunmasters without attempting completeness, for the material at our disposal is far from sufficient for biographical purposes.

Gunmaster Abraham von Memminge tells us something of the qualities and activity of a gunmaster of his time. He says: 'His first duty is to honour God and keep him ever in mind and go in fear of him, for when he is at work with the gun and gunpowder, he has his greatest enemy in his hands.

The master must also be able to read and write, for otherwise he is not able to keep in mind all that is needed for his art, whether distillation, separation, sublimation, or combination. He must also be able to prepare all sorts of wildfire and tame works, he must know about ranges and measures, about strengthening walls, lining moats, and attacking with towers, rats, and screens. He must also be friendly in his words and behaviour, always clear-headed, and abstemious in drink.'

The document confirming the appointment of gunmaster Heinrich Roggenburger in Augsburg in 1436 gives us a picture of the various technical arts possessed by a gunmaster of that time. In this document we read: 'He is able to cast great and small guns, to fire them as quickly as has ever been known, and to make powder for them. He can shoot and throw fire arrows, and make great and small cast weapons such as have not yet been seen in Germany, for they stand still after being fired without moving or recoiling, and without it being necessary to bind them and fix them, and throw stones of from five to six hundredweights; he also makes tackle by which it is possible to lift 100 hundred-weights, then armour for guns and war carriages, bridges which can be transported overland for use over ditches and running water. Besides all this, he understands the con-struction of towers, houses, and water-, wind-, and horse-mills, cast, earthen, and wooden pipes, how to lead springs over hill and valley, and to make sculptures. His yearly wage is to be 110 gulden.' This tells us how far he was beyond the mere art of gunmaster, and at home in all branches of the technology of his time.

Heinrich Grünwald, the gunmaster, was in the service of the town of Nürnberg from 1382 to his death in 1427. He is said to have reached the age of about seventy. The town provided him with all his raw materials, for they were able through their wide connections to buy more cheaply than the master could. Grünwald provided the workmen and paid them. He was allowed in 1394 to cast the great cannon for Frankfort. He also worked for the Bavarian duke in Ingolstadt with permission from his town. Later on the duke wanted to employ him again, but Grünwald refused. He believed that he could make a good living in Nürnberg by casting bells and other work. But the chief reason was no doubt that these highly placed persons were frequently very bad paymasters. Grünwald was held in high honour. Even on the field of battle he was given the leadership of the artillery. He improved considerably the quality of gunpowder. In addition to guns, he cast thin-walled bells with a wonderful tone. Every gunmaster in these early days attempted to improve his gun. The customer frequently called the gun after the man who made it. Thus people spoke of the 'Grünwaldin,' or the 'Steudin.' Nürnberg itself soon became the greatest industrial town for cannon. The most important stages of its development were carried out there. There was a great trade in armaments in Germany. It was soon possible to buy even quite large stone-throwing cannon in the open market.

The town of Hagenau had in its service in 1391 the cannon-maker Johann von Oppenheim. He was a highborn knight, who, according to his contract of service, was at the disposal of the town as a horseman with two horses. He was also able to cast cannon, and it was stipulated in his agreement that he should teach one of the members of the town council the art of firing cannon and making powder.

In 1419, Hans Fry von Weissenburg was appointed as gunmaster to the town of Frankfort.

In Nürnberg we have in 1448–9 the master Erhard, bell-founder and overseer of the town; he cast great wall-breakers. The town supplied the material and utensils, and also paid the wages. The master himself was paid a wage. Just as the cannon on fortresses were fired by preference at night, so also, perhaps for romantic reasons, was the casting of guns carried out by preference in the evening and with

DE

special ceremony. In those cup-loving days wine and beer were naturally not wanting, and the sums paid for them and carefully entered in the accounts, lead to the conclusion that the town councillors took care to do themselves well on such occasions at the cost of the town.

In Trèves, in 1373, Gyllis was gunmaster. Two years later we have in addition another master, Welter. In 1380 a famous gunmaster was fetched from Strasbourg to teach the town the new art, being highly paid for his services with 50 Mainz gulden. The professional cannoniers formed themselves into a society for the cultivation of their art. They are already mentioned in 1370 in the accounts, and we learn that the town took pains to be agreeable to the cannoniers. They were made a present of wine, which makes the heart glad. Rathgen has tried to calculate from the amount paid the quantity of this wine and so to draw conclusions concerning the number of the cannoniers concerned. But his efforts were in vain, and he consoles himself with the fact that, after all, the thirst of these cannoniers would have to be regarded even to-day as an unknown quantity in the calculation.

Another famous German gunmaster is Walter von Arle. He came from the present town of Arlon in Belgium, which had many connections with trade in the Middle Ages. Walter ranks as a German gunmaster, who made in Cologne the first stone-throwing cannon. From there he was engaged by Frankfort in 1377, but the cannon which he had to make there was not successful. The master was put in gaol, but the council of the town of Trèves pleaded for him. Nine citizens of Trèves went bail for him, among them six smiths. In 1378, Walter von Arle was working in Augsburg, and a year later in Passau. It is supposed that he was also in Nürnberg.

A much-travelled master of high skill was the overseer Hans der Derrer of Augsburg, given the title of 'the Bold.' He was a daring man who worked as mason, joiner, and then as cannonier, and finally acquired the art of making a good powder. He also taught this art to three Augsburg patricians, and here again we have an account of a cheerful carouse which crowned the work.

Gunmaster Albrecht von Soest cast great cannon in 1402 in Göttingen. Here we also get the name of gunmaster Heinrich Grosse, who came from Erfurt. Amberg in the upper Palatinate was the scene of the activity of Martin Mercz, who died in 1501 and whose portrait has come down to us on his tombstone.

Gunmaster Henning cast in 1411 the giant gun of Brunswick, 'Faule Mette.' The gun weighed nearly 9 tons, the ball had a diameter of over $16\frac{1}{2}$ in., and weighed 270 lb. The five shots fired in earnest by this gun all failed to hit their mark. In 1414 the Göttingen gunmaster Hinrik Heisterbom cast a number of cannon. He was given the task of casting, in 1430, a cannon weighing 5 tons for Mühlhausen in Thüringen.

In 1432, we have Bertold Sprangke casting cannon in Brunswick, producing a considerable number up to the year 1449. His name already appears in 1421 in Hildesheim as a bell- and gunfounder. We further know that he made his will in 1476 and probably died soon after at a great age. He was in business on his own account. The town provided him with workmen, but he paid them himself. The money paid to him by the town was reckoned as 10 per cent. of the value of the material cast. As we have already seen, the casting of guns was, like that of church bells, a great event. People were glad to make the occasion that of a popular festival, the town band played, and beer and wine flowed freely. The workmen were allowed to bathe free of charge in the town bath. The relations of German gunmasters to iron-founding are also very important. It is supposed to-day that the gunmasters were also the first to cast iron in the form of cannon balls. This was an advance of great importance. Iron cannon balls had a fundamental effect on the art of fighting. Very soon, the art of casting small cannon in iron was learned, in which connection we may name the Frankfort master Merckln Gast, the first iron-founder mentioned in documents. Our information comes from a document of the year 1400 in the archives of Frankfort. He was able to recover the expensive saltpetre and sulphur from spoiled powder, and to make powder of a quality which would keep for 60 years. He was able to fire great and small cannon, and above all he was able to make small hand guns, and also other guns from cast iron. With this a great technical advance was made by a gunmaster. We may assume that he was already working as an iron-founder from 1391 onwards. It is believed that he came from a Frankfort family.

Konrad Kyeser von Eichstädt comes down to us as a gunmaster who had also the admirable gift of putting on paper, in a 'firework book,' his own knowledge and whatever came to him by hearsay. This valuable manuscript is in Göttingen. Kyeser's book, to which he gave the title of *Bellifortis*, 'the strong in war,' remained for a century and a half the model for similar works. It consists of 130 pages of parchment illustrated for the most part by shaded pen drawings, but also by many beautiful miniature paintings; it has a text full of information and shows us what such a book of the time contained. We see rockets and fire dragons, and a long poem gives us the name of all the sciences necessary to such a gunmaster. But the author admits, nevertheless, that 'God alone can master all these sciences.' Kyeser was born on August 25th, 1366, and died after 1405. The manuscript was closed by him on May 3rd, 1405. It is assumed that he worked on it for three years.

Eastern Germany also took an early and successful interest in the development of the new art. In Marienburg, the bellfounder Dümichen, who cast great cannon in 1409, was highly esteemed. It was also said that he produced one of the first breech-loaders, provided with a wedge and screw breech block, whereby the rate of fire is increased;

this was 100 years before Leonardo, who sketched a breech-loader of this sort in his notebook. Other famous gun-masters were Steynkeller, born in Glogau, and Werderer from Preussisch-Holland. The German Orders had a special foundry in Marienburg, and were the makers of the famous 'Faule Grethe,' which broke the resistance of the castle of the rebellious Quitzows in Brandenburg, and thus enabled the Markgraf Friedrich, the Hohenzollern, to become master in his own land. The gun weighed over 10 tons. Under the management of the gunmaster, it destroyed, in February 1414, the 14-ft. thick walls behind which the robber barons felt themselves perfectly secure. We have further to remember that art in the fourteenth century was closely connected with the activities of the bellfounder and gunmaster. Thus we may take Peter Vischer, whose works are justly praised in every history of art, as a typical great Nürnberg gunmaster. His son-in-law, Peter Mülich, was one of the most famous of them.

Gilg Sesselschreiber, who, along with others of his art, made the monument to Maximilian I in Innsbruck, was a noted gunmaster. Along with Peter Vischer, there worked Gregor Löffler, a famous gunmaster of the time, whom one may describe as a great engineer. Jorg von Strasbourg had a high position as gunmaster to the Emperor Maximilian.

In view of the importance of this art of gunmaking, it is natural that even the highest in the land, emperors and kings, took an interest in it.

But no one did more for this branch of technical work, as general, prince, and engineer, than the 'last knight' on the German Imperial Throne. The Emperor Maximilian I, who was born on March 22nd, 1459, died on January 12th, 1519, and ruled from 1493 up to his death. Lamprecht in his German history says of him: 'His were great achievements as engineer and military technician.' An account of his own life, drafted by him and written by his confidential clerk in 1512, a message from the wise king, named the *Weisskunig*, gives us a striking picture of him. Hans Burgkmair made 120 pictures, wonderful wood-cuts, for this book of Maximilian's. Pictures and text provide us with an excellent survey of the technical achievements of that time. We well understand that the young king desired to learn everything about the technical work of war. We hear that he laid great stress on throwing bridges quickly over rivers, in order to get his men at the enemy with the greatest possible speed. He also clearly recognized the extraordinary importance of the mines in his territories, and did everything possible to develop them in all directions. The output of mining was equally important for his finances and as a source of raw material for armaments. In the chapter dealing with the construction of iron armour, the king subscribes to the view that works are more than knowledge. Knowledge comes not only from observation, but is created by the work ; many failures came from those who believed that they knew, and nevertheless had not done the work themselves.

In connection with our present theme of the German gunmakers, we are above all interested in the picture in which we see the young king standing before the gunmasters, taking advice, anxious to learn about this art as well. The book itself tells us that he was desirous as a young man to learn everything in connection with gunnery. He learned how to make powder, and he also wanted to lay the gun himself. When he came to the throne, he built great arsenals. But above all, he was the first to take up standardization in gunnery on a large scale. In the beginning, every gunmaster probably thought that he owed it to his art to make each gun different from the previous one. Again and again the idea was to try whether other proportions might not give greater effect. No one would have anything to do with mass manufacture. Every gun was to bear the stamp of its maker in its appearance. This overwhelming abundance of different forms is always found at the beginning of great

9. THE EMPEROR MAXIMILIAN I AT THE GUNFOUNDER'S
From a wood-cut by Hans Burgmair from the *Weiss-Kunig* (1514)

How the Young Wise King was Skilful with Artillery

The young wise king had even in his youth a great passion, desire and affection for all firearms, and everything to do with them, such as sulphur, saltpetre and the rest, and gave much thought to guns. And when as a youth he was able to lay hold secretly of a gun, he started such a shooting and a turmoil that he had in the end to be stopped to save him from coming to harm; and this love and affection which he had in his youth for the gun remained always in his heart. And when he came to govern and to manhood, he built many great arsenals in his kingdom for use in war, and thought out many a wonderful new gun.

10. JOHANNES GUTENBERG (1397–1468)

From an engraving by Hans Kohl, Gutenberg Museum, Mainz

technical developments. But in this field, complete chaos in the matter of dimensions must make it almost impossible to supply ammunition in a war. Maximilian created definite classes of guns, and attempted, as far as it was then possible, to bring some order into development. This was an engineering achievement which enormously increased the power of firearms in warfare.

JOHANNES GUTENBERG

AND THE DEVELOPMENT OF THE ART OF PRINTING

1397–1468

Language is the necessary presupposition for human development. The purpose of writing is to put on record what has been spoken, thought, and experienced. All the civilized nations whose history we study have taken this great step and created systems of writing which have given the learned much trouble and work to decipher; this problem has not yet been completely solved to-day. The raw materials of writing have changed. The eternal stone of Egypt—the hardest granite there—the clay tablets of Babylon, the skins of animals, parchment, the papyrus of Egypt, paper and textiles, all these and other substances as different as it is possible to imagine, have been covered with writing of the most different forms.

Writing remained an aristocratic art in the service of the great ones of the earth. Priests and kings were well aware of its value as a means for transmitting their deeds to posterity. As scientific knowledge grew, the need became greater to enlarge the circle of those who could take part in it through the medium of writing. Books came into existence, and though few of these have come down to us from the great periods of Greek and Italian civilization, we have still some idea of how great already was the output of literature in those times. There were already publishers who made numerous copies by dictation to a number of writers simultaneously, and copies of the books of Virgil and Cicero were on sale. The culture of the Middle Ages linked up with them. The monks in their monasteries developed writing to an art, the church had a need for the sacred books, the ancient writers were discovered again, new writers arose, and rich men were thus able to think of creating collections of books, the number of which, however, was still very modest as compared with the home library of a learned man of the present day. When it was necessary to sell a large vineyard in order to pay for a copy of Livy, we see how greatly relative values have changed. Even at this period, the art of reading did not yet extend to the great mass of the people. Reading was still a privilege of the nobles of Church and State, and of the small number of those who devoted themselves to science. But the great spiritual upheavals, which we designate by the terms 'Renaissance' and 'Humanism,' the great religious wars which shook the nations to the depths, gave rise to a desire to seek instruction and encouragement in, above all, religious writing. The making of books one by one by copying them was much too dear and tedious to fulfil in anything like the required degree the demand which now came into being. Besides writing, there were pictures, by which anyone could communicate what he had to say in a manner readily intelligible even to the illiterate. The art had been developed of cutting such pictures on wood blocks which could be inked and made to give mechanical copies. Copperplate engraving had also been developed, and handwriting could be treated in the same way as pictures, being cut into plates from which printed copies could be made. Manifolding of this sort had been in use for hundreds of years by the Chinese for their picture writing. This process had also been used for printing on cotton and silk textiles. Thus the art of printing was already developed.

The uninitiated have again and again felt justified in the conclusion that only a small step was necessary to cut out the individual letters from the wood blocks and then make use of them in different groupings to form words and sentences. But this process was far from simple. Very accurately cut letters of metal were necessary in order to print a book which would look as if it had been written by hand. The master mind which gave this new art of printing to the world was Johannes Gutenberg.

It is taken for granted to-day that everyone can read; for many people it is no longer possible to cope with the flood of print, and we find it very hard to put ourselves back into the time when printing was unknown. Perhaps no technical advance in any field had so great an effect in promoting development in all other fields of human labour as the invention of printing, for only by its aid was it possible to acquaint the whole company of those working in a given field with what others before them had already thought and worked out. With its coming, the acceleration in the development of human work began to take on values hitherto unknown. Millenniums shrank to centuries, decades, years. The science of that time had the further advantage of a language intelligible to the whole civilized world, Latin, so that in those days, when only few in every nation were at work in any special field, community of effort among Europeans was successfully brought into being.

The far-reaching importance of the art of printing being generally recognized, it is clear that one question has been very thoroughly examined and discussed: 'Who was its inventor, and how was the invention made?' What a number of inventors are supposed to have been responsible for the art! A Chinese smith is said to have been already printing with types of burnt clay 400 years before Gutenberg. Cast copper types are said to have been already used in Korea in 1407. A man from Prague taught people to write artificially. A monument has been erected in the North of Italy to a physician as inventor of the art of printing. Strasbourg also claimed the invention, as did Holland. But the more thoroughly the question is investigated, the plainer did it become that the art of printing came into being in Mainz, and that Gutenberg was the author of this great technical achievement. It was a matter of great labour to separate the irrefutable proof from a mass of assumption and supposition, to distinguish between fiction and proof. Again and again, right down to the present day, efforts have been made to penetrate into the darkness of that time. We have in fact still very little positive knowledge, and more could be written about the things of which we are ignorant.

The work of research has been concerned with the inventor and his life history, with the place in the history of art occupied by his great achievements, but least of all with his actual technical deeds. Gutenberg was at pains to keep his art a secret, in which he was to a great degree successful. His contemporaries frequently made a practice of not saying whence their skill came. They wished Gutenberg to remain in the background, and hence endeavoured to suppress as far as possible even what was known at the time.

We do not even know the year of the inventor's birth. It lies between 1394 and 1398. We follow to-day an old tradition in assuming the year to have been 1397, and believe that he was born on the 24th June, St. John's or Midsummer Day, since in those days a child was given the name of the saint on whose day he was born. Gutenberg was born on the estate of Gutenberg, which was at the corner of two existing streets of Mainz, the Schusterstrasse and the Christophstrasse. The name of Gutenberg's father was Friele Gensfleisch. He was owner of the Hof zum Gutenberg, when he took to himself as his second wife the inventor's mother, Else Wirich. The parents took their

name from their estate, and their three children, of whom
the inventor was the youngest, did the same. We know
nothing at all about his youth.

Times were bad in the Mainz of those days. The national
government fell more and more into decay, the internal feuds
between the town nobility and the guilds became fiercer
and more embittered, the towns on the Rhine suffered
financial disaster. In 1444 Mainz, with scarcely 6,000
inhabitants, had a debt of 2,900,000 marks, a monstrous
burden for those times. Between 1326 and 1400 there were
32 plague years, while the fifteenth century actually saw 40
of these terrible years. The father of Gutenberg belonged
to the town nobles of Mainz, and his pedigree can be
followed back to the thirteenth century. He stood by his
own people in the increasingly embittered struggles. He
had specially close relations with the Archiepiscopal Master
of the Mint. He supplied the metal for minting, and was
also concerned with the disposal of the different sorts of
coins. When cases involving false money were being dealt
with, he was a member of the court. It is frequently
assumed that these relations gave the inventor an early
acquaintance with the metals which he was later to use in his
technical work. In any case we know that excellent seals
and dies for coins were cut in his time in Mainz.

Mainz strove to get out of its financial difficulties by high
taxation. But the patricians were asked to grant the taxes
for ten years ahead without knowing how high they would
be. The majority of them preferred to leave the town, and
allow themselves to be outlawed. The struggle became
more and more violent. Johannes Gutenberg was one of the
emigrants, having his own ideas in his head, and not the
slightest intention of obeying the new decrees of the guilds.
Peace was concluded in 1430, but it seems that Johannes
Gutenberg did not accept this peace. Whether he went
direct from Mainz to Strasbourg is unknown to us; we are
again completely without any light on a number of years.

But legal documents and taxation records give us proof that he was in Strasbourg from 1434 to 1444—that is to say for a decade. Here also he was very badly off for money, for Mainz was not willing to pay him the yearly income of 12 gulden due to him from a legacy. An agreement was finally come to about this, but these 12 gulden were not enough for his needs. A citizen of Strasbourg helped him with a loan. Gutenberg joined the town nobles, but we also find him entered in the list of the Goldsmiths' Guild. He was not only obliged to work for his living; it no doubt lay in his nature to need an occupation.

His great ability and lively imagination showed him again and again new openings. In 1437, he founded a business with the Strasbourg citizen Hans Riffe, and they were joined later by two other Strasbourg citizens, Andreas Heilmann and Andreas Dritzehn; their object was the manufacture of mirrors for the pilgrimage to Aachen, which took place every seven years. The partners had to pay 160 gulden to Gutenberg, but when they discovered that Gutenberg had knowledge of other things besides making mirrors, they begged him to teach them all his other arts, and keep nothing back. They were ready to pay for this a further 250 gulden. We are unfortunately unable to derive much technical information from the purely legal agreement. But the secret art appears already to have been a question of the mechanical reproduction of writing, for there is talk of 'trucken' (*drucken*, printing), a press and also of formes. According to the agreement of 1438 between the partners, no stranger was to learn the secret. The agreement also provided that even in case of death, the heir was not to be told. When this event actually occurred, Gutenberg definitely refused to take in the heir, and judgment was given in his favour in 1439. Other statements give us ground for assuming that Gutenberg was already interested in printing from 1436 onwards. His name is not to be found in Strasbourg documents after 1444, while the first mention of him again in Mainz documents occurs in 1448. We do not know where he was in the intervening four years.

The Gutenberg Museum in Mainz has a sheet of paper, a hand's breadth in size, printed on both sides, and it is assumed to be one of Gutenberg's first pieces of printing, from the year 1445. We know still less of the life and the work of Gutenberg in Mainz than we do of his Strasbourg period. He printed some textbooks and calendars, and perfected himself to such an extent in the new art that, about 1450, he set to work on the printing of the Book of Books, the Bible. That was a mighty undertaking. The cost of a well-written Bible in those days was about 300 to 500 gulden or 2,300 to 4,000 marks. When anyone had succeeded in printing so well as to imitate handwriting, and was sufficiently unscrupulous as to think only of getting money, the purchasers could be deceived into taking the book for handwriting, and hence paying the highest price. It is said that Gutenberg's successors occasionally profited by this trick.

But what was the nature of the technical achievement ? Gutenberg naturally had a knowledge of woodcut printing. He knew how pictures and letters could be cut in wood blocks, and was familiar with the block books printed in this way. But as a goldsmith, he understood how to manage metals, he worked with stamps and punches, with gravers and chisels. He knew that if one wanted to produce a book to look like the excellently handwritten books, one could not think of cutting out the wooden letters and printing with them. Quite other methods would be necessary. Our knowledge of the technique of printing enables us to trace the invention backwards. Gutenberg also knew the cast bronze plates put on tombstones, often having much lettering on them, and he knew how these were cast in a sand mould made from a wooden pattern. Ornaments of the noble metals are still cast to-day in sand moulds. The lettering used by present-day bookbinders is made in the same way. The strips of letters are cut up into single letters with a saw, and these are accurately worked. The book-binder cements his letters together to form words and lines, and thus produces the inscription. This method of working, sufficient for a few words, was much too cumbersome to be used for books. A complete change in the process of casting was necessary. In place of sand as a material for the mould, which had to be remade every time, some form of permanent mould had to be created. Instead of sand he chose lead. We are acquainted with the flat brass punches of the year 1524, which were cast in sand from a wooden pattern. These brass punches were struck into lead, making an impression which was then used as a mould for the letters. In this way a casting mould was created, which could be used for the mass manufacture of types. This was Gutenberg's invention. The brass punches were soon replaced by engraved steel punches. We do not know what the first type moulds were like, for none have been preserved. They would have been like those immediately after Gutenberg's time, much the same as those employed far into the nineteenth century until type-casting machines came into use. These moulds had naturally to be very accurately worked, and this was also the case with the finished types. The finishing was done by grinding and filing, in a way which lasted well into our times. Here, again, it was the casting machines that first made this handicraft superfluous. A further great achievement of Gutenberg's was so to transform the press, already in use in a number of industries, as to make it applicable to printing.

In order to print so great a work as the forty-two-line Bible by means of these technical appliances, which had been tested over a period of years, considerable financial means were necessary. These were not at the disposal of the inventor, who had all the time been in need of money. A citizen of Mainz, Johannes Fust, helped him out. He lent Gutenberg 800 gulden, which, however, were used up in two years. The same sum again was necessary, and Fust was ready to provide this, but wanted to have a share in the business, in which case he was ready to provide a further 300 gulden annually as working capital. This co-operation between the inventor and the capitalist unfortunately ended in a legal dispute. Fust demanded his money back. Though we are not fully acquainted with the details and outcome of the action, it is certain that Gutenberg's means were exhausted. The further great printed works which appeared in his lifetime all came from the press of Fust and Peter Schöffer. It is frequently supposed that Gutenberg had to hand over the whole of his plant to Fust. In 1457 he worked in a press in Mainz belonging to the Mainz Syndic, Konrad Humery. He is supposed, on many sides, to have produced here a great work, the *Katholikon*, and a number of other smaller works.

He was again involved in political struggles. The Emperor and Pope had deposed the Archbishop of Mainz and named another in his place. Gutenberg seems to have been on the wrong side. It is supposed that after the town had been conquered by the new Archbishop, he was obliged to leave it in 1462. But the new prince of the Church recognized the great importance of the inventor, bore him no grudge for the side he had taken, and made his peace with him. He took the poor old man, on January 17th, 1465, into his entourage, gave him a dress such as that worn by the knights, and presented him with an annual allowance of 20 malters (12 bushels) of corn, and 2 fuder (270 gallons) of wine. But this allowance was on the condition that he was neither to sell them nor give them away. He thus got free clothing and food. The prince also released him from all taxes and duties. The inventor ended his life in Mainz, but the date of his death is not known to us. The documents only give us evidence that he was no longer alive on February 25th, 1468. Some believe that he was blind in his old age. He was buried in the Franciscan Church in Mainz.

This was pulled down in 1742, and therewith his grave disappeared for ever.

The art of printing spread over Europe from Mainz with astonishing rapidity, the result of a very strong demand. The struggles in Mainz had much to do with this rapid dissemination. For though the printers had had to take oath to keep their art strictly secret, this promise was no longer kept when the conditions of the time forced them to leave their native country. A French savant, Guillaume Fichet, already wrote in 1470 of these German printers, who were now carrying with them their art into the whole world: 'They are pouring out into the world as once the warriors poured out of the belly of the Trojan horse. They are carrying the light from Germany into all parts of the earth.' It is said that in 1500, 16,299 works had already been printed in 208 different places, and in 1,213 different presses.

From the year 1507 we have Wimpfeling's words of praise: 'There is no invention or product of the mind of which we Germans can be so proud as of printing, which made us the new spiritual bearers of the doctrine of Christianity and of all sacred and secular science, and so benefactors of the whole of humanity. What a wonderful new life has come into being in all ranks of the people; and who should not bear thankfully in mind the first founder and promoter of this art.'

LEONARDO DA VINCI

AND THE GREAT ENGINEERS OF THE RENAISSANCE

1452–1519

Italy, with her great past, went through a forceful and remarkable time in the fifteenth century. The world of antiquity was discovered anew. The greatest enthusiasm arose for the art of the Greeks and Romans, and their achievements in science were studied. The country, it is true, was divided into many small states, the ambitious

rulers of which were continually attempting to extend their
territory by war. It was a time of unrest and violence. The
tension of a political struggle was carried over into the intellectual field. The desire everywhere was to attain to the
best and most perfect; this time of New Birth, of Renaissance, was also a time of eager rivalry in the sphere of
intellect. Never before had artists been held in so high
esteem, and paid so much honour by rulers. Every one of
these wished to have the greatest painters and sculptors
among his subjects. Honour and fame were the reward
for acquiring a great artist. This high regard for art and
science spread to the whole nation. A new work of art could
excite the enthusiastic sympathy of a whole city. Art and
handicraft were still intimately bound up with one another,
and handicraft led to trade and industry. The rulers of those
days knew how great was also the economic importance of
the technology of that time. Bloody wars were carried on
in order to transplant flourishing industries from one
country to another. Inventions were regarded as national
property. He who gave away the secret of them was a
traitor to his country, and could be punished by death.
Silkworm culture and the silk trade were looked upon as
particularly profitable, and Greek skill in them was brought
over to Sicily as the result of a war. In Bologna, spinning
machines had been constructed which for a long time gave
the town a monopoly. The industry was particularly well
developed in Florence, and here again textiles took a fore-
most place. Florentine cloths were famous throughout the
whole western world, and nowhere was the art of dyeing
scarlet so much at home as there. The Netherlands, France,
England, and Spain sent great quantities of raw materials to
Florence, where they were worked up. Wonderful silks were
woven, gold and silver brocades.

This age of great advance in all fields saw the birth of
Leonardo da Vinci, a contemporary of Raphael and Michel-
angelo. He was famous even in his lifetime as a painter

EE

and sculptor far beyond the frontiers of his state, indeed far beyond Italy itself. But his genius cannot be confined to the history of art. The histories of medicine, of the sciences, and above all of technology, tell of the full measure they received from this universal genius.

Leonardo was born in 1452 in a little place Vinci, near Florence. He was the natural son of Piero da Vinci, one of the council of government in Florence. His mother Catherine was a country girl. His father and mother both married in their respective stations, shortly after the birth of Leonardo. But his father took as much care of Leonardo as of his legitimate children that were born later. Of his youth we only know that he was early seized with the desire to record everything with his pencil. His drawings pleased his father, who showed them to a well-known Florentine artist, Verrochio, who was painter, sculptor, and goldsmith. He sensed the genius revealed by the boy's sketches, and readily agreed to take him into his house. Thus we find the fourteen-year-old Leonardo a pupil of Verrochio, and here he became conscious of the many impulses that were latent in him. He painted, modelled, wrote verse, and composed music. At first music was his chief enthusiasm. Leonardo left Florence in 1480. He travelled for four years through Italy, and then was called to the Court of the Prince of Milan, Lodovico Sforza il Moro. Here again it was Leonardo's music which first attracted the Count's interest. The Court of Milan was a great place for festivals, and Leonardo, now thirty-two years of age, was able to gain fame and respect as Master of Revels at Court. He aroused great enthusiasm by being ever ready with new ideas to astonish wedding guests and princely visitors. Leonardo could hardly have imagined when first he went there that he would remain for an uninterrupted period of fifteen years.

The theatrical spectacles and many songs which he produced were not the end of his activities. He concerned himself with greater tasks. The world-famous 'Last

Supper' was only one of these achievements. In 1494 he
went to Pavia. Here anatomy took hold of him, and he
began by first studying the human body from the point of
view of the artist. But this work led him far beyond mere
sketching, and he has not unjustly been called the greatest
anatomist of his time. He worked at the most varied
branches of science, and, animated by the desire not only
to collect knowledge but to apply it, he took a very great
interest in technical work. He built great canals, he planned
a great equestrian monument to the predecessor of the
Prince. The monument was to be gigantic, and the horse
excited great astonishment as a model. The technical
daring involved in the desire to cast such a piece was looked
upon as unimaginable. Unfortunately, this also belongs to
one of the many works which Leonardo planned but was not
able to carry out. Wars prevented it, and French soldiers
destroyed the model.

When the French conquered Milan in 1499, and the
Prince fled to Germany in search of help, Leonardo went
temporarily back to Florence. He then obtained a commanding position with Cesare Borgia as a military engineer
and carried out for him the fortification of the Romagna
towns. The letter in which Leonardo offers his services to
the Prince has been preserved, and gives us in the style of
those times an insight into the work of Leonardo in the field
of military technology. He proposes to build the Duke long
military bridges which may be quickly put together and
pulled down, to drain away the water from the besieged
fortress, to build drawbridges. He promises mysteriously
to break down even such walls as cannot be attacked by a
cannon. He understands how to make guns, and transport
them conveniently. He is able to dig tunnels without noise,
he proposes to attempt to force a way into the midst of the
enemy by carriages on which guns are mounted. For sea
warfare also he has the most varied weapons and machines
ready for attack and defence. But when it is peace-time, he

will build great buildings and waterworks. In addition to all this, he is a sculptor and painter.

When he had completed his tasks as a military engineer for Borgia, he is found again in Florence. Milan, now French, did him the honour in 1508 to ask him to return. Leonardo, now fifty-six years of age, accepted the call. Seven years were now occupied chiefly with scientific questions of the most varied description. He worked as an engineer, and many will not forgive him for often being more occupied with scientific and technical work than with art. But he finally became weary of the perpetual dissension and never-ending warfare between the small states of the Italy of those days. Francis I, King of the great country of France, invited him to come to him in 1515, offering him every sort of support. He was to be free in his activity, free from every sort of material care, to spend the evening of his days as a prince of art and science in the great land of France. Leonardo accepted, and was given by his royal friend the Château of St. Celoux, near Amboise on the Loire. He was spared for a further four years, which he passed in close intimacy of old Italian friends and scholars, held in high honour by the King. He continued to work at a number of problems, planning great canal construction, and without doubt acting as an ever-ready adviser on every imaginable technical problem.

He died on May 2nd, 1519, in peace with his surroundings. We find in his manuscripts a saying which might have served as his epitaph: 'Just as a day well spent gives us peaceful sleep, so does a well-spent life bring us a peaceful death.'

Why are we justified in giving Leonardo one of the first places among the great in science and technical work? Are any works of his still remaining for our wonder and admiration? Did he write great books about science and technology? Nothing of the sort. But there have been preserved to us in almost incredible profusion sheets of his notes, covered with sketches, calculations, remarks on all the fields in which he was active; and his desire to get to know everything and conquer new territory was so comprehensive, that a table of contents of these notebooks would almost amount to a lexicon of the technology and science of his time.

Not only books, but also manuscripts have their fate. Leonardo had early accustomed himself to record with his pencil everything that interested him. But he drew on the same sheet, quite without any order, whatever he was occupied with at the moment. We find parts of machines, whole machines, next to them anatomical studies of man and horse, then figures from mathematics and mechanics, astronomical calculations, a plant, a tree, and in the midst of it all some profound philosophical remark, and again a caricature, a horrible human face, drawn by the hands of a great artist, and seeming to make fun of the whole mass of knowledge recorded there.

Leonardo stood with his two feet in life. It was known in the Italy of those days, and above all in the towns where he had worked, how great was his interest in technology and industry. His advice was asked, he was shown new works, and he recorded in his sketch-books whatever seemed valuable to him. In the same way, when he found statements or drawings in literature, he no doubt extracted from them also whatever appeared to him specially noteworthy. For this reason it is certainly not right to assume that everything contained in these sketch-books is an original idea or invention of his. But when we set aside a number of things which we are able to prove to be derived by him from his predecessors, there is nevertheless much remaining to show us that Leonardo was one of the most original thinkers and engineers. In his sketches he is by no means satisfied with a few general views of a machine, but goes deep into their details, taking them apart, viewing their different elements, and giving with his wonderful gift for representation so many details that it is possible to work from them. He ever understands much about manufacture, and is able to help when the simple master's experience comes to its limits. His learned contemporaries, who knew these notes of his, have reproached him, in the professional pride of which they were not free, of not having a literary education, and hence have said that his writing was of no value. Leonardo calls this 'the chatter of fools,' and tells his opponents that he needs for what he has to say, experience, and not fine words. 'Words are made for quarrelling !' he might have added with Goethe, but Leonardo did not wish to quarrel; he sought truth. 'And since experience has always been the mistress of those who have written well, I take her as my guide, and follow her in all things.'

But did Leonardo then not know the great writers in his own field ? Of course he did. He quotes in his notes no less than seventy-two books and writers. Naturally, not all of them gave him anything of value. Leonardo kept to his own independent thought and investigation in the face of Aristotle, whose teaching was accepted in those days almost as a creed, and even regarded as unexceptionable by the Church, though with some regrets for the fact that he was a heathen. The only authority which he recognized in all things was experience. He had a specially high regard for Archimedes. He owed much to Vitruvius, and also studied thoroughly Hero of Alexandria; he learned much from these men. It would be valuable to study in the light of scientific criticism these authors, whose book knowledge Leonardo made his own, and to determine what he took over from them, what he put into new form, and what he added of his own.

Leonardo took all these numerous notebooks with him as a precious treasure to France. He doubtless thought of using them as material for books, for he must have had the desire to treat in a connected way one or other of his spheres of interest. But the mass of new problems presented again and again by everything that interested him, gave him no opportunity. Vasari, who was born in 1511, while Leonardo was still living, and was a colleague of his as painter and architect, was one of the first to endeavour to set down the life history of his great contemporaries—above all the artists. He remarks that many of Leonardo's works were not completed, and he assumes 'that his noble and masterly spirit was hindered by all too great striving, that his endeavour, to pile excellence upon excellence and perfection upon perfection was responsible for this, and, as Petrarch says, eagerness hindered the work.'

What do we know of the fate of these notes of Leonardo's ? We are unable to say even to-day how many such notes have existed, but we have fairly good information of over 5,300 leaves of his notebook. He made his pupil and friend Melzi a trustee in his will for the writings he left behind, and this friend took faithful care of the treasure. But when he died in 1570 there remained no one who took any especial trouble about it. The notes were scattered in all the world. Three volumes with 1,222 pages form the famous *Codex Atlanticus* in Milan. Paris has twelve volumes with 2,200 pages, England 1,728 pages. Others are in Rome, Turin, Florence and Venice. It is not easy to find one's way in these pages, which, as already remarked, deal with the greatest imaginable variety of subjects. All notes are written by Leonardo in mirror script from right to left. It is assumed that he was left-handed, and that this way of writing was not difficult for him. Perhaps he made use of it to prevent anyone, seeing the notes by chance, from becoming acquainted without his permission with the results of his thought. He also often uses abbreviations, and runs words together, which were obvious to him, but are not readily understood at once by anyone else. But the most curious fact is that these notebooks were completely forgotten. Only in 1797 do we find them again mentioned. For over 250 years nothing was known of them. How fruitful might have been Leonardo's work in its effects on the development of science and technology ! Through ignorance of the work of Leonardo, many who come much later have been given credit for ideas and inventions which are to be found centuries earlier in Leonardo's notes. Even in the works of Galileo, there is much that was said a century earlier by Leonardo. Our opinions have to be changed on many points, and we should do well constantly to consult Leonardo in the history of technology. It is at times difficult to believe, when we are reading his writings, that he lived from 1452 to 1519.

What have these 5,300 leaves got to say to us ? We will not deal here with astronomy, geology, botany, anatomy, and physiology. We are concerned here above all with his position with respect to natural science, to the fundamental sciences of technology. Mechanics, for Leonardo, takes the foremost position. He calls this science 'the paradise of the mathematical sciences, for here we reap the fruits of mathematics.' Geometry, also—above all, the study of perspective —is regarded by him from the standpoint of the artist: he calls perspective the rein and rudder of painting. Acoustics, and above all optics, the doctrine of colour and heat, occupied his detailed attention.

We have already seen how he took part as a technical engineer in the wars that were perpetually in progress. He built fortresses able to resist guns, and made guns which were able, again, to destroy these fortresses. Above all, he gave attention to manufacture. Much that played a great part in the Great War was already anticipated by Leonardo. Steel helmets, breastplates, movable armour plates, tanks, and—a fact that is little known—poison gases and gas masks. In the great field of architecture we have large buildings by him, and he was also concerned in building the Cathedral of Milan. He was a great builder of towns, and he proposed to introduce into a great town a system of streets one above the other. The streets were to be as broad as the height of the

houses. He designed a model town. He had a great liking
for water engineering. He designed and built great canals,
irrigated land, built harbours, and went so far into detail
that he also paid attention to all apparatus and tools, and
investigated how the greatest effect is to be obtained with
the smallest exertion—motion studies, as we would say
to-day. These technical labours led to testing materials,
and here again one would never believe that such tests could
be carried through in his day with so much understanding.
All the results of his experiments in hydraulic engineering
were collected by him in a treatise, which includes practically
all knowledge of his time. He made a considerable advance in the measurement of water, a matter of great
importance to him in his irrigation work, where the water
taken from the canals had to be measured.

He divides up machines into their parts, paying particular
attention to gearing. How is rotational motion to be
changed into reciprocatory, as by crank and connecting rod ?
He attempts to replace sliding friction by rolling friction.
He collects together all that is to be said about valves.
We find in his pages a description of lifting tackle of the
most various sorts, while pumps, dredges, pile-drivers are
not wanting. He gives us a windmill with a turning roof.
He also pays attention to tools. He shows us screw-cutting
machines, and is quite at home in the textile industry. The
Florentines, whose cloth-finishing was famed far and wide,
frequently inspired him to execute beautiful drawings
of shearing machines, washing machines, pressers, and
calenders. Furthermore, we find great boring machines for
boring tubes for wells, an automatic file-cutting machine,
and spinning machines in all details. Weaving is not
missing, nor are wire-drawing machines, spring hammers
for gold-beating, measuring instruments, and, among the
machine parts, the universal joint hitherto ascribed to
Cardan, and playing a great part in the modern motor car.
He also worked on very interesting chain constructions for

driving purposes, which are known to-day as Gall's chains. The above list does not nearly exhaust the contents of these sketch-books.

We have still to say something about a matter which least of all occurs in thinking of the fifteenth century, the art of flying. The desire to conquer the air for humanity occupied this great engineer for decades. He made little figures of thin wax, filled them with warm air, and let them fly about his room, to the great astonishment of his friends. This might easily have led him to the fire balloon, but Nature was his model. His desire was to imitate the birds, and so he made the most exact studies of their flight with his pencil. He was a sharp observer. But he also knew that he must get the most exact knowledge possible of the air itself, if he was to have success with his great bird, as he liked to name the flying machine which he built. He knew how dangerous practical experiments must be. He held it to be safest to fly at a great height over the clouds. Here one would have a better view, and be able to avoid all the dangers arising from whirlwinds rising up from mountain valleys. In connection with flight, Leonardo was already dealing with that most modern question, streamlining. His objective was gliding flight, and an English author who has recently been going in detail into this section of Leonardo's work, adds that the Germans—excluded by the Versailles Treaty from the development of motor-driven aeroplanes—have now carried out gliding flights in the most brilliant way. It is in this way that the daring work of our own time is linked with the wish-dreams of the great master who lived 400 years ago. Leonardo was spared the experience of the tailor of Ulm. In this field, again, one improvement after another, made as a result of further study, prevented him from getting as far as an actual trial. But if he had succeeded in actually getting into the air in his flying machine, he would have been able to save himself in case of a crash by a parachute, for even that had been invented by him. He said prophetically of his great bird, his flying machine, that it would make its first flight from a hill in the neighbourhood of Florence. 'It will fill the universe with paeans of praise, and the town from which it sprang will win everlasting fame.'

The reason why we, in our time, feel Leonardo so close to us is that in a time when belief depended almost exclusively on authority, he was ready to trust only experiment, experience. Again and again we find in his notebooks the brief remark 'tested by experiment.' Experience he calls the common mother of all sciences and arts. She never deceives. It is always only our own judgment which promises us the impossible. Again and again he points to experiment. On one occasion he writes: 'Before you make this result into a general rule, test it by experiment two or three times, and see whether you always get the same result.' It is Leonardo's object in these rules of his to prevent engineers and inventors promising themselves and others the impossible.

We must not be surprised that people in Leonardo's time were full of the hope of discovering perpetual motion, for this race of inventors is not dead even yet. Leonardo studied the question, and points out repeatedly how foolish it is; in one place he exclaims: 'O ye who cudgel your brains in search of perpetual motion, how many delusions have you not created in this endeavour? Go and take your places among the alchemists.' Here, again, his judgment is far ahead of that of his time.

As regards the physical form of this man who spent sixty-seven years on this earth, we have many witnesses to the strong effect of his personality on people. He was a powerfully built man of aristocratic appearance, strong and healthy, of great physical skill, and was gifted with great powers of conversation which aroused enthusiasm in those with whom he came in contact. He is praised not only for his deep knowledge, but for his kindly and helpful attitude to mankind, ever ready with help. We also know that he was very fond of animals, above all of horses, and birds, the flight of which he was anxious to emulate. 'The gigantic outlines of Leonardo's nature will ever be only sensed by us from a distance' is Jacob Burckhardt's opinion.

We may take leave of Leonardo with the words of his biographer, Vasari: 'We often see rich gifts showered by nature, with the aid of the heavenly powers, on human creatures, but now and then we find united in a single human being, as by an overwhelming and supernatural prodigality, beauty, good nature, and a skill in art so splendid that every one of his actions appears divine, all other mortals are surpassed, and it seems to be revealed that his achievement is the gift of God, and not attained by the art of a mortal. This was the case with Leonardo da Vinci; his body was graced by a beauty beyond praise, every action of his was full of the greatest attractiveness, and his artistic powers were so perfect that wherever his spirit turned, he solved with ease the most difficult problem. Unusual strength was joined in him with agility, his courage and daring were great and noble, and the fame of his name spread so far that he was praised not only by his contemporaries, but very much more by posterity.'

GEORGIUS AGRICOLA
1494–1555

Mining and metallurgy have always stimulated engineering and found work for engineers. Germany in the Middle Ages was one of the countries richest in metals of the then known world, and mining was largely a German development. The ores and metals from German sources supplied the greater part of the means necessary for building up the power of princes. They paid attention to mining, and great capitalists made it their field of action. The Fuggers and Welsers of Augsburg were the greatest capitalists of their time, and their mines were to be found far beyond the confines of the German Empire.

11. LEONARDO DA VINCI (1452–1519)

From the self-portrait in red chalk, in the Royal Library, Turin

12. GEORGIUS AGRICOLA (1494–1555)

From an engraving by an unknown artist, Graphische Sammlung, Munich

Metals were more and more sought after, and the prices were very high. The demand sometimes stimulated mining to such an extent that the no less necessary agriculture was neglected. The oldest sources take us to the Harz. In the famous Rammelsberg, German miners have been digging for silver and other metals for more than a thousand years. Starting from Goslar, mining was also begun in the upper parts already in the eleventh century. Soon the Harz became the high school of German mining. At the end of the twelfth century the famous silver mines of Freiberg came into existence. At the beginning of the thirteenth century, mining for copper began in Mansfeld. Copper ores were then soon found in the Alps and in Silesia. Silver was got in the Erzgebirge, in Alsace and Tirol, lead in the Eifel, tin in the Erzgebirge, gold in Bohemia, Mahren, Salzburg, and Karnten. The mines in the Erzgebirge between Saxony and Bohemia were very important.

Iron ore mining is, in the age of iron, one of the most important problems. The Erzberg in Steiermark near Leoben rewarded the work of mining richly. Iron ores were plentiful in Sieger and Sauerland, also in the Harz, in Thüringia, in the Eifel, in the Fichtelgebirge, and in many other parts of Germany there were deposits of iron which at that time were worth mining.

Mining and metallurgy, and the trade in their products, dominated German economy round about the fifteenth to the sixteenth century. Karl V in 1525 named the mines 'the greatest gift and utility which the Almighty has given the German lands.' The Emperor estimated the value of the annual production of the German mines at 2,000,000 gold gulden, a gigantic sum when we allow for the purchasing powers at that time. It allowed of much being done politically, more so since in those days, as ever, the first requisite for waging war was money. One hundred thousand persons are said to have been employed in 1525 in German mining and smelting. Germany's production of silver exceeded that of all other countries together up to about 1545, when the rich ores of Peru and Mexico were exploited. Still greater was the production of copper, the metal which was used on the largest scale for casting monuments, and above all for cannon. Mining and smelting had need of wholesale trade for the disposal of their products. Augsburg and Nürnberg were the leading towns for this. Jakob Fugger owed his title 'the Rich' to the metal industry. These great merchant princes of the Middle Ages, the Höchstetter, Fuggers and Welser, to name only a few, controlled this industry far beyond the confines of Germany. They used their money to open up again and again new sources. They were the successors of the great Hanseatic merchants of the fourteenth and fifteenth centuries, who for 200 years had a fortress-like colony in London named the 'Steelyard,' and who carried on trade with mining products through their other great houses in Norway and Russia, Hungary and Poland, and so became the pioneers of the German mining and smelting industry. The Fuggers controlled the winning of silver and mercury in Spain in the sixteenth century. The Welsers paid early attention to the Spanish mines in Central America. Germany led the way, and when the English desired to develop their own mines, they sought to gain the help of German capital, German enterprise, and German technical skill.

But here also money was not enough, there was need for first-rate German skill, often inherited from one generation to another. The greater the undertaking became, the deeper the mines had to go, the more necessary became German engineers of the time. But they were outside the ranks of the masters and rulers. It was enough that they did their work. No one thought of paying them especial honour, however indispensable their ability, best known to those who were dependent on the income from mining.

We know nothing at all of the life stories of these technologists, who laboured to develop step by step the appliances without which the ore could not be won; only a name here and there has been handed down to us. But concerning the works created in the fifteenth and in the first half of the sixteenth centuries by German masters of the art, we have a curiously detailed account, which we owe in the first place to Georg Bauer, who, in accordance with the custom of the time among the learned, took the name of Georgius Agricola. He put his own intimate knowledge of the mining of his time into a book written in Latin, then the universal language of the educated, and entitled *De Re Metallica*. This was the technical bible for the whole world of mining for 200 years. It was soon made accessible in a German translation, and everyone who wrote on mining drew his material from Agricola. This treatise led to the knowledge presented to us by Agricola flowing through innumerable channels and fertilizing, stimulating, and instructing all those who had to do with mining and metallurgy: indeed, even with glass-making. When we give an account here of Agricola's life, and pay tribute to his great importance, recognized far beyond the confines of Germany, we are also celebrating the excellent German masters of the art of mining and smelting, of whose great knowledge and powers Agricola gives such an excellent account. We see in him the herald of the fame of the engineers of his time. In the Hall of Fame of the German Museum in Munich there is a portrait of Agricola with the inscription 'Georg Agricola, famous as investigator and physician, became herald of the great achievements of German technology, a great experimenter, and expounder of mediaeval mining and smelting.'

Georg Agricola was born in Glauchau in Saxony on March 24th, 1494. We know nothing of his parents nor of his early youth. He must have gone to school in Glauchau, and we know that he went at an early age to the Latin School at Zwickau, then very highly esteemed. His parents were in a position to give their son a good education. In 1514, at the age of twenty, he went to the university in

Leipzig. He absorbed with enthusiasm the learning of his time. He became a great Latin scholar, and what at the time was rare in Germany, he learnt Greek, and soon became highly proficient in this language. Agricola became a great humanist, whose striving after knowledge led him deeper and deeper into the most varied fields. In 1518 he was called as a teacher of Greek to Zwickau, to an academy from which a number of famous men have come. In the next year he was chosen, when only twenty-five years of age, as rector of the newly founded school. The fame of the Zwickau school spread. Melanchthon speaks in the highest terms of the praiseworthy town of Zwickau, which does so much to advance study. Luther also finds words of praise for it, bearing witness to his hearty appreciation 'that the people of Zwickau on their own initiative take up and pursue matters of this sort so seriously and courageously.'

Agricola's first book, a Latin grammar, was the outcome of this field of his work. The famous humanist Mosellanus, the teacher and friend of Agricola, then called him as his assistant to Leipzig, and so he became a teacher. Here he was in the midst of the intellectual currents of that great epoch; he attracted attention, and gained friends.

In 1524, when he was thirty years of age, he put aside philosophy and theology in order to study science and medicine in the famous universities of Italy. He went to Italy in 1523 or 1524. He studied in Bologna and Padua, but his longest stay—he himself mentions two years—was made in Venice. Here he worked in connection with the famous printer Manutinus. He had also an opportunity to learn much about industry, and visited the famous glass-blowing works in Murano. In 1526 he was in Rome. It was in Italy that he gained most of his astounding knowledge of the scientific, medical, and philosophical works of the ancients, and also of mediaeval and Oriental learning. While there he paid close attention to Arabian and Moorish literature as well. His friend Georg Fabricius tells us of his 'tireless enthusiasm for learning, and insatiable reading.' But we know that he was able to learn not only from books, but from practical experience, to which he attached the highest importance.

In 1527, Agricola was again in Germany. He was then in Joachimsthal as town physician. He himself writes: 'When I once returned to Germany from Italy, where I had studied medicine and philosophy for a few years, nothing was nearer to my heart than to go to the Erzgebirge, at present the richest silver mines in the whole of Europe. I had scarcely arrived there before I was full of a burning desire to get to know about mining, because I found everything beyond my expectation. A year later I took the advice of my friend, who had a great influence over me, to settle as a physician in Joachimsthal.'

His studies had drawn his attention to the fact that the ancients made use of many drugs of mineral origin, which were no longer known in his time. He wanted to re-discover them. These studies introduced him to geology, mineralogy, petrology. This brought him to mining, to men skilled in the knowledge of rocks, who burrow under the earth after the treasures so hotly desired by mankind.

The mining town of Joachimsthal was only ten years old when Agricola settled in it. The news of the rich discoveries there ran through Germany like a prairie fire. Miners streamed together into the place from all sides. Fourteen years after the foundation of the industry in 1516, there were already 914 undertakings, in which 800 surveyors and 400 foremen were in charge of 8,000 miners. One might really speak here of an American speed of development.

This new community needed a capable physician. Agricola needed all the expert men who had come together there. He became the friend of the mining experts, knew personally the masters of the art, and had the highest opinion of their invaluable labours. What he did not understand he had explained to him. This association and collaboration with

FE

the ablest men led to his thorough knowledge of mining and smelting, which he then gave to the world in language of wonderful clarity. The first fruit of this work was his catechism of mining, which he named after his friend, the expert in mining, *Bermannus*. The work was printed in 1530 by the famous press of Fröben in Basel.

The great humanist Erasmus, also a friend of Agricola, praises in this book not only the novelty of the subject, but above all the almost Attic simplicity of language and the incomparable clarity. But as he says, he would not have expected anything of a mediocre sort from such a mind as Agricola's.

From Joachimsthal he went to Chemnitz, where he lived from 1535 to 1555. This great industrial town needed him, not only to care for the health of its citizens, and to minister to the sick, but also for his knowledge of the world, his skill in negotiation, and the great reputation that he enjoyed, all of which were of advantage to the town in its many and various problems. He was called three times to the highest office by his fellow citizens; he was three times the chosen burgomaster of the town of Chemnitz. He did his best to serve the town amid the everlasting struggle for power of the princes round about it.

The mighty spiritual struggle of the Reformation broke out also in Chemnitz. Sides were taken passionately for or against the new faith. Priests of new faiths demanded unconditional agreement, and the warlike spirit of those days detested every concession. What position did Agricola take ? He had naturally the closest contact with this great spiritual movement. He no doubt recognized clearly how great was the need for reform in the Church of his time. He was certainly the man with courage enough to draw conclusions from what he knew of the facts. But his whole disposition made him hate revolution. What he saw and experienced daily in his town and state appeared to be a revolution, going far beyond the limits of what he was prepared to recognize as reformation. It appeared to him as if revolution here was often only a pretext for the struggle between local princes greedy for power and the might of the Emperor who gave unity to Germany. This political turn of events and so much that repelled him in the external forms of the movement made it impossible for him to support the Reformation as he experienced it. But in the meantime the new faith had conquered Chemnitz. His services were forgotten, and he was looked upon only as an enemy, a Papist. When Agricola, now a lonely man, closed his eyes on November 21st, 1555, in his sixty-second year, fanaticism was so powerful that burial was refused to this great German man of learning, physician, investigator, and burgomaster. The Abbot of Zeitz gave him a resting-place in his Abbey.

Agricola's tireless industry, of which his friends speak repeatedly, gave to the world, especially in his Chemnitz days, work of great importance in addition to his practical activity as physician and statesman. We are not now referring to his medical works, among which a book on plague has received especial recognition, nor of his other writings; in this place his great literary life-work is at the same time the most important witness to the achievements of German technology. A letter of Agricola's dated in March, 1533, already tells us that he intended, if his life was spared, to publish twelve books of his entitled *De Re Metallica*. Modest though he was, he knew all the same that this would be the greatest achievement of which he was capable. We know that he went more and more deeply into the material. He had opportunities to make journeys for purposes of studying German mining, and his friends gave him news from the whole world concerning the subject about which he had undertaken to write. Fabricius wrote in a letter to one of his friends: 'The books *De Re Metallica* are awaited with the greatest eagerness,' and he further says that if Agricola treats of the material with the industry which is natural to him, he would then earn such praise as no one has earned in literature for a thousand years. Agricola finished the work in 1550. The book, decorated with 273 wonderful woodcuts, also of great historical value, was ready in March, 1553, and the manuscript with the pictures went to Fröben and Basel. It was also a great undertaking for the printer, and it was only in March, 1556, four months after Agricola's death, that it appeared in Basel. Agricola was no longer able to fulfil the desire of his prince and to issue it also in the German language. This task was undertaken by the Basel professor, physician, and philosopher, Philip Bechius. It was thereby made accessible to the men who had provided the chief material for it. A suggestion made shortly before the Great War to issue it in modern German could not be carried out on account of the conditions of the time. In the meantime an excellent English edition was produced by the mining engineer Herbert Clark Hoover, later President of the United States. Hoover carried out this great work, with the assistance of his wife, in five years, and thus presented the English-speaking world with an excellent translation of Agricola, enriched by numerous valuable historical notes. Hoover, in his Preface, points out quite justly how inadequate the old German edition is, and expresses his surprise that we Germans have not yet made our great fellow countryman accessible to the German-speaking world by a translation of his masterpiece.

The Verein deutscher Ingenieure and the Deutsche Museum in Munich then undertook to produce the edition of 1928, thanks to the wide support of influential circles and above all the co-operation of those who were chiefly concerned in the translation. The Reich Press printed the book with great artistic insight, and the wonderful cuts are effectively displayed. Agricola divided his work into twelve sections, which he named 'books.' So great a reader as Agricola naturally made use of all literature on the subject accessible to him, and again and again we are astonished when reading his work at the amount of knowledge which this one individual had absorbed. Among newer writers, Agricola himself mentions a book by an Italian, Vannoccio

Biringuccio, who was born in 1480 in Siena, and brought out his work *Pirotechnia* in 1540 in Venice. It was described as a textbook of chemical metallurgy and of gunnery. We know concerning the writer that he studied German mining and its technology in two journeys, and that he was not unacquainted with the old German military literature, and Agricola's *Bermannus*.

Agricola was naturally familiar with the extensive literature of the alchemists, and it is characteristic of his acute mind that he would have nothing to do with it. His opinion is that no one had ever grown rich by this art, although they were all applying themselves to it day and night with the greatest industry with a view to making great heaps of gold and silver. 'Their books also reveal their untruthfulness, for they write on them the names of Plato and Aristotle, and other philosophers, in order to awaken in simple persons by these boastful inscriptions a belief in their learning.' He then proceeds to talk of his own work, and gives us in his clear language at the same time a short survey of his twelve books: 'The first contains all that can be said against the art, and against mines and miners by their opponents; the second instructs the miner concerning the sort of man he is to be, and goes on to discuss the discovery of veins; the third deals with veins and faults, and their distortion. The fourth describes the method of following the veins, and also describes the various offices of the mining community. The fifth describes the getting of the ore, and the art of separating the values. The sixth describes mining tools and machinery. The seventh deals with the testing of ores. The eighth gives instruction in firing the ore, pulverizing it, washing it, and roasting it. The ninth describes the art of smelting the ores. The tenth gives an account of separating silver from gold, and lead from the latter and silver. The eleventh shows how silver is to be separated from copper. The twelfth gives recipes for preparing salt, soda, alum, vitriol, sulphur, mineral wax, and glass.'

He then tells us further how much trouble and work he has expended without counting the cost, and he has not only described all the tools, machines, and furnaces, but also engaged paid draughtsmen to make illustrations in order that the things described in words, but unknown to present or future readers, shall not offer any difficulties to the understanding. And now follow in the 564 pages of the new German edition a detailed account in simple and clear language of all the knowledge and experience possessed by his time in the field of mining. The importance of this work for the further development of mining technology cannot be over-estimated.

Not many books live for 400 years. Let us close this account with Goethe's wonderful words of praise for Agricola, taken from his treatise on colour: 'So let us remember our fellow countryman Agricola, who performed in the first half of the sixteenth century the service for mining, which we would have wished for our own field of work. It is true that he was fortunate enough to enter into a realm of nature and art complete in itself, which had for a long time been worked in, which though highly complex had always been instilled with a purpose. Mountains opened up by mining, important natural products sought out in their raw state, mastered, treated, worked up, separated, purified, and put to human purposes: this is what interested him in the highest degree as an outsider, for he lived in the mountains as a physician, he himself being of an energetic and highly observant nature, at the same time acquainted with antiquity, educated in the classical languages, and able to express himself readily and attractively in them. So we still admire him in his works, which take in the whole subject of old and new mining, old and new knowledge of ores and stones, and come to us like a valuable present. He was born in 1494, and died in 1555, and thus lived in the highest and best period of the new art and literature which had just come into being and immediately reached their highest peaks.'

OTTO VON GUERICKE

ENGINEER AND SCIENTIST

1602–1686

In the Hall of Fame of the Deutsche Museum of master-pieces of science and technology in Munich, the Pantheon of great German scientists and engineers, the portrait of Otto von Guericke was one of the first to be hung. It bears the inscription:

'The German founder of experimental science. The air pump and the electric machine have made his name famous. With their aid he opened up wide fields of physical knowledge, and created essential foundations of machine technology.'

Two hundred and fifty years have passed since he died in Hamburg in the house of his son. Almost 300 years have passed since he thought out those experiments which startled the world, and whose effects to-day were undreamed-of in his time; they were carried out by him with the technical insight of genius. Guericke the engineer and scientist is not forgotten. His fame survives the centuries.

He himself built his own greatest monument in his book on the 'new Magdeburg experiment,' which appeared in the last years of his life, when he was beginning to fear that he would no longer live to see it published on account of the endless delays in the Dutch Press in Amsterdam; it came out, however, in 1672, fourteen years before his death. Written in the learned language of the time, Latin, no German translation of it has yet appeared, but on the occasion of the celebration of the 250th anniversary of his death, the Siemens-Ring-Stiftung, which has taken up the task of paying honour to great men of technology and science, determined in 1936 to join the Agricola Society of the Deutsche Museum, and the Verein deutscher Ingenieure in presenting the German nation with Guericke's work in its own language. It will be printed by the Reich Press in a worthy manner.

Guericke was born in Magdeburg on November 20th, 1602. His ancestors may be traced back there as far as 1315. He came from the landed gentry. His father, trained as a lawyer, held diplomatic posts under the kingdom of Poland in Moscow, Constantinople, and Copenhagen. The family was wealthy, owned a noble house, brewing concessions, and great estates on the fertile Magdeburg land, which it farmed. The father was able to give his only son a good education. He was taught by tutors. At fifteen years of age he went to the University of Leipzig, then to Helmstedt, then to Jena, and then to the Dutch University of Leiden, world-famous at the time. While in Jena he had studied chiefly jurisprudence, in Leiden he was attracted to mathematics and science. The applied mathematics of the great Universities of those days included everything that a school could teach concerning technology. He learned surveying, but above all military technology and fortification. He was introduced to astronomy, and to the scientific thought of his time.

Just as an apprentice, after serving his time, had to go on his travels in order to become a master, so also were men of learning accustomed to see the world as part of their education. Guericke was able to travel for nine months in France and England. He took everything in with lively senses and open eyes. His view extended far beyond the limits of his own native city.

After this upbringing and education, he returned to his native town, and married in 1626. He put his youthful powers at the service of his town. The young patricians were enrolled in the ranks of the councillors. The knowledge and experience which he had acquired in the world led to his being entrusted with the engineering task of strengthening the fortification of the town in a manner appropriate to that warlike time.

Germany was once again, and on the greatest scale, the battle-field of Europe. The mighty spiritual struggles of the Reformation had given rise to political questions of the first order. Once more Germans were fighting with Germans. Magdeburg was Protestant, the Imperial troops marched against the town, and before Gustavus Adolphus was able to relieve it, the town was taken in spite of its very brave defence. The wealthy Magdeburg was subjected to the most monstrous outrages. The greater part of the citizens lost their lives, their goods and chattels were plundered, the town was burned. Guericke only saved the lives of himself and his family with the greatest difficulty. He entered the service of Sweden, worked at the fortifications of Erfurt, but immediately returned to Magdeburg when he saw that the survivors were willing to rebuild their wonderful town, its wrecked bridges, and its churches. Guericke became the town architect, but his far-reaching proposals came for the most part to nothing in face of the desire of the impoverished citizens to restore the little narrow alleys by rebuilding on the existing foundations.

Guericke's diplomatic skill, a legacy from his father, was of especial value to Magdeburg in those difficult times. He had to journey to Osnabrück and Munster, where preparations for the conclusion of peace were going on, for Magdeburg was not willing to give up its struggle for independence, but wished to be, as in old times, a free city on the great European highway, and on the Elbe, the waterway connecting north and south. Guericke succeeded in extracting important assurances. Much was promised to this tall Magdeburg burgomaster with his noble bearing, sharp blue eyes, narrow firm face, who moved with such assurance in the dignified dress of his office as an equal among the high dignitaries present. The citizens of Magdeburg were thankful to him, though they were able in their poverty to pay him but little, but they promised him and his family freedom from taxes for all times, they gave him privileges, and even allowed him to pay for these, now and then, out of his own pocket. We know that Guericke as town architect contributed very considerable sums on his own account to the carrying out of the town plans.

But matters were not settled by the conclusion of peace. Again and again he had to go to the meetings of the Reichstag in Regensburg, or to the Imperial Court in Vienna; he was not able to achieve a permanent success on the lines desired by Magdeburg. The power of the princes of Brandenburg and Saxony, whose territories lay next to Magdeburg, was too great for him. Magdeburg was compelled to pay homage in 1666 to the Elector of Brandenburg. The free city was made a part of the greater Prussia then coming into being, which was destined to become the centre of German unity.

A more peaceful time was now the lot of Magdeburg's burgomaster, and he used it to complete his historical studies of his town, and above all, for his scientific experiments, which, however, had been begun considerably earlier. We have here to give an account of these works, on which his world-wide fame was founded.

The men of that time had long ceased to pay sole attention to the purely theological world of thought of past centuries. Scientific thought had awakened, and sought for satisfaction, though it was for long anxiously concerned to reconcile the new knowledge with the opinions of the theological schools. It was dangerous to move outside fixed dogma. Added to the Heaven of the theologians, with which humanity is so concerned, were the heavens which we see. Men strove to understand the infinity of the heavens with their sun and innumerable glittering stars. Only pure thought could solve our problems here, said the learned. And this thought was organized as a profession. The academic learned claimed that they alone were able to discover new solutions in this field. The learning of the Schoolmen strove to solve the riddle of the universe by continually greater subtlety of thought. The Emperor's astronomer Kepler, called by his friends the prince of astronomers, had opened up for us the laws of planetary motion in a mathematically scientific form. The effect of his work was enormous.

Young Guericke also had not been to the Universities in vain, and great as were the cares of every day, he nevertheless turned his eyes to this problem of the universe. He may well have often found in this occupation a way of getting at a distance from earthly matters, and so gaining calm and certainty for his daily problems.

Kepler, when engaged in getting one of his great works printed, in spite of the greatest difficulty, wrote: 'In the midst of the collapse of cities, provinces, and states, of old and new families, in the midst of the fear of barbaric attacks, of violent destruction of hearth and home, I see myself, a disciple of Mars . . . without giving signs of fear, at work here. . . . With God's help I will also really carry this work to an end, and that, too, like a soldier, inasmuch as I to-day give my orders with defiance, rage, and fury, leaving to the morrow the care for my burial.' These were warlike words of great fighters in a warlike time. Guericke might also have spoken thus as he set to work to take his own part in his own way in this battle of minds.

The Schoolmen fought with words and with the power of their pens. Is there such a thing as a vacuum ?—that was the question which stirred men's minds at the time. Some proved with the greatest skill that such a thing as a vacuum is impossible, others with no less a gift of eloquence, proved the opposite. 'Words are wonderful things for dispute, words for making systems, for believing in, not a letter can be taken away from a word,' and Goethe goes on to say, 'I tell you a fellow who speculates is like an animal on a dry pasture led around in a circle by an evil spirit, while all around is splendid green pasture.'

Guericke saw this fine green pasture. He did not wish to speculate, nor to argue with the learned, but to question Nature herself; he would attempt to create a vacuum, a space empty of air.

He filled a beer cask, one especially well made, with water, and fixing to it an ordinary syringe, and two valves, he attempted to pump out the water. When the water is got out the cask must be empty of all matter. The work was not easy; two strong and powerful men pulled the syringe off. It had to be fixed much more firmly. The work went forward with great difficulty. But Guericke discovered that the air got in through the wood itself. An air-free space cannot be created in this way. So he put the cask in a larger one filled with water, thus sealing it with water. The work was begun again, but this still led to no success; water and after it air now got into the cask which was to be pumped out. Wood was not a suitable material for this experiment.

Guericke went to the coppersmith and had a sphere of copper made. The work was begun again. The air became thinner and thinner, and suddenly to the terror of all present, the external pressure of the air crushed the copper sphere, 'as one crushes a cloth in one's hand.' The extraordinary power of the external air pressure was manifested.

For further tests a stronger and better worked spherical vessel was used, and the experiment was finally successful. Guericke had produced a space empty of air, and though the learned had hitherto supported the all-too-human idea that nature abhors a vacuum, which furthermore contradicts the nature of God and hence cannot exist: there *was* a vacuum, which nature actually put up with in spite of the opinion of the learned. 'There are more things in heaven and earth than are dreamt of in your philosophy.' Guericke made a number of further experiments. He proved that a flame cannot burn in a vacuum, that a sparrow dies in one, that sound cannot be conveyed without air, and many other things. But he wished, above all, to make an impressive ocular demonstration of the great and undreamed-of power of air pressure. He conceived for this purpose the idea of constructing two exactly worked hemispheres, fitting together closely, but the coppersmith was not able to make them with sufficient perfection. Guericke put a leather packing between the two hemispheres, so getting an airtight joint. The sphere was then pumped out. Strong men were no longer able to pull the two halves apart. Guericke calculated the force of the pressure, and knew that with the dimensions he had chosen, even sixteen horses pulling against one another would not succeed in separating the hemispheres. In this way he gave his contemporaries the most striking presentation of the magnitude of the atmospheric pressure. These experiments were not carried out at the Reichstag in Regensburg, in front of the Emperor and the German Princes, as has hitherto been assumed, but only some years later in Magdeburg.

Guericke carried out other experiments in the manner of an engineer. He built in his yard a scaffolding of wood, and in place of the hemispheres he arranged a cylinder, in which an air-tight piston was fitted. A strong rope went from the piston over two pulleys. A number of men could pull on the ropes, but they were unable to hold the piston in place when the space between it and the cylinder was pumped free of air. Or he hung on this wooden structure the two hemispheres, loading the lower one with weights, and so being able to determine the magnitude of the air pressure. Further, he thought out an instructive experiment, by which he could determine the weight of the air.

He further allowed water to be forced by external air pressure into a vessel, and wished to know how high this pressure is able to lift the water in a pipe. For this purpose he went to the top story of his house, and proved that the external pressure of the air is able to support a column of water 20 Magdeburg ells high—about 30 ft.

Also, he was already aware that this height is not invariable. If it is true that the whole earth is covered by a sea of air, at the bottom of which we human beings live, then the pressure of this air should be greater at the ground level than on the top of a church tower, or a high mountain. The reading of an instrument measuring the air pressure will also change with the weather. Guericke put on the column of water a little carved figure of a man, which showed the height of the barometer at the moment. This Magdeburg weather-man, who was so clever as to foretell the weather, excited the greatest admiration, and astonishment. Guericke could venture to foretell the weather by means of his barometer. He prophesied a mighty storm two hours before it broke out, a feat which was looked upon as marvellous. He set out with a servant to test his instrument on the Brocken, but the servant had a fall during the climb, and the instrument was broken. The experiment was not repeated.

In the meantime, he heard from a learned man at the Reichstag in Regensburg that in Italy Torricelli, the learned pupil of Galileo, had already invented the mercury barometer. He recognized the value of this invention, but was right in believing that he too had achieved great success by quite different means. In France, too, Pascal undertook measurements at high levels based on the Italian experiment. He also went over to mercury later, but at first made use, in wine-loving France, of red wine as a liquid.

The majority of Guericke's experiments on air pressure appear to have been carried out between 1657 and 1662. But there can be no doubt that he had already mastered these problems at an earlier date. He appears to have been working on the air pump in 1635 onwards, and we know that he carried some of his apparatus with him on his long journeys, so as to be able to work further on it, and also to convince the many who were only willing to believe when they saw the experiments with their own eyes. His son later on proved that his father had spent on his scientific experiments 20,000 thalers, a very great sum in those days.

But Guericke also carried out world-famous electrical experiments, though we have not yet been able to discover how they have been done. He reported on them in 1662 by letter, and demonstrated them in Magdeburg at the same time. Leibniz learned of them, and Guericke gave him a full account of them by letter. Here again the intention of the experiments was to explain problems of the earth. What the great English scientist Gilbert wished to show with his spherical magnet, Guericke wished to prove with a sphere of sulphur. A ball of sulphur mounted so that it can be spun round gives electrical effects when the hands are laid on it. He was the first to discover electrical repulsion after previous attraction by means of a down feather, while he used small hop leaves for showing repulsion. He observed the effects of sharp points, and discovered that electricity can be conducted through a thread. Though he was not able to solve cosmic problems, and Leibniz pointed out to him that his assumption of 'world forces' was not sufficiently scientific, his experiments are nevertheless a proof that Guericke was a pioneer in a new field of work, one which to-day dominates the technical world by its immense effects.

Leibniz wrote to Guericke on August 17th, 1671: 'If you, most honoured Sir, had never invented or discovered anything else than the sphere which has had so much effect in the illumination of human science, and the pumping out of air, whereby human power has been increased, you would have rendered sufficient service to the human race.'

We can scarcely form any conception of the enormous effect of Guericke's experiments on the minds of his contemporaries, for we are ceasing more and more to be astonished by the mighty events which take place in the technical sphere. For the learned men of all the world were agreed that a vacuum could not possibly exist, and along comes the burgomaster of a German town, a member of no academic body, and shows everyone that he can produce a vacuum, and, furthermore, what enormous effects the external pressure of the air is able to produce. The whole affair seemed like a miracle. The air all round us, which we take as naturally as a healthy person takes his good health, the air which we cannot see, to which we pay no attention, which goes through us and surrounds everything, without which no life on earth is possible, without which no fire can exist, this was now exhibited in its properties and powers by experiments. A learned Jesuit father of Würzburg, Professor Schott, who before the appearance of Guericke's work did much by his own books to spread a knowledge of the experiments, says in his essay *On the Magdeburg Experiments*:

'I do not hesitate to confess frankly, and to say boldly that I have never seen, heard, read, or thought of anything more marvellous of this sort, indeed I believe that since the creation of the world the sun has never shone on anything like it, to say nothing of anything more wonderful.'

Such a judgment by a learned contemporary must bring before our eyes how great the effect of this work of Guericke's was, reaching far beyond the circle of the learned. That which gave rise in those days to incredulous amazement is to-day self-evident to every schoolboy, and Guericke and his experiments are mentioned in every elementary physics course.

We admire Guericke for the ingenious engineering style of his experiments, which, far removed from mere theoretical notions, produced the greatest effect on men's minds. And it was not enough simply to think out these experiments; they had to be carried out with the very inadequate technical resources of that time. We know that Guericke himself had often put his hand to the work, that he used both his head and his hands accurately in connection with it, and we may recall in this connection the remarks of a great German scientist, Helmholtz, who when speaking in 1869 in Innsbruck on the aims and progress of natural science, pointed out that the human memory is patient, and is able to store up in itself an almost incredible amount of learning, but the scientist needs, in addition to such knowledge, senses with the power of close attention. He needs abilities which can only be acquired by persistent attempts and long practice. His senses must be sharpened for certain powers of observations, and his hand must be practised now to undertake the work of a smith or mechanic or carpenter, now that of a draughtsman or a violin player. More than this, he must possess the courage and coolness of a soldier, when confronted by overpowering destructive forces.

These were demands which Guericke fulfilled in a high degree, but in addition he had love for the work itself, and the power of concentrating all his senses on it. We find wonderful examples of this enthusiasm in his work. We experience Guericke's grand view of the Cosmos, which raises him far above his contemporaries. His description of 'nothingness' rises in his work to poetic heights: 'Nothingness contains all things, is more precious than gold, coming and going is strange to it . . . nothingness is full of all wisdom. Where nothingness is, there ends the king's command, only nothingness knows no pain, the earth hangs over nothing, says Job, besides the world is only nothing. Nothingness is everywhere.'

Equally powerful is his praise of God at the close of his work: 'but as God is immeasurable so also is the host of his fiery servants without end. The immeasurable vastness of heaven is peopled with innumerable standards and flags of the heavenly army. Of this mortal life our knowledge is but fragments, but when the hour of accomplishment shall come, all barriers will fall.'

But what is Guericke's great significance for our own time ? Why did the German engineers put a statue of Guericke over the entrance to their house in Berlin ? Because Guericke, by his direct questioning of nature and high regard for experiments, led the way for us as an engineer into the present land of scientific knowledge and technical work.

Since the seventeenth century we see an ever-increasing acceleration in the great development of science and technology. These successes we owe to the companionship in work of science and technology, which by mutually stimulating, helping, and supporting one another, make possible

GE

that which has been held to be impossible. In those times, in which the learned thought to solve the riddle of nature by words alone, Guericke in his great work confronts them with the sentence:

'In scientific questions fine talk and good argument are not of the least value. When facts may be made to speak, ingenious hypotheses are not needed.'

That was the only possible way which could lead to our present successes. Practical recognition of reality, discovery of facts: these were the foundations on which the proud edifice of present-day technology had to be reared.

When the learned and unlearned pressed him all too closely with trifling objections based on no sort of experiments, he defended his position openly and clearly. But finally his patience gives way in the face of all too stupid objections, and he writes:

'I take it to be superfluous to confute this and other talk, for more weight is to be laid on experiments, than upon the judgment of stupidity, which is always ready to invent prejudices against nature.'

Guericke, as the combative burgomaster of Magdeburg and great scientist, made short work of these preconceived ideas. But many who came after him still had to fight for the decisive importance of experiment. How long is the time before discoveries made by the great become common property is seen in a remarkable example given us by Helmholtz in his discourse on 'Thought in Medicine' in the year 1877. He tells us how a much admired professor who was invited by a physicist to witness an experiment, rejected the suggestion indignantly, on the ground that the experiment had nothing to do with true science. And another learned professor begged him insistently to divide up the course in physiology and lecture himself only on that concerned with pure thought, leaving everything to do with experiments to a lesser colleague, who would be good enough for the purpose. When Helmholtz declared that he regarded experiments as the origin of all science, intellectual inter-course with his famous colleague was interrupted.

Facts determined by experiments often need a long time before the knowledge of them becomes widespread. The fundamental experiments of Torricelli resulted from the desire of Italian makers of pumps to get their pumps to suck water from greater depths than 10 metres. Guericke's work showed that water cannot rise higher in the suction pipe of a pump than the external air pressure is able to lift it. But a famous German professor, who has also done great things as a practical machine designer, tells of his experiences with a much esteemed practical pump maker from a waterworks forty years ago, who was once again attempting to make a pump suck water much higher than the external air pressure allows. The professor gave the practical man a long discourse on the physical impossibility of his attempts, with the result that the pump maker summed up his own opinion by saying that even a difficulty like that could be got over by goodwill and energy.

Guericke determined in his old age, feeling perhaps that he had been unfairly treated by his fellow citizens, but chiefly no doubt in view of the plague which was approaching the town, to spend the last years of his life far from his native town with his son, who had the post of Ambassador of the Great Elector in Hamburg. He died there on the 11th May—the 21st by our present calendar—1686. He was first buried in Hamburg, but his remains were after-wards taken to Magdeburg. Here, however, they were taken out of the church which was hastily transformed by the French into a hospital in 1806, and destroyed with the remains of other Magdeburg citizens, so that no one now has the opportunity to lay on Guericke's grave a wreath of honour.

The great deeds of great men are not bound up with their life-time. They take ever-growing effect in course of time, far beyond the earthly existence of the individual.

GREAT MODERN ENGINEERS

JAMES WATT
1736–1819

A DIRECT path leads from Guericke's work on the pressure of the air to the production of the first heat engine, a prime mover ready for human service at all times, independently of the wind and weather. Many remarkable men combined to develop it in the eighteenth century. The greatest genius who took part in this engineering achievement was James Watt, whose fame justly stands much higher than that of his predecessors and co-workers.

The importance for human history of the invention of the steam engine cannot be over-estimated. We have to go far back to the time before the beginning of history to discover a technical event, the use of fire, of like importance. Perhaps one may further reckon among these technical events in world history, the invention of firearms in Germany in the fourteenth century. Later times will lay even a greater stress on the decisive importance of the steam engine as a historical event. Such a development as the steam engine, the starting-point of a new epoch extending far beyond the limits of trade and industry, must have a great influence also on the social life of mankind, upon their thoughts and feelings. In the history of the steam engine, there are not wanting those great dramatic movements, the storm and stress of human passion, the outpouring of love and hate, which always appear with especial prominence when new times are coming to birth, when world events are taking new directions, and men are being torn out of the habitual round of daily life.

Great convulsions of the whole of social life also accompany the entry of the steam engine into history. It meant the beginning of the fight against the old home industry, against handicraft; mighty factories sprang from the ground, with an immense output concentrated into a small space, and the factory worker and the factory owner came into being. Social displacements unheard of in extent begin to be felt. The steam engine makes man independent of his physical power, and in many cases also of the acquired skill of the individual. The battle against the machine, which always breaks out when considerable displacements in the employment of labour are caused by it, often took on revolutionary forms, particularly in England. This was not the fault of the steam engine, which is beyond good and evil, but of man's lack of social skill, whereby he was baffled by the flow of new possibilities of development, seeking to guide it into the shallow channels of his traditional existence, and then wondering when this great new flood burst all dams and barriers, and deluged all the land.

The study of this movement shows us plainly how greatly the steam engine has changed the rhythm of human life. The development went forward with the inevitability of a law of nature. When engineers succeeded in using the steam engine for transport, when the first steamship, and the first locomotive came into the world, the influence of the steam engine on human life was increased to an extraordinary degree. If you were to attempt to plot from decade to decade the number of horse-power of heat engines at work in the world, we would see how slowly the curve was still rising in the eighteenth century, how it started to rise a little faster in the first half of the nineteenth, how at the turn of the century we already believed that the rate of advance could continue no longer, only to see in the twentieth century the transmission of electric power and the steam turbine result in a still steeper rise in the curve. While the total world-production of electric energy amounted in 1931 to 310 thousands of millions of kilowatt-hours (B.O.T. units), in 1937 it was already estimated at 450 thousands of millions.

In Guericke's day, and after him far into the eighteenth century, want of motive power hindered all further industrial development. The first source of power was the muscles of men and animals, and we can hardly imagine to-day how severely human strength was tried, how overworked, according to our present ideas, were the animals employed in pulling loads, turning wheels, and driving machines which, at that time, were already present in numerous forms. But when many mines in the eighteenth century had to use as many as 500 horses merely to get the water out of the workings, we see also how nearly the technical and economic limit was already reached. The most valuable workings had to be abandoned to subterranean water without resistance. Before the coming of the steam engine, mankind had other natural powers at his disposal. Thousands of small water-wheels were working for him, and windmills were used to drain low-lying land, and for grinding the farmer's corn wherever wind conditions were reasonably favourable. Above all, wind power was of the greatest service on the sea, and the achievements in the building of sailing vessels were also most admirable in the eighteenth and nineteenth centuries. But water and wind were bound by place and time, and the longing grew for a source of power available to man everywhere and at all times.

Guericke had shown by his experiments, impressive also to the laity, that a great number of strong men are not able to hold back a piston moving in a cylinder, when the air between the bottom of the cylinder and the piston is removed. The external air pressure forces in the piston, and

13. OTTO VON GUERICKE (1602–86)

14. Denis Papin (1647–1712)

15. John Smeaton (1724–92)

From the portrait by George Romney,
National Portrait Gallery, London

it was clear to everyone that very considerable work could be done in this way. The problem was, therefore, that of creating a vacuum under the piston. There was no lack of proposals; stout fellows might be put to work at the air pump, said some, and others proposed to use a water-wheel for the purpose. These suggestions show how little the actual problem had been grasped, for it would, of course, have been considerably simpler to have the strong men, or the water-wheel working the machine directly, without troubling the air pressure, which is only able to get to work with their work.

Other means had, therefore, to be thought out for producing the vacuum. The idea of using gunpowder for the purpose was then put forward in France. It was to be exploded on the bottom of the cylinder, and the gases rushing out at great speed were to drive out the air through a valve in the piston, whereby a vacuum would be formed, and the external air pressure would close the valve, and force in the piston. The forerunner of the steam engine was thus this atmospheric explosion engine, driven by powder; it was taken up again in Germany 160 years later in an effective form, the atmospheric gas engine of Otto and Langen. The Dutch physicist Huygens, then living in Paris, also worked on this explosion engine, and for this purpose he engaged the services of Denis Papin.

Denis Papin was born on August 22nd, 1647, in Blois, in France, as the son of a royal official in a high position. We know nothing of the first fourteen years of his life. At fifteen years of age he went to the University of Angers, and studied medicine and natural science. We then find him bearing the title of Doctor, in Paris, where he was much admired for his great skill in making his apparatus for the most part with his own hands, and for his sharp powers of observation. In 1675 he went to London, where he worked on the air pump with the famous physicist Boyle. There also he was very much appreciated. The Royal Society of London made Papin a

member at the age of thirty-three. By way of thanks he
dedicated to it a paper in which he described the 'digestor'
named after him. The economic development and application of this on a large scale, already hoped for by Papin, was
left to our own time. But in those days also, many famous
men turned their attention to this invention of Papin's, which
made it possible to cook food under high pressure, and so
protect it from going bad. The invention of the safety valve,
also ascribed to Papin, was a necessary adjunct to the use of
this apparatus. Papin recommended his apparatus at the time
to 'confectioners, cooks, brewers, and dyers.' He himself
made use of it to make fruit jelly by evaporation.

Papin's desire for travel, and his hope of getting on more
quickly in other conditions, took him for a short time to
Venice. But he returned to London again a few years later,
where he was employed by the Royal Society to carry out
scientific experiments. Here he undertook a whole series of
remarkable researches. He proposed to use compressed air
for the transmission of power. He attempted to hurl projectiles by the aid of a vacuum, new forms of artillery seeming
to him to promise well in the warlike times in which he lived.
But in the meantime France had revoked the Edict of Nantes,
and his return to his native country was now closed to him
as a Protestant. He belonged to the many thousands of
French citizens who were now destined to carry science,
industry, and trades, in which the France of those days was
superior to many of its neighbours, to England, Holland,
Germany, and above all to Prussia. Religious persecution
plays a very important part in the history of the spread of
industry.

Among the many German princes who were less interested
in alchemy than in mechanics, was the then Landgrave of
Hessen. He had heard of Papin, and called him to the
University of Marburg. Papin accepted this call, in order to
get on in the world. He was appointed Professor of Mathematics in 1688. He spoke in his inaugural address of 'the

uses of mathematical science, especially of hydraulics,' but
Marburg was a disappointment to Papin. He was embittered
by the narrow and petty conditions of life there. The Landgrave himself was mostly absent from his country at the wars
of that time. The sciences which Papin had to represent were
not part of the course of study for any profession; people took
little notice of this French savant; the income was extremely
small, it was hard to live on 200 thalers a year, especially since
he had married in 1691. But his work as an inventor is of
uncommon interest. He invented the centrifugal pump, he
wanted to take up again the transmission of power to a
distance, he made experiments with the diving bell, and even
with a submarine boat, this in 1692 at the request of the
Landgrave in Cassel. But after all, what use was a submarine in Cassel ?

The owners of the mines and smelting works applied to
Papin for advice as to how they might improve their work
technically. Above all, they were concerned about the
consumption of fuel. Papin helped with the evaporation of
brine; the learned Professor had plenty of work, and lost all
interest in the endless scientific controversies which at that
time were a chief occupation among the academic. Papin
had already made the acquaintance of Leibniz in Paris, who
took a lively interest in all his work. Papin wrote to Leibniz
in 1696: 'As regards my theoretical labours, I must admit
that I have completely abandoned them. The number of
machines and new inventions which I have in my head
becomes ever greater, and I have no stronger desire than to
live to see their effect, which they will produce as soon as they
can be properly constructed.' He complains that he only
goes ahead very slowly. He has to do everything himself, he
has no money to pay a mechanic, he will certainly not be able
to carry out half his plans. 'Hence, I will,' he continues,
'limit myself to serving the world with the talent which God
has given me, leaving it for the great and versatile spirits such
as yours, to penetrate into eternal truths, and create for

posterity short and easy ways, along which they may move to ever greater progress.'

Of all his projects, the one which makes him the great forerunner in the invention of the steam engine, is the atmospheric piston machine invented by him. The Landgrave had ordered him to concern himself in Marburg also with Huygens's powder engine. He added a touch-hole to it, and improved it in this way. The vacuum produced was very poor, the machine could hardly stand the violent explosions, and so the user took his life in his hands. Papin's idea for improving it was a stroke of genius. He proposed to produce the vacuum by the condensation of steam instead of by the explosion of gunpowder. The air is driven out of the cylinder by boiling some water in it, the steam finally filling the whole cylinder. Heating is then stopped, whereupon the steam condenses again, the resulting water taking up only a small space in the cylinder. We then get a partial vacuum, which brings the external air pressure into action. In 1690 Papin published his work: *New methods of producing the most powerful driving forces with little trouble*. Papin was thus the first to invent and carry out a practical engine in which steam is used. He was the inventor of the atmospheric piston engine.

He was not, however, satisfied with adding another to existing clever pieces of apparatus; the ultimate aim of his work was practical utility. He proposed to use the power of his machine to raise water and ore out of mines, to hurl iron balls against the wind; ships were to be provided with paddles driven by his engine. Indeed, he also thought of using it to drive a carriage, and, if words were deeds, he had already invented the steamship and the motor car. But such things were not to be thought of. Even the famous boat with paddles, in which he wished to travel to England, and which was destroyed by the river sailors of Münden out of jealousy of their privileges, was no steamboat, but a boat with a paddle driven by man power, as expressly stated by Papin; and he ought to know more about it than the numerous writers who refuse to allow the legend of Papin's steamboat to die out.

But Papin's great hopes could not be fulfilled. He, himself, was able to construct a physical apparatus, but not a machine serviceable for practical work outside the laboratory. He himself recognized that the chief difficulty would be the construction of the great cylinder. He states that only long experience would be able to abolish this obstacle, and hence recommends that a factory should be founded concerned only with the construction of steam cylinders. But naturally at that time he could not get as far in Marburg as carrying out his plans on a large scale. The tragedy of his life, so rich in work, and so poor in success, lies in the contrast between his desires, and the needs and powers of his time.

Other plans put back the work on the heat engine. Leibniz wrote to him in 1705 that Savery in England was constructing a steam pump. The Landgrave desired Papin to concern himself once more with this idea. He was to build a pumping engine, and the water thus raised was to drive a mill. In June, 1706, experiments were actually carried out in Cassel with a pumping engine newly built by Papin. A marble tablet in the Square in front of the Science Museum in Cassel records this event, but a practical result was not attained.

Papin again determined to change his place of work, and the Landgrave gave him his freedom and a testimonial to his work. In 1707 Papin went to London again. Armed with introductions from Leibniz, he wanted to demonstrate his machine there, and enter into competition with Savery, but he was not able to get any help. Deserted by his earlier friends, Papin found himself poor and solitary in London. Again and again he sought the recognition of the Royal Society. He did not cease to work, but no success rewarded him. His last letter of the year 1712 closes with the words: 'I am in a miserable position, even when I do the best of work, I gain only enmity, but be that as it may, I fear nothing, for I trust in God who is all-powerful.' It is supposed that he died in 1712 destitute in London. His misfortune in life was to have lived a century too early.

In the same year that Papin departed this life, the wooden and iron limbs of a heat engine, built on his principle, moved for the first time; it was devised by Thomas Newcomen. The inventor was born at Dartmouth, in the county of Devon, in 1663, and baptized there on February 28th. He was apprenticed to an iron merchant, and then set up on his own account in his native town. We know nothing of his early years, we hear only that he visited as a dealer in tools the neighbouring county of Cornwall, the great mining field, and there experienced personally the desperate position of mining which could no longer cope with subterranean water. It may well be imagined that this led him to concern himself with the question whether help might not come from a new power-giving machine. He was not the only one who took an interest in this problem at that time. Among those working in this direction, was Thomas Savery, who received in 1698 a patent for an apparatus '. . . for raising of water, and occasioning motion to all sorts of mill works, by the impellant force of fire.' Savery's steam pump corresponds to our present-day pulsometer. The steam is used alternately to produce a partial vacuum and to lift the water sucked up to a height corresponding to the steam pressure. Here also it was not possible to get results of importance with the technical means then available. Though he brought out in 1702 a pamphlet entitled *The Miner's Friend*, he was not yet able to meet the needs of mining with this steam pump.

Savery was a fellow countryman of Newcomen. It may be that both attacked the problems at about the same time. But Newcomen took another road. He used, like Papin, a cylinder and a piston, but he separated the steam boiler and the cylinder. The steam cylinder was hung from the rafters of the machine house. The boiler was situated underneath it. The piston hung on strong chains from the radially curved end of a two-armed lever, the beam, at the other end of which the piston rod of the pump was also hung by chains. The steam from the boiler filled the space between the piston when at the upper end of the cylinder and the bottom of the latter. It drove out the air, and when it was condensed the vacuum was produced. The external air pressure forced down the piston, and raised the plunger of the suction pump fixed in the shaft. The steam was condensed by surface condensation. The machine made about four strokes a minute, and then by chance, condensation by a jet of water was discovered, whereby the speed was raised to twelve strokes a minute.

But there was much to be done before this engine could be put to work for the first time, in the years 1711 or 1712. The first engine is said to have been used in the county of Stafford. Savery, who had very good connections in Government circles, received a patent before Newcomen learnt about it, and the latter had to consider himself fortunate in being taken into partnership by Savery. Success was soon attained in causing the machine to regulate itself, so that it worked quite automatically. Up till then the only automatic motion of this sort known had been the clock. When we realize what enormous difficulties lay in the construction and use of this new form of machine, we must pay the greatest respect to Newcomen as engineer and inventor. Savery, who was born about 1650, died in 1715. The patent rights were then transferred to a Company, which in a special advertisement in 1716 pointed out that atmospheric piston machines of this sort were in use in various parts of England. The needs of the mining industry forced this machine into use to an ever-increasing extent.

The news that success had been attained in raising water by fire, soon spread beyond the frontiers of the country. In Hungary a steam engine was running as early as 1722, in France in 1726, in the same year in Sweden, in Vienna, and in Cassel; yes, even in Siberia the attempt was later made to build an atmospheric engine as a blower. Newcomen died in London, on August 5th, 1729. We have no portrait of him. We know nothing of his outward appearance, nothing of his life, but we know from the history of his great technical achievements how heavy must have been the cares of this master, but how great must have been the joy which final success brought to him.

While the Newcomen engine remained unchanged in principle, many important improvements were made in its construction in the course of the next few decades. This we owe to the great engineer John Smeaton, who succeeded in making great improvements in it by correct design and careful construction of the parts without making any change in its method of working and general arrangements. Smeaton's atmospheric engine remained for long after his time in use as a motive power for all sorts of purposes.

Smeaton, who was born at Leeds, on June 8th, 1724, the son of a successful lawyer, devoted himself to technology, which at that time was little esteemed in educated circles. He learned in London the art of making mathematical instruments, and understood how to make good use of the connections with scientific circles brought about by his instruments. He attended the lectures of the Royal Society, and was soon made use of for scientific work in this circle. His excellent work on experimental investigations of water and wind power for moving mills, and other machines with a rotary motion, was rewarded in 1759 with the gold medal. Smeaton extended his knowledge considerably by travelling in England and Belgium. In association with the great canal engineer Brindley, he planned and built canals, so taking part in his time in developing this first means for the large-scale transport of goods. Canal traffic preceded the railway, and its advantages were of great economic importance to England. He became famous as builder of the Eddystone Lighthouse, which enjoyed in its day world-wide renown as a masterpiece of engineering.

He first turned his attention to the steam engine in 1767. The way in which he grappled with and solved this problem, shows him to have been a born engineer: first thorough study of existing plants on the basis of numerous and exact experiments, then criticism of these results, followed by a search for means of making good the defects so revealed. Smeaton built a very large engine in 1775 for a mine in Cornwall. The cylinder was over 70 in. in diameter, and 10 ft. high. The machine house, built of granite, and forming also the framework of the machine, had a height of 60 ft. The mighty beam was made up of twenty strong fir beams, ten in pairs placed one over the other. The output of this huge machine, as calculated from the water raised, was about 70 h.p. Such were the means which had to be employed in those days to save a mine from drowning. We may understand contemporary critics who said of these atmospheric engines that an iron mine was needed to construct them, and a coal mine to drive them. They could no longer work economically where coal was dear and the mines had to be driven deeper and deeper. What was earned by the mine was eaten up by the steam engine. At this point began the pioneer work of James Watt.

In the little town of Greenock near Glasgow, James Watt, who was employed in shipbuilding, was presented on January 19th, 1736, with his fourth child, who also was named James. The father came of an old Scottish family. He was not blessed with this world's goods, and had to work as a carpenter and shipbuilder at any job which he could find. He, therefore, built not only houses and ships, but also furniture of all sorts, and did a trade in equipment for ships. He even tried his hand at mathematical instruments such as are used in navigation. The mother of the great inventor is described to us as a clever, kindly woman, remarkable both physically and intellectually. The childhood of little James Watt was lonely and quiet. He was frail and sickly, the joyous games of children of his age were not for him.

He thus became a shy child who anxiously avoided human society. He much preferred to play in his father's workshop. Taught reading, writing, and arithmetic by his mother, his intellectual development was very rapid, and even precocious, spending as he did all his time in the company of grown-up people. Loneliness led to the powerful development of the imagination of this mentally most active child; he was never tired of inventing fairy tales, and the pleasure of making up stories remained with him into old age. Even as an old man of eighty-one, he delighted Walter Scott, the great Scottish writer, by his art of telling fairy stories. He went to school later than other children, and was not greatly drawn to Greek or Latin, but did extremely well in mathematics.

His joy in constructive work in his father's workshop, his pleasure in discovering the secrets of all instruments which could be bought from his father, the uncommon skill of his slender hands, determined his choice of a profession. James Watt became a mechanic. His apprenticeship began in the then very small university town of Glasgow, in which little was to be seen of technology and industry. Here also he obtained entry into learned circles where he was able to add considerably to his education. But much was not to be learned in Glasgow in connection with his profession, and so he was determined to go to London. He arrived there after a journey on horseback which took him twelve days; such was then the time for a distance now covered by aeroplane in forty-eight minutes. He succeeded only with difficulty in finding a place where, for payment of a heavy premium, he could work for a year as apprentice. His health was not equal to hard labour and the privations which he imposed upon himself; to this was added an attack of homesickness, and so he returned to Glasgow at the age of twenty. The University offered him a cellar as a workshop. Here he began the experiments, the results of which were to extend far beyond his own life, and here he met with scientific stimulus of all sorts in the circles of the professors and students.

This modest University mechanic became a friend of professors; and men such as Black, to whom the science of heat owes so much, and Robison, a master of mathematics, a man of the world who knew America and Russia, were never tired of talking of the modesty and great knowledge of this mechanic. 'Everything became science in his hands.' James Watt was a great reader all his life, able to separate the wheat from the chaff. His friends provided him with reading matter in all fields, and later on, men who found entry into the small circle of James Watt's intimates were again and again astonished to find how 'uncommonly well educated' this famous engineer was. He was given the possibility of independent work outside the University, but from the point of view of earnings, the prospects were not so good. He was unable to do without assistance from his father. A living was not to be made out of the two or three mathematical instruments needed every year in Glasgow, so he gave his attention to mending and constructing musical instruments. Soon he was occupied with building an organ of considerable size for which he received an order. Watt went to work on building organs in the same methodical way as later he employed in constructing the steam engine. First he studied the literature of the subject, above all a treatise on harmony. Then he constructed a model, with which he carried on fundamental experiments of all sorts, only setting about the work itself after acquiring knowledge and experience in this way. The testimony of one of his friends to his character is to the effect that his superiority was always recognized by everyone, yet nevertheless he won all hearts, for James Watt always concealed his superiority under the most generous recognition of the merits of others.

Robison, who uttered this judgment, had already as a student concerned himself with a plan for building a steam

HE

carriage, and, in 1759, was the first to direct Watt's attention to steam power. But the matter went no farther. Robison went abroad and Watt had more pressing work to do. Not until 1762 did he again turn his attention to the steam engine. He built himself a small non-condensing high-pressure machine. This taught him how difficult it was to make the machine steam-tight, and how dangerous it might be to work with high-pressure steam. He did, however, include this form also in his widely drawn patent, but more in order to bar this road to others, than to follow it himself.

A decisive event was the request made to him in the winter of 1763 to 1764 to put in order the small model of a Newcomen engine belonging to the University collection. This was a suitable task for a university mechanic. But Watt's gift of first observing, then asking questions, and not resting until an answer to them was given by experiment, led to this professional work of his becoming the starting point of his pioneer inventions. Watt was soon able to get the little engine working. But the boiler only gave steam enough for a few strokes, the engine had then to wait till there was more steam in the boiler. Watt was astonished at the enormous amount of steam used, many times the content of the cylinder. He sought in vain information on this point from technical publications. He made experiments with simple apparatus. He immediately consulted his friend Black, who had already made the same discovery of 'latent heat,' and had described it for the first time to his students in the summer of 1764. What consequences were to be drawn from this fact? Months of meditation and thought followed. How was the steam to be used to the best advantage? One thing became clear to him. If the waste of steam by the condensation taking place as it enters the cylinder is to be avoided, the cylinder must be at least as hot as the steam going into it; on the other hand, if as high a vacuum is to be obtained, the cylinder space must be as cold as possible.

But the steam cylinder is also the condenser, and so the same space is required to be at once as hot and as cold as possible according to the position of the piston. It is impossible to fulfil this condition. How was the problem to be solved? It was not inspiration that brought the invention into being, but methodical, often painful, hard thinking which became almost an obsession. Watt himself tells us that the solution occurred to him suddenly when taking a walk by himself one Sunday; it was to make the condenser separate from the cylinder. Watt said to himself that the steam, being an elastic fluid, would rush into the empty vessel. But how were the cooling water, the condensed water, and the air to be got out of the condenser? Two ways occurred to him. In a mine, a long fall-pipe would be a solution, but otherwise it is necessary to get the air and the water out with a pump, which would of course be possible in all circumstances. Was the idea right? Watt hurried home to his workshop, and built as quickly as he could a small experimental apparatus—to-day the most valuable possession of the Science Museum in London—and this told him that what he had thought was correct. The first real steam engine with air pump and condenser separate from the cylinder, with a steam jacket and closed cylinder, was working in the form of a small and insignificant-looking experimental apparatus. The heart of the great inventor must have been filled at that moment with the most profound joy. We will call it good fortune that he, the instrument maker, had at the time no inkling of the enormous difficulties to be overcome by the mechanical engineer in order to turn this idea into a practical working machine. If Watt had been able to foresee all the hard labour necessary in the coming years to overcome these difficulties, he would hardly have had the courage to continue to work at the steam engine. Here he needed the help of men filled with enthusiasm for the greatness of the problem.

People who think that an invention is complete with the creation of the idea, and that the construction of a marketable product is only a straightforward technical job, are living even to-day. All inventors perform a service in telling the story of the hardships to be undergone by anyone who is finally to reach his goal by steady persistence.

The first machine of considerable size based on Watt's idea was built. An old plumber assisted Watt the instrument-maker, and neither of them had much notion of machine construction. The machine was a failure, and Watt was in despair. He had already spent £1,000 on the steam engine, far more than was justified in view of the fact that he now had a family, for he had married in 1760. He had neglected his other work, which brought in money, and had now to set about looking again for remunerative work. His own experience had made him acquainted with the instruments used for surveying. There was at that time a great demand for men able to survey canals, roads, and harbours, and he was easily able to find employment; he then began to take an interest in their construction, and was soon well on the way to achieving a reputation as a civil engineer. But he was compelled, as he writes to his friends, to devote all his thoughts to the engine. He was quite unable to think of anything else, he was in the grip of the great problem.

He needed help with the engine, and found it in the person of Dr. Roebuck (1718–1794), who had come into the chemical industry as a practising physician, and had been the promoter of great undertakings, chiefly in ironworks and mines. Roebuck founded in Scotland the famous Carron Ironworks. Black drew his attention to Watt and his invention. Roebuck himself was best able to judge the potential industrial importance of the engine, and he found the money and gave what other help he could. The results of Watt's experiments also interested him personally as a scientist and man of learning. But the invention could only be exploited commercially if broad protection by patent could be got. Watt then went to London, and succeeded, with the help of his friends, in getting through a very wide patent

16. JAMES WATT (1736–1819)

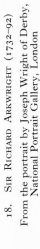

18. SIR RICHARD ARKWRIGHT (1732–92)

From the portrait by Joseph Wright of Derby,
National Portrait Gallery, London

17. MATTHEW BOULTON (1728–1809)

From the portrait by Sir William Beechey

claim without limiting himself to any details. The form of this claim enabled it to be upheld later in face of bitter litigation.

This English patent, one of the most famous in the history of industry, was numbered 913 and dated January 5th, 1769. Watt now began to build a larger machine at Roebuck's own house, but this machine seemed never to get finished. Watt was overworked. Only his surveying brought in money, and he was not able to neglect it in favour of the steam engine. 'Of all things in life, there is nothing more foolish than invention,' he wrote at the time to one of his friends. Roebuck had compromised himself financially too deeply, he had a load of debts round his neck, and was in despair. Watt was no longer able to pay the costs of the patent. He had been working on the steam engine for twelve years, and thought himself farther from success than ever. 'To-day,' said he, 'I entered the thirty-fifth year of my life, and I think I have hardly yet done thirty-five pence worth of good in the world; but I cannot help it.' But the care of his family left him no time for gloomy meditation. Watt, at the time, was carrying out the surveys he had undertaken in a dismal and lonely stretch of country. Autumn storms and continuous rain made work in the open air still more cheerless. And then came suddenly the news that his wife was severely ill. Watt hurried home, but his wife was dead. She, whose happy temperament had often driven away his cares, who had encouraged and consoled him, was torn from his side. The most desperate hour of his life had come.

And now came the great turning point. His friend, Dr. Small, introduced him to the great English industrialist Matthew Boulton (1728–1809), and the result was a collaboration and friendship out of which grew the practically useful steam engine, though only after long and hard struggle. Boulton was, at that time, when he met Watt in 1768, a first-rate industrialist already known far beyond the confines of England. He had greatly extended his father's business; his chief field of activity was metal and ironware. He gave special attention to applied art, and made wonderful silver table services, produced gold leaf, and works in gilt bronze. The manufacture of buckles for shoes and knee breeches, with which he had already had to do when he entered into his father's business at the age of fourteen, brought in much money. He knew how to make a profit from the belief of his fellow countrymen that everything which came from France was particularly up to date; he sent his buckles to France, and then imported them from there into England, in order to be able to sell them at a higher price as made in France. He soon became a partner in his father's firm, and then took up the manufacture of clocks, chiefly with a view to their cheap mass-manufacture. He paid the greatest attention to the training of apprentices. All apprentices who showed promise had to learn drawing. The result was the growth of his business, in a day of small undertakings, into one on a great scale, which in 1775 employed 800 workmen. He built new great factories in Soho near Birmingham. Many other branches of industry interested Boulton, and it was his custom to found a special Company for every department of his work. We may anticipate our story by saying that he had hardly overcome the difficulties connected with the steam engine before he was interesting himself as an engineer in the improvement of minting money. Here he introduced new machines which worked so excellently that he equipped mints for a great number of European governments. James Watt later said quite rightly that Boulton would deserve a place of honour in the history of industry even if he had done nothing else than improve the minting of coins.

Boulton's great undertakings were known far beyond England. He never tired of showing off his factories, because he knew that everyone who came to know about his achievements would be instrumental in increasing his sales. He not only took visitors round his works, but was also a charming host at the house in Soho built specially for the purpose, and called by his friends 'the house of friendship.' In August, 1767, he wrote to his London representative: 'I had Lords and Ladies to wait on yesterday, I have French and Spaniards to-day; and to-morrow I shall have Germans, Russians and Norwegians.' The crowned heads of Europe also visited him and the Empress Catherine was his guest in 1776. Princes, diplomats, artists, writers, and merchants all paid a visit to Soho. Such was the position of the man who now made himself responsible for James Watt's invention.

Boulton, the enterprising and tireless industrialist, took a great personal liking to James Watt, the quiet Scot with the crystal-clear mind. It is rare that two men have been so complementary to one another. Boulton, for whom no business could possibly be big enough, who found refreshment in the daily battle, and Watt, who wrote in 1770 to his friend Dr. Small: 'Nothing is more contrary to my disposition than bustling and bargaining with mankind— yet that is the life I now constantly lead. Use and exertion render it rather more tolerable than it was at first, but it is still disagreeable. I am also in a constant fear that my want of experience may betray me into some scrape, or that I shall be imposed upon by the workmen, both which I take all the care my nature allows of to prevent.'

Then he goes on to complain of headaches and other ailments, which incapacitated him for days, and which only left him when an old man. Two years later he wrote to the same friend: 'I would rather face a loaded cannon than settle an account or make a bargain. In short I find myself out of my sphere when I have anything to do with mankind; it is enough for an engineer to force Nature, and to bear the vexation of her getting the better of him.' James Watt did not feel equal to coping with the great difficulties of practical life. Here he needed the industrialist as a support, who took from off his shoulders the cares about earning money, and filled him with fresh courage when Watt thought that the ever-increasing load of debt would land him in prison.

But if Boulton was now ready to let go the money owed him by Roebuck, if he could enter into the agreement with Watt under the same conditions, and while he was further ready to put down very large sums for the future development of this machine, it was necessary to prolong the life of Watt's patent, which now had only eight years to run, to twenty-five years—till 1800. An agreement with Roebuck was easily come to, for none of his creditors were ready, as Watt wrote, to give a penny for the patent for the steam engine. But the fight with the Patent Office in London was very difficult. Every kind of opposition was raised against 'monopoly'. But Watt and his friends were finally victorious, mainly on the ground that money could only be obtained for developing so great an invention if there were a prospect of commercial success, for further improvements not contained in Watt's patent might still be made, whereby all the work and money put into Watt's invention would be sacrificed in vain. This risk had to be taken by the capitalist, and even a patent would not free him from them. To the great annoyance of all opponents, Watt's very wide patent claim was extended for another twenty-five years. Boulton and Watt now made their agreement by which Boulton took over all costs and the whole of the business direction in return for two-thirds of the profits from the patent. Watt had in return for his third to design the machine, and to give his advice in erecting it and working it.

It now seemed as if difficulties were at an end, but, so far from this being the case, the struggle went on. The constructional difficulties were scarcely to be overcome. No machine builders of the sort needed were yet in existence. Turning things on the lathe by hand is an art. When the great ironfounder Wilkinson produced a steam cylinder accurate to one quarter of an inch, the feat excited astonishment. The construction of Watt's steam engine demanded incomparably greater perfection in its construction, than that of the atmospheric engine of Newcomen. Accurately turned piston rods were now necessary, and the hitherto unknown stuffing-box had to be used; at times it seemed as if Watt's engine would come to grief altogether in face of these difficulties in its manufacture. There were no machine shops such as we have to-day; a machine was a thing built up like a house on the spot where it was to be used. Soho supplied only a few small parts, such as valves. Boulton and Watt acted as consulting engineers, and not as manufacturers. Watt produced the drawings, working at home, and helped in erecting and working the engine. For this he was paid at the rates customary at the time. But how was money to be made in this fashion? Every practical man advised against a Watt engine being put in. They said it was so complicated that it could never be kept in working order. But Boulton and Watt did not want to make and sell engines. They were satisfied to be paid a third of the value of the coal saved, as compared with the consumption of the existing atmospheric engine, stipulating only that the cylinders should be bored by Wilkinson. The mine owners were to pay this royalty year after year, as long as the patent lasted. They were at first very ready to make this arrangement, which could only result in a profit. But later, when the quite trustworthy Watt engine consumed only a quarter of the coal for the same output as compared with the old engine, they became angry at having to pay the yearly royalty. The monopoly was bitterly attacked; it was said to be ruining the industry, and every attempt was made to get round the patent, a fact which aroused the greatest indignation in Watt. The result was embittered patent litigation, which, however, was finally won by the firm.

Anyone to-day who is not willing to admit, as frequently

happens, the great and decisive part played in the development of technology by the far-sighted capitalist, may learn much from this story of the steam engine. For there were still grave financial difficulties to overcome before a profit could be made. Boulton's great metal works did not earn anything like as much as the steam engine cost. Heavy indebtedness was incurred. But Boulton's faith in final victory was unshakable. He hung on. Boulton had to raise a sum of over £40,000, enormous for those days, before commercial success was attained. The invention began earning money only in 1785, twenty years from its start. It was Cornwall, poor in coal and with deep mines, that paid. In 1783, all steam engines in Cornwall had been replaced by those of Watt. Every one of these engines brought a very considerable yearly royalty to the firm. Watt could now be satisfied with his machine. He wished to confine his energies only to the development of this pumping engine, and again and again advised his friend Boulton to leave all new problems to young people who had neither money nor reputation to lose.

But Boulton, the industrialist, was of a different opinion. The pumping engine business was not indefinitely expansible, but suppose it were possible to introduce this heat engine into factories and so replace the clumsy and feeble water-wheels and the muscular work of men and animals ? Boulton would have nothing to do with the view of some engineers, even some of great reputation, that the pumping engine could be used to raise water to drive a water-wheel. He pressed Watt with increasing urgency to build a steam engine giving rotary motion. But Watt hesitated, fearing a number of new great difficulties. But finally he set about the fresh task. He turned the existing single-acting machine into a double acting one, and replaced the chain by his wonderful link motion, the Watt parallelogram. But he was prevented by an English patent from applying the crank, a device which had long been known, to his engine. He got round the difficulty by a new device. If we add to this that Watt was perfectly clear about the economic importance of expansive working, and had already taken this possibility into his patent, and if we further recollect that he introduced the throttle valve for regulating the power and actuated it by a centrifugal governor, we have a picture of the machine as constructed by Watt. This machine was everywhere in the greatest demand; people in London, Manchester, and Birmingham were mad after the steam engine, as we read in a travel story of those days. The construction of complete machines was begun in Soho, and it was scarcely possible to supply the demand. A means of measuring their power was now required, and since they were mostly used to replace horses, the natural thing was to measure their power in terms of the number of horses actually replaced. But not all horses give the same power, and so Watt came upon the idea of introducing a fixed unit. He introduced the horse-power unit, familiar to us to-day as H.P. Only in the age of electrotechnics was a new unit of power proposed, and this was given Watt's name in his honour, so that to-day millions of people calculate daily in watts and kilowatts, without thinking of the fact that they are uttering with the name of this electrical unit, that of one of the greatest engineers of the world.

Among the great collaborators acquired by Boulton and Watt, the Scotsman William Murdock deserves first mention. He was twenty-three years of age when he came from his native land and visited Watt. Boulton recognized his value, and engaged him. Murdock was a machine constructor of genius, and a type of man better able than Watt and Boulton to deal with the stubborn Cornish mine-owners. This big, quiet, meditative, and powerfully built Scot, who loved deeds rather than words, was successful in constructing the pumping engine, and in getting it to work. He lived for many years in the mining district of Cornwall. His life there was not made easy for him. He had to do with rough people, and it is credibly reported that he laid the foundation of the extraordinary esteem which he enjoyed in Cornwall by squaring up silently to the biggest talker who was attacking him and giving him a thorough beating amid the enthusiastic applause of the other mine-owners, who loved a fight. After that he was respected, and when anything was not in order, the call was for Murdock. He remained true to his firm in spite of the most dazzling offers from other sides. He improved the steam engine considerably after 1800. He even built in Cornwall a small steam carriage, but the anxious Watt insisted that he should confine his attention to his pumping engine, not wanting to have his best man spend his energies on all sorts of far-reaching plans. Murdock already made use of coal gas in Cornwall, and carried out the first gas lighting installation on a large scale in Soho on a national holiday in 1803. He is rightly regarded as one of the pioneers of the generation and application of coal gas. He was at work for the firm in Cornwall for twenty years at an extremely modest salary. 'We need more Murdocks' were the words with which Boulton and Watt recognized the great value of his work for them. Murdock went on working in an important position after James Watt, up to 1830. He died in 1839 at the age of eighty-five. He lived to see the coming of the steamship and the railway.

Let us return to James Watt. At the beginning of the nineteenth century the hard-fought patent for the steam engine expired. Watt rejoiced that this fact put an end to his business obligations, and could not endure another day in industry. Boulton, eight years older than Watt, was of quite a different nature, and had no idea of withdrawing from commercial activity. Rest, resignation from his life's work, would have been for him equivalent to death, and though his advanced age with its infirmities warned him against excessive activity, and though Watt begged his friend again and again to take a rest, Boulton remained faithful till his death to the business which he had created. An old ailment brought him to a sick bed in 1809, from which he was released by a peaceful death on August 17th. Watt, deeply moved by his death, wrote to his son and successor: 'Few men have had his abilities and still fewer have exerted them as he has done, and if to them we add his urbanity, his generosity, and his affection to his friends we shall make up a character rarely to be equalled.'

But James Watt, now at the age of sixty-four, free from material cares and better in health, rejoiced to be able to live according to his scientific and technical tastes in his modest home, where there was naturally a well-appointed workshop. He was not even able to refrain from inventing, but he would have nothing more to do with patents. The evening of his life lasted another nineteen years. Mentally vigorous, giving and taking ideas, he continued to take the closest interest in the further development of science and technology, art and literature. Anyone who was fortunate enough to know the tall spare old engineer, anyone who looked into his deep grey eyes, and heard his deep quiet voice with its strong Scottish accent, gained the impression, one to which contemporaries testified again and again, of a great, profound and modest genius, who was never tired of singing the praises of others, but who exclaimed to one of the friends who wished to write about him, 'Preserve the dignity of a philosopher and historian; relate the facts, and leave posterity to judge.' Posterity, when James Watt had passed away quietly on August 9th, 1819, erected a monument to the great engineer in the venerable and world-renowned Abbey of Westminster, among kings, marshals, heroes, statesmen, and poets. The inscription states that the King, his minister, and many of the Lords and Commons of the realm erected this monument

To

JAMES WATT

who directing the force of an original genius, early exercised in philosophic research to the improvement of the steam engine, enlarged the resources of his country, increased the power of man, and rose to an eminent place among the most illustrious followers of science, and the real benefactors of the world.

MASTERS OF THE MECHANICAL ARTS

The eighteenth century gave us the steam engine through the agency of James Watt and his collaborators. The same period saw an England grown poor in wood replace it for iron smelting by her rich resources in coal. Among the great achievements in this field, we may recollect the work of the ironmasters Abraham Derby, father and son, and of the famous ironmaster and engineer John Wilkinson, whose portrait, painted by Watteau, is to be found in the Kaiser Friedrich Museum in Berlin. But especial importance attaches to the creative work of Henry Cort, who at the time when the first Watt steam engines were revolutionizing the driving of industrial plants, produced good wrought iron in the reverberatory furnace fired with coal, by means of the puddling process. When one remembers that up to the time of Cort's invention, English wrought iron was so poor in quality that it could not be used in the English Navy—iron being obtained at the time from Sweden and Russia—we recognize what this deed meant for England. Lord Sheffield said in 1786 that the inventions which England owed to James Watt and Henry Cort more than compensated for the loss of America, for England became, by the achievement of her engineers, the superior of all other countries in the production and application of iron.

But in the eighteenth century, almost simultaneously with the discovery of the steam engine, men of the most humble origin succeeded in introducing machines into the technology

of textiles. Arkwright, Hargreaves, and Crompton replaced the work of the sensitive human hand in spinning by
ingeniously constructed parts of machines. These machines
were then soon mechanically driven, first by water-wheels
and then by steam engines. Soon the new machines were
able to spin much more yarn than the old hand looms were
able to take. Then a clergyman, Edmund Cartwright
(1743–1823), developed the machine-driven loom in 1785.
The spinning machines were now unable to produce enough
yarn, and a yarn famine set in which continued for a long
time until spinning and weaving were again adjusted to
one another. In France, an inventor of genius, Joseph Maire
Jacquard (1752–1834), made numerous inventions in the
textile field, which were of especial importance as regards the
weaving of patterns.

The result was an enormous expansion of the English
textile industry. It was here that the modern factory system
came into being. It was here that men were first trained on a
large scale to working in a way determined by machines.
Here, too, the hatred of the man-conquering machine arose:
a hatred first expressed in the sharpest revolutionary forms
in England by the revolt of those directly affected against
inventors, engineers, and machine owners. Much could
be told of the men who were responsible for these achievements. Of Arkwright, who finally gained the day after
the fiercest struggle, and died one of the richest men in
England; of Crompton, the gentle idealist, who allowed himself to be deceived by promises and lost almost the whole
reward for his invention of genius; over and over again,
was a human destiny closely interwoven with the machine
created by it.

When kings build, there is work for carters. In technology
also, there are a few real kings, who by their achievements
exercise a decisive influence on the development of their
times. But the execution of their plans, their application
in all sorts of directions and in the most diverse countries,

demand a multitude of workers. Of the work of these men we have a detailed account in the history of technology, but their lives, as far as posterity is concerned, are spent without leaving a trace in their work. The battles of technology cannot be fought by generals alone; privates are needed as well.

The engineers of the eighteenth century were given the most varied professional designations. The methodical education and training of our days was unknown. Mining, at once the greatest stimulus and source of orders for engineering, had its master technicians. The machines used for raising water and ore to the surface were called 'arts,' and the man who could build and run such works of art was called the Master of Arts. This fine term for the profession, *Kunstmeister*, has been kept till to-day in Germany.

The machines used in the art of mining are characterized by reciprocatory motion. Mills, on the other hand, are revolving mechanisms, and in English the word mill was used for all rotary motions; in England we speak of cotton mills and so on. Here we have the mill builder, the 'millwright,' the man who long ago worked his way up from the ranks of the handicraftsmen, and, without a place in the craft guilds, had to do everything connected with building and running mills for the most varied purposes. We owe to the great English engineer William Fairbairn, who himself came from among them, a valuable contribution to the professional history of this same class of the old engineers. 'The millwright of former days was to a great extent the sole representative of mechanical art, and was looked upon as the authority in all the applications of wind and water, under whatever conditions they were to be used, as a motive power for the purposes of manufacture. He was the engineer of the district in which he worked with equal facility at the lathe, the anvil, or the carpenter's bench.'

The millwright of the eighteenth century carried on his

trade as engineer and mechanic peripatetically. He lived far
from the town, in the heart of the country, and usually
relied completely on his own resources. As Fairbairn says,
'he could calculate the velocities, strength, and power of
machines: could draw in plan and section, and could construct buildings, conduits, or water-courses, in all the forms
and under all the conditions required in his professional
practice; he could build bridges, cut canals, and perform a
variety of work now done by civil engineers.' Fairbairn
considers these country millwrights to be some of the most
useful and independent men who have ever worked technically. However, he was well aware of his own achievements,
and this at times makes him a little too pleased with himself.

JACOB LEUPOLD

1674–1727

But who then were called mechanics? Here again it is
naturally impossible to draw a sharp line of division, for
these professional designations were not titles protected by
law, and acquired by examination; but as regards the
mechanic and the work he was required to do, Jacob Leupold
gives us a very exact picture of the situation in the first half
of the eighteenth century. He himself considered himself a
member of this class. He was born in 1674 in Planitz near
Zwickau, and died in Leipzig in 1727. His fame has lasted
into our day by reason of his great work *Theatrum Machin-
arum*, which is one of the most voluminous technical works
in the German language. The Latin title is in the language
of the learned, but it is translated as 'exposition of the
foundations of mechanical science.' The first volume
appeared in Leipzig in 1724. The whole work has the stately
dimensions of 1,764 pages and 472 full-page copper engrav-
ings. Seven volumes appeared in Leupold's lifetime, and the

IE

eighth immediately after his death, followed by a supplementary volume twelve years later. Anyone desirous of
becoming acquainted with the achievements of machine,
instrument, hydraulic, and bridge construction at the
beginning of the eighteenth century has here the source of
information to hand. By studying Leupold he is able to
penetrate into the knowledge and mode of thought of the
engineers of that time. He will find, again and again, how
valuable a service is performed by presenting the knowledge
necessary at a certain period in daily professional life, in
simple language understandable by everyone.

Leupold's father was a craftsman with skill in a number of
different trades. The son was to follow in his footsteps, but
he was physically too frail for heavy work, and hence he was
allowed to study. He went to the famous school of learning
in Zwickau, thence to the Universities of Jena, and later
Wittenberg. Here he wished to study theology, but the poor
student could not live by studying, and hence he had to
think about going back home. On the way he thought of
making one more attempt at Leipzig, where he succeeded
in giving private lessons, and also in instructing masons and
carpenters in the 'civil building art.' But this business of
teaching drove him from his studies. He needed applied
mathematics for the lessons which he was giving, and he had
qualms of conscience about giving up his study of sacred
learning. Here a sensible clergyman helped him to overcome
them by pointing out that there were enough preachers in
Leipzig, but no workers in the arts with mathematical and
physical knowledge. So in 1699, Leupold determined to
open a mechanical workshop at Leipzig. He succeeded
some years later in considerably improving the air pump,
and he then carried on his workshop with varying success.
He raised his own status to such an extent that Prussia gave
him the title of 'Commercien-Rath,' Councillor for Commerce. He was made a member of learned societies, and in
1724 the first volume appeared of the work to which we have

referred, and which laid the foundations of a fame lasting till our day.

He points out in his preface that he has not written the book for the learned, who would certainly know better than he on all points, and had the opportunity of studying existing writings; he has 'had in mind artists, craftsmen, and such persons as have no command of foreign languages or other studies, and have no opportunity of making use of "informatores" and other aids, or of seeking out from so many writings what is necessary, and are nevertheless more than anyone in need of these foundations, not out of curiosity, but because they are actually using such machines, and even have to build them and apply them.'

Leupold tells us also on the first page of his work his conception of a mechanic: 'but a mechanic (of whom we are here talking) ought to be a person who not only understands well and thoroughly all handicrafts, such as wood, steel, iron, brass, silver, gold, glass, and all such materials to be treated according to the arts, and who knows how to judge on physical principles, how far each according to its nature and property is adequate or suitable to withstand and endure this or that, so that everything receives its necessary proportion, strength, and convenience, and neither too much nor too little is done in the matter; but he must also be able to arrange according to mechanical sciences or rules for any required proportion, or effect according to present or proposed force or load; for which purpose he must also have learned from geometry and arithmetic all that is necessary for calculation of the parts of the machine. And when he desires thoroughly to understand his profession, he must have a complete grasp of all the arts and professions for which he will have to make and invent machines; for otherwise he knows not what he is doing, and has also no power to improve anything, or invent anything new, such as is chiefly demanded of a mechanic. But above all he has to be a born mechanic, so that he shall not only be skilled in invention by natural instinct, but shall also grasp with little trouble all arts and sciences, in such a way that it may be said of him: what his eyes see, that also are his hands able to do; and that love of his art lets him avoid no trouble, labour, or cost, because throughout his whole life he has daily to learn something new and to experiment.'

We also learn from Leupold that a distinction was made at that time between a 'mechanicus' and a 'machinarius.' According to him, a machinarius is the man who invents the machine, while the mechanicus is he who is able himself to make machines and instruments, and so has a very good knowledge of handicraft. But Leupold makes the observation, very true in his time, that both are so closely connected that it is rare for one to accomplish anything without the other. The great mathematicians, he says, were often very unfortunate with their inventions, because they had no knowledge of handicrafts.

FRIEDRICH WILHELM HOLTZHAUSEN
and
FRANZ DINNENDAHL
1768–1827 & 1775–1826

We will now talk of two German engineers of great attainments in the century after Leupold. These are the Masters of Arts Holtzhausen, who came from the Harz, and built his great machines in Upper Silesia; and Dinnendahl, who, born of the humblest parents, became a great master in Essen in the west.

The problem was to introduce steam power into Germany, and the great King of Prussia, Frederick II, stands at the head of this development. In 1780, the king, a great promoter of industry in his state, had ordered his minister, the Freiherr von Heinitz, to give his attention to the heat engine, which 'could be used in all mines to get the

20. JACOB LEUPOLD (1674–1727)

From an engraving by M. Bernigeroth
Photo: Deutsche Museum

19. SAMUEL CROMPTON (1753–1827)

22. FRANZ DINNENDAHL (1775–1826)

21. FRIEDRICH WILHELM HOLTZHAUSEN (1768–1827)

From a portrait by F. Rolan

water out,' but the minister was further, above and beyond this special task, to make use of the steam engine wherever it could be applied usefully and effectively. It was necessary to take a lesson from England. The minister therefore decided to send specially gifted mine officials into the Promised Land of technology; they were to study the English machines, and particularly to attempt to get at the secrets of Watt's steam engine. One especially successful mining engineer was Carl Friedrich Bückling, who was born on July 23rd, 1750, at Ruppin, the son of a merchant. Bückling had a good education. He was at first trained for building, but later he took up mining and smelting. He was sent together with four colleagues, the first Prussian mining men, to the newly founded School of Mines at Freiberg. An essential part of education in those days was travelling for study. Bückling had in 1780 visited England and the Scandinavian countries, commissioned by the minister. When he came back, he constructed, with the help of two mechanics in Berlin, a working model of a Watt steam engine. He thereupon got the order to erect a steam engine in Hettstadt in the neighbourhood of Mansfeld. But the task was not so easy to carry out. He had to go once again to England. He travelled over the famous mining district of Cornwall, where he succeeded, in spite of all prohibitions by the English Government, in engaging a machine master by the name of Richard for the Prussian mining industry. On August 23rd, 1785, the first steam engine was put into regular industrial use in Hettstadt. It was the first steam engine made of German materials by German workmen. Its importance was recognized 100 years after it started to work by the Verein deutscher Ingenieure, which erected a monument on the spot where it had worked. Bückling also built a whole series of machines, including boring machines and lathes. He died at Berlin, on February 22nd, 1812, highly esteemed and appreciated in his own line of work.

It was Upper Silesia, however, which attained the greatest importance in technical work for the Germany of those days. Frederick the Great found helpers of genius in Freiherr von Heinitz and Count von Reden, for whom it was a work after their own heart to carry out the great task entrusted to them by their sovereign in Upper Silesia, which hitherto had been completely neglected. Count Reden wrote in 1786: 'I delight in anticipation of the times when busy industry, faster circulation, and culture will raise this unconsidered corner to the rank of a jewel in the Prussian crown, and will turn its inhabitants from poor oppressed slaves into educated and happy men and women.' Heinitz and Reden knew that this was only possible by the aid of the new technology. The first steam engine was ordered from England for Tarnowitz. This was the engine, perhaps the only one, seen by Goethe. When on a journey with his Grand Duke to Upper Silesia, he was taken by Reden to look at this machine, and while under the impression made by it, he wrote in the visitor's book:

'To the company at Tarnowitz, 4th of September 1790.
Far from educated men, at the bounds of the Empire, who shall help you
To find treasures and to bring them with success to the daylight ?
Only wisdom and honesty help; these two
Are the keys to every treasure in the earth's possession.'

But these men needed help, and they found a master of genius in August Friedrich Wilhelm Holtzhausen, who was highly recommended to Count Reden as having a good head for mechanics. Holtzhausen was born on March 4th, 1768, at Ellrich in the Southern Harz. In 1790 he learned mining and machine construction at Andreasberg. It was Bückling who gave him the possibility of becoming acquainted with the first steam engine in Hettstadt, but Reden sent him as early as 1792 to build steam engines in Upper

Silesia. The twenty-four-year-old engineer now set about energetically building steam engines, without which the development of Upper Silesian mining was impossible. Three steam plants were under his control. Holtzhausen began to build new steam engines under the most difficult circumstances imaginable, using only the simplest and roughest tools, and with the help of entirely untrained workmen. The parts were first made at the smelting works at Malapane, and later at Gleiwitz. In 1808 he was made machine inspector and manager of the machine works laid down in 1806 at the Gleiwitz smelting works. At the same time all steam engines of the Upper Silesian mining and smelting works, and of the Waldenburg coalfield were put under his control. German engineers pay him homage as one of the greatest of their professional forerunners. Holtzhausen and his co-workers made Upper Silesia in those days into the cradle of German machine construction. The building of steam engines spread thence all over Germany, and the first steam engine used in the industrial district of the west came from Upper Silesia. Built by Holtzhausen, it was set going in 1801 at the Zeche Vollmond at Langendreer. The machine house for it was built by a carpenter, Franz Dinnendahl, who on this occasion received his first incentive to the building of steam engines.

FRANZ DINNENDAHL

1775–1826

Dinnendahl's father was the miller at the Horster Mühle, near Steele, which to-day is part of the town of Essen. Here Franz Dinnendahl was born on August 20th, 1775. Perhaps the mill itself made on the child an impression which determined his future career; be that as it may, he refers again and again in his autobiography, which unhappily was never finished, to the fact that the joy in building machines was in his blood. He wanted to become a 'master of arts,' or as he later liked to call himself, a 'mechanicus.' But how was a poor miller's son on a lonely mill to find and travel the road to an art which had hardly yet received a name ? Dinnendahl referred to the simple village school, in which he managed to learn by his twelfth year a little reading and writing, as a 'miserable school'; then came the necessity to earn money. Dinnendahl himself, when telling the story of his life, loved to describe how he had had to work his way up from small beginnings. He was very proud at having risen by his own powers, and he tells us that though he had to start by tending swine, he never forgot his 'irresistible leanings to mechanics.' Thus, while looking after his pigs, he cut out all sorts of models of little machines, with the consequence that he brought home at night barely half the number of pigs that he had driven out. The farmer may be excused for having dismissed young Dinnendahl as 'unsuited to the business.'

Young Dinnendahl now tried his hand at mining, and at sixteen had himself enrolled as a miner. He made the acquaintance of all the necessary operations, which was an advantage later when he had to make mining machinery. But here as well he got no nearer to the goal which he had set himself. An uncle advised him to become a carpenter. Wood was at that time the most important material used in machines, and a builder might in this way quite well become a 'mechanicus.' Young Dinnendahl loved variety, and so he laid aside mining and went to a village cabinet-maker, who was also a carpenter, to learn the trade. He kept at it for scarcely a year, when he had learned, as he thought, enough. He was lent fifteen reichsthalers to buy tools, and Dinnendahl then began to build everything he could get orders for. Still, he was all the time pondering new ideas. But what use was it for him to make plans; he had no money, and at first no one would entrust him with any construction. At last someone was sufficiently courageous to order from him a modest wooden house. Others followed this example, and in a few years he had built ten houses and some sheds.

These were hard times for him. He had to put in sixteen to seventeen hours daily, including what was often a long journey, in order to earn the barest necessities. But as he tells us, his passion for machinery was strong enough to keep him designing his machines far into the night, though he no doubt found time to think about them when at his work. Finally he received from the farmer who owned the coal-mine in Kupferdreh, an order to build a water-lifting machine. He now learned drawing and succeeded in getting running not only the machine ordered, but also a hand-driven hoisting engine 'to the amazement of the public.' And then, as we have already seen, he built in the Vollmond mine at Langendreer the house for the steam engine which had come from Upper Silesia, the first in Westphalia.

The machine master did not quite know how to deal with the machine and Dinnendahl thought he knew better. His advice was sharply rejected, for what could a simple carpenter be expected to know about the highest achievement of machinery of the day? Finally he got a hearing from the owner of the mine, Freiherr von Romberg. He never afterwards failed to remember that this nobleman, 'though I came to him in a linen smock, and had never had any personal acquaintance with him before, did not repel me with indifference, but at once saw my value.'

Dinnendahl was then allowed to take a hand in getting the machine erected. People began to have confidence in him, and one here and there began to believe in his 'mechanical genius.' The hand-worked pumping apparatus built by him for the Wohlgemut mine near Essen no longer sufficed, and Dinnendahl was asked to build a heat engine. It was got going in 1803, and had done its work by 1815.

With this, a very important milestone in Dinnendahl's professional career was passed.

He who would raise water by fire, had to be an excellent master of arts. But what difficulties had to be overcome by an engineer of those times ! Let Dinnendahl tell us of them in his own words. 'It was in truth a weighty undertaking, the more so because there was not even a smith in this neighbourhood who could make a proper screw, let alone produce other forged parts needed for the machine, such as valve gear, piston rod, boiler work, and so on, or could do boring and turning. I myself was trained in carpenters and joiners work; but I had now to undertake smithing without having learned it. However, I did almost all the ironwork on the machine with my own hands, even the boiler, so that for a year and a half I did hardly any work but smithing, and so made good myself the absence of such craftsmen. But there were also no sheet iron hammers or skilled plate workers in this neighbourhood, for which reason the plates of the first boiler were almost all imperfect and cold-short. Equally defective were those parts of the machine which the ironworks had to supply, such as cylinders, steampipes, pumps, pistons, and the like. This difficulty also was overcome, for with the help of my own ideas and the skill of Herr Jacobi, owner of the ironworks at Sterkrade, I got this firm to the point of supplying all necessary parts of an engine, at first, it is true, imperfectly, but now as good as they can be made. The boring of the cylinder put fresh obstacles in my way, but even they did not daunt me; I built myself a boring machine without ever having seen one. And so at last I overcame untold difficulties and got so far as completing the first engine according to the old principle.'

His name was soon known far and wide. He was called to Aix-la-Chapelle to build an engine. He was to get 5,000 reichsthalers for a machine with a 32 in. cylinder. This machine also was to be an atmospheric engine, but in the meantime Dinnendahl had learned of the great advance made by James Watt.   He determined to show that he could build an engine according to the new principle.   Such an engine would naturally cost considerably more, and he knew that the agreed sum of 5,000 reichsthalers would not even suffice for the old type.   'But,' he writes, 'my courage did not even then desert me; all these circumstances were rather a spur to new exertions.'   First he built the engine on the old principle.   He was careful 'to guard against losing my credit at the start.'   The machine was a complete success, and now he had the courage to convert it to the new principle.   To everyone's satisfaction, the engine now ran as a Watt low-pressure engine.   We read in his autobiography: 'The joy I had in seeing that the machine likewise did its duty is beyond my powers of description.'

This great joy over the success of a daring step is for many a recompense for all the trouble and anxiety which fall to the lot of every technical pioneer.   At about the time that Dinnendahl was working in Westphalia, we hear of a master Scharl, who had to build the great water-wheel for a brewery in Munich.   The story then runs: 'This great wheel caused the builder, Scharl, many sleepless nights, he read, he studied, he asked mathematicians, mechanics; he calculated, experimented, altered and altered again, until at last, after a great expenditure of thought, money and time, it was set up, and the joy of the inventor may be guessed from a phrase, written in capitals, in one of his letters: FRIENDS, AT LAST THE GREAT WHEEL IS WORKING!'

In 1806 Dinnendahl built for the coal-mine Salzer and Neuack near Essen a pumping engine with a 40 in. cylinder.   The Office of Mines called the proprietors together, and Dinnendahl put before them a new and unheard-of proposal.   He wanted to build not only a pumping engine, but also a steam winding-engine, and both were to get their steam from one boiler.   He got the order.   He was to get 12,800 reichsthalers for the two machines.

Dinnendahl now became a 'mechanicus,' and gave up

carpentering and joining. He went to Essen and set up a machine works. The new machine gave rise to great difficulties. The Gutehoffnungshutte took eleven months to make a satisfactory cylinder of the required dimensions. It had to be cast five times, and made in three parts, for the capacity of the furnace was not sufficient for the cylinder. The engine was set to work in 1809.

Dinnendahl's achievements were soon known far beyond Westphalia. Even the Emperor Napoleon gave him orders. A fort had to be built in the greatest haste at the fortress of Wesel; horse machines were not adequate, and Dinnendahl could not build a steam engine in time. But he succeeded in getting one from England. His work was so satisfactory that he received an order for a like plant in Metz. The political position changed, and so this order was not carried out. But the plant in Wesel had at last made some money for him. It is said that in those days whole casks full of hard thaler pieces stood in the entrance to his house, and being the man he was, he must have had the greatest joy in being able to give his fellow citizens so striking a demonstration of his wealth.

Dinnendahl had reached the pinnacle of his life and success. He established close personal and business relations with Gottlob Jacobi in Sterkrade, with the great German industrialist Friedrich Harkort in Wetter, and with Friedrich Krupp, father of the great Alfred Krupp. He let Krupp's children share the teaching given to his children by his secretary and tutor Sartorius.

Dinnendahl even made a gas-lighting installation for his factory, long before the first gasworks was built in Germany by Englishmen. A friend of Dinnendahl's, a pharmacist in Essen, had made coal gas in his laboratory, and shown this curious light to his friends. Dinnendahl, delighted by every technical advance, determined to light his works with it. In order to avoid the jumping and flickering of the light, he put in a gasholder. The journal *Hermann* gave an enthusiastic

report of the success of this lighting installation, under date
March 27th, 1818. The first eight or ten days the courtyard
of the works was full of sightseers every evening, who
cheered Dinnendahl in their enthusiasm for the new and
beautiful light.

He then went on building engines, the largest being for the
coal-mine Kunstwerk in Steele, of which Dinnendahl says
in a communication to the Chief Office of Mines, that this
work 'is unique of its kind, at least in this neighbourhood.'
Dinnendahl's achievements were known outside Germany.
Thus he was applied to from Holland to build ten great
steam engines with all accessories, which were to be used
to pump out at long last the Haarlem lake. He answered
that 'he felt himself equal to the task of taking over the
business and carrying it through to everyone's satisfaction.'
This vast undertaking attracted him, but the Dutch made
it clear that a heavy financial risk had to be taken, though
a profit of two millions, or even much more, might result.
Dinnendahl wanted to negotiate directly with one of the
leading Dutch Ministers. But he had not the courage to
risk a million on his own account for land reclamation. Thus
the negotiations dragged on, Dinnendahl being well aware
that the machines alone would not accomplish the work.
The engines were the least part of it, and the work of the
drainage engineers would cost an enormous amount. When
he was advised not to demand cash, but to accept payment
in the form of shares in the reclaimed land, he was unable,
he said, to agree, because he had not the money to carry out
the work.

Dinnendahl considered it necessary to set up his own
foundry, the more so because the Gutehoffnungshutte had
started, in 1819, to compete with him in steam engines.
After his factory in Essen was destroyed by fire, he combined
the new building with a foundry. But competition now
began to make itself felt more and more keenly, Friedrich
Harkort having joined the Gutehoffnungshutte in 1819

for building engines on English lines. Worst of all, Dinnendahl had proved himself too optimistic in his business undertakings. He had taken shares in mining ventures; he was no doubt compelled to do this in order to get orders. But now these business ventures began to show heavy losses. The money he earned he lost again; the poverty of his early years threatened to return. He was no longer able to take up the struggle. He died on August 15th, 1826, at the age of fifty-one. In 1936, the town of Essen gave him a tomb in its cemetery of honour, after his resting-place in Steele had been absorbed by an enlargement of the town.

Dinnendahl, like so many other technical pioneers, was of the humblest possible origin. A characteristic of his was his faith in his own powers. His enthusiasm gave him an enormous capacity for work. He was stimulating and attractive in personal intercourse. Full of temperament, fresh and decisive in his manner, he made many friends, though his self-esteem sometimes went too far, and made personal dealings with him difficult.

He found it especially hard to manage officials. So he complains in his autobiography how unpleasant it had been for him when 'I had to see myself delivered over hand and foot to the ignorance and arbitrariness of an official body.' It was no doubt more especially the middle class of official that made trouble for him, for they believed in their own omniscience, and saw in Dinnendahl an upstart. What indeed was to be thought, in those days when authority was a superstition, of a man who went so far as not only to think, but to say: 'Ministers and state officials are not at all times the cleverest people'? But this struggle with officialdom was much to the taste of Dinnendahl's fellow citizens, who had not themselves the courage to stand up for their own opinions against the authorities.

He stood up for his own people and never forgot how much his success depended on their collaboration. One of the simple songs, written and composed by his apprentices in 1811 for a works festival, has come down to us. In this the pride of Dinnendahl's men and their joy in their work and their master, is expressed in a manner which warms the heart. But they also remember to thank Madame Dinnendahl for the French brandy and beer which she had given them: *'Mit Vergnügen, Lust, und Pläsier Gesellen Dinnendahls sind wir.'* And so we catch an echo of the joy and love of life of Dinnendahl and his men, specially necessary in technical work when a great and new advance has to be made in face of all difficulties. Dinnendahl was one of the pioneers, and for us he is a path-finder on the road of technical progress, for he added important material to the structure of German technology and industry.

GEORG FRIEDRICH REICHENBACH

1771–1826

Georg Friedrich Reichenbach came of a family of well-to-do artisans. His grandfather was a mechanic in the Mint at Mannheim, his father was a master mechanic, who had worked his way up to the grade of master cannon-borer. His grandmother was the daughter of a master mason. His father had migrated from the Palatinate to Durlach in Baden, because he hoped to get on more quickly there, and here his son Georg was born to him on August 24th, 1771. When he was two years old, his father moved to Mannheim, and became, in close competition with others, the manager of the great cannon-boring works, thanks to his great manual skill. He had much work to do; the army made great demands, and technical output had to be increased again and again. He was given the opportunity of looking round everywhere; he went to Hanover and got acquainted there with the latest English work; he had to work in Munich. He was allowed to add to his modest salary by accepting private orders. So Reichenbach *père* did not spend much time at home, and paid little attention to his child's schooling, the more so because Georg, in his early years, did not seem to promise much. At that time the chief thing was learning by heart, but the boy had no aptitude for it and was never much use at it. On the other hand, he loved all the more everything to do with mathematics and science, and so the opinion of his teachers finally changed for the better. He succeeded at fourteen in getting into the Military School at Mannheim, at that time known as the 'Chief School of Genius.' Here young Reichenbach began to acquire many friends. He was short, he had dark brown hair and steel-blue eyes, a high forehead. He was a joyous man of the Palatinate, lively, enthusiastic for everything that attracted him, and never forgot in the midst of his work to enjoy life. The early careers of father and son were much the same, both received commissions, both became captains. In their professions, they were both advanced from 'Untermechanicus' to 'Obermechanicus.'

In addition to the knowledge he gained at school, he acquired in his father's workshop the latter's great practical skill; thus was laid one of the chief foundations of his success, for sensitive hands were needed to carry out what Reichenbach's brain had conceived, and we know from his life that he always set to work with his own hands when the highest accuracy was needed for his famous instruments. Another important part of Reichenbach's education was the two journeys to England which the King of Bavaria made possible for him at the suggestion of Count Rumford, who at that time was engaged in Munich in successful technical and scientific work.

A determining factor in Reichenbach's career was the fact that when still at the Military School he chanced to become acquainted with the astronomer at the Mannheim Observatory. Here the cadet got a knowledge of mathematical instruments hitherto strange to him, and his ambition was aroused to test his own manual skill by attempting to construct similar instruments in his father's workshop. He was allowed to try his hand, and the Director of the Observatory, Abbé Barry, who wanted to help his young friend, sent a sextant made by Reichenbach to Count Rumford with the warmest recommendations. He then received a grant of 500 gulden for the journey to London, and more important still, the best possible introductions to Watt and Boulton in Soho, for he was commissioned to order a Watt steam engine for the town of Munich. He was nineteen years of age, and had not been much out of Munich. For him a journey to England meant more than does for us a journey in a fast liner to America.

At the same time as Reichenbach another young Bavarian engineer, Joseph Baader, who was eight years older and already knew England, also wanted to journey to the Promised Land of technology. It was thus natural for Count Rumford to entrust young Reichenbach, who had never been abroad and knew no English, to the guidance of Baader. This acquaintance with Baader caused Reichenbach all his life much worry and unhappiness, for Baader inherited from his father an excessive desire for prominence, and if possible developed it still farther. He was an excellent speaker, and understood how to make his presence felt. Backed by all that he had seen, experienced, and accomplished in England, he thought that he alone in Germany understood anything of technology, and persecuted with biting criticism everyone who achieved anything in the same field independently of himself. So Baader is not a very attractive figure in the technical history of those times. The determination to get one's own way at all costs is a challenge to criticism, and it now seems that there is little left of all his plans, specially as regards the introduction of the railway. In any case he could not prevent the rise of Reichenbach, but he caused him many unhappy hours, for there were few who dared to take up the cudgels seriously with Baader.

KE

They knew his method of fighting and preferred to come to a peaceful arrangement with him whenever possible. This was impossible in Reichenbach's case, for Baader always showed a passionate dislike for him.

Reichenbach's first stay in England lasted from June 1st, 1791, to January, 1792. He then went home for a short time, returning to England for over a year. For the first months he lived in Soho. Boulton, who was his earliest acquaintance, was not very pleased over Reichenbach's intention to work with him. But since he brought with him an order for a steam engine, he could not well object. It was now Reichenbach's task to learn as much as possible about building steam engines. His diary tells us something of these first weeks. He was glad that he soon got to know Mr. Watt. We learn further how every endeavour was made to keep things secret from him. By giving some small tips, he tried to hear and see at least a little. At his inn he attempted to make drawings in secret of all he had seen and heard. 'This work cost me indescribable trouble, for the reason that not only could I not ask anyone anything, but dare not for fear of arousing suspicion; all I was allowed was to see them from time to time.' Young Reichenbach nevertheless succeeded in making a careful drawing of the machine, and in describing the boiler and engine very accurately. But he was only able to stay eight weeks in Soho, for Count Rumford had cancelled the order at the threat of war, and Reichenbach had to leave. He then went on to work as an engineer in managerial positions in large English ironworks, and during this time built quite independently a large blowing engine. Reichenbach received very good testimonials from the English: his abilities were said to be deserving of every support, and Mr. Reichenbach was specially commended to the Elector of Bavaria. He also used his stay in England to study as far as possible English instrument making, which at that time was famous all over the world.

At the end of May, 1793, Reichenbach went home again from Edinburgh via Rotterdam. His diary tells us that he examined the Electoral fortress in Düsseldorf. But it was the collection of pictures there that roused his enthusiasm most. In Remscheid he examined the smithies producing war material. A wide range of military duties awaited him at home. It was a warlike time, and one had to be ready for anything. Reichenbach attempted essential improvements in the military workshops of Mannheim and Munich, and here it was chiefly Reichenbach *père* whose aid was called for. He received as a recognition of his achievements a gold medal for 'the only boring machine in Europe so well constructed.' His father had also been concerned in directing the construction of the Amberg Small-arms Factory, and in equipping the foundry and boring mill put up in Augsburg in 1806. He died in 1820 as Lieutenant-General of Artillery, and a much admired 'mechanicus.'

Georg Reichenbach had made for the Austrians, at the time when the French were besieging Mannheim, bomb mortars with a long range. In 1796 he came with the rest of the Electoral Bavarian troops to Munich. Here he set to work on the making of his famous mathematical instruments, though military tasks had to be carried out at the same time. He made a rifled breech-loading gun, but it did not find favour; people were not ready to depart from custom. Further experiments seemed to him too costly an undertaking. From the year 1807 onward, the great scientific and technical problems of instrument making occupied him more and more completely. He therefore determined in 1811 to ask the King to accept his resignation from the army, 'in order to be able to devote all my strength more to mechanics and science, and never again to be diverted by the inevitable details of military service.'

The chief foundation of Reichenbach's great successes in instrument making was the invention of the dividing engine. He has himself told us how this technical advance was only achieved after much thought and great trouble. 'Many hundreds of plans, ideas, and experiments to improve the circular dividing engine died immediately after birth.' When in quarters during the campaign of July, 1800, he discovered the extremely simple principle of his dividing engine, and he goes on to tell us to what a degree the graduation, hitherto carried out by means of the compass, was dependent on the material, however exact the work. Measurements made in this way were quite unable to give the accuracy required. But he considered himself, a young officer, somewhat daring in attempting to beat the great English instrument-maker Ramsden, whose method of graduation was known to him. 'After much cogitation,' he tells us, '(for in such matters the simplest solution usually occurs to us last of all), I at last extracted the fundamental principle that a perfect graduation can only be obtained when it is carried out without any previous visible marks drawn as divisions between the given limit, so making it as it were in the air, before the lines of division are drawn: and in stating this basic idea we have given the main principle of my new method of graduation.' When he set to work to carry his invention into effect, many difficulties had to be overcome. At this point no doubt he owed much to Liebherr, a man trained as a watch-maker, and very skilful with his hands, whose acquaintance Reichenbach had made and whom he had taken as partner. Later on there was a quarrel between these two men, but even if we admit that Liebherr made many useful additions to Reichenbach's invention, the technical feat remains to the credit of Reichenbach when the discovery is carefully examined.

Thereupon he went to work to found in Munich, as had long been his intention, workshops for mathematical instruments. The Benedictine Professor Ulrich Schiegg from Württemberg, who was for a time Astronomer in Munich, gave him great support in this undertaking. He caused the Academy of Sciences to grant him 600 gulden for his workshops. Schiegg also recommended his instruments to the government authorities. Very soon the excellence of his machines made them known beyond the confines of Bavaria, and in 1803, the King of Bavaria granted him an honorarium of 60 louis d'or in recognition of his valuable services as a mechanic.

An important matter was that he got into contact with Joseph von Utzschneider. Utzschneider was at home in many fields of work, and was particularly desirous of encouraging trade and industry. Mainly, as he said, because they were calculated 'to advance the prosperity of all, and not the wealth of individuals.' Here he was dealing with the right man in Reichenbach, as later in Fraunhofer. On August 20th, 1804, Reichenbach, Utzschneider and Liebherr formed themselves into a company with the object of running a mathematical and mechanical institute. Reichenbach was to take over the whole technical and scientific direction. He had to design the instruments, and to carry out with his own hands all work demanding the highest perfection. Liebherr was to be the first foreman. Utzschneider agreed to attend to finance and to be the business head of the institute. In the meantime Napoleon had closed the frontiers of the Continent, optical glass could no longer be obtained from England, and it thus became necessary to incorporate an optical workshop in the undertaking. For this, Utzschneider succeeded in discovering the glassmaker's apprentice Joseph Fraunhofer, whose value was also recognized by Reichenbach: 'that is the man we are seeking; he will supply us with what we are lacking.' And so Fraunhofer began to calculate and grind the glasses produced in the new works at Benediktbeuren. The optical part of Reichenbach's institute was now transferred to this place. But Reichenbach continued to be engaged in other work as well. He set up a mathematical workshop in Vienna, and in conjunction with a very capable mechanic, Ertel, inaugurated in Munich the mathematico-mechanical institute of Reichenbach and Ertel, which also obtained its glasses from Benediktbeuren.

If we seek to form a picture of Reichenbach's great attainments in the field of geodetic and astronomical instruments, we must recognize how this great German engineer, a master held in high esteem far beyond the confines of Germany, created monuments of mechanical art. His theodolites were famous. He worked out a model which thoroughly proved its work in the trigonometrical survey of Germany undertaken in the 'forties. Indeed, the essential design has remained unchanged until to-day. The Deutsche Museum affords wonderful examples of Reichenbach's achievements. Gauss said of these theodolites made in Munich, that they were being used for the most accurate measurements of angles on the Earth. Gauss himself was an enthusiastic admirer of Reichenbach's instruments, the importance of which no one was better able to estimate than he. In a letter in March, 1813, Gauss writes joyfully to one of his collaborators: 'We have two splendid Reichenbach instruments,' and he stresses the fact that the measurements hitherto made at the observatory with the theodolites prove 'that it is an unbeatable instrument.' He admires the fineness and exactitude of the scaling, the almost incredible sensitivity of the levels, the perfection of the telescopes and the accuracy and beauty of finish of all the individual parts.

Reichenbach was right in valuing very highly an opinion from such a source. It was of Gauss that Reichenbach said, 'If he wants a divided circle from me, I will do it for nothing.' He felt the best work of his head and his hands to be so closely bound up together, that he thought more of how he could be of service to science with his instruments, than of how he could earn money. Hence he took special pains to see that his instruments came into good hands.

The famous Frenchman Laplace gave him the same recognition as that paid to him by Gauss. He calls the astronomical instrument, in a letter to Reichenbach, the most perfect astronomical instrument in existence. Again and again, contemporary reports praise these astronomical tools as the most perfect ever built by human hands.

An important source of income of the State of Bavaria was salt, which was produced in the salt-pans by the evaporation of brine. Salt had been prepared for over 1,000 years in the neighbourhood of Reichenhall, Traunstein, and Berchtesgaden. For 200 years apparatus for bringing the brine to the boiler-house had been in use. In these two centuries, machines of the period had done valuable work. The Bavarian directorate of the salt mines had now to cope with new and great problems. Reichenbach, who in reality was only incidentally a renowned instrument maker, but in his chief capacity was a member of the Advisory Council of the Bavarian Crown for the salt works, was selected to deal with these new problems. First of all a pipe-line for the brine had to be built from Reichenhall to Rosenheim. In 1810 this considerable work was finished. But now came the really great task, that of sending the brine from Berchtesgaden to Reichenhall, passing over only Bavarian territory. The distance was shorter, but the task was uncommonly difficult, for Reichenbach determined to force 44 gallons a minute to a height of 1,218 ft. in one throw. Here, as in the former case, only water was available as motive power, and there was only a small amount available, with a high fall. What machine was to be used?

The water-power would not be sufficient if used with the low-efficiency water-wheels of that day. Reichenbach now remembered the water-column machines of the Hungarian mechanic Hell. These were piston-engines, in which the head of water acted on the piston as does the pressure of steam in the steam engine. He had no intention of simply copying these machines, but designed new ones on this principle, which, however, called for considerably better workmanship and mastery of mechanics than the water-wheels. At this point, his great experience of accurate work in astronomical instruments came to his aid, and his knowledge of the manufacture of cannon was also most valuable. When his old opponent Baader ridiculed him as the instrument maker who knew, in his opinion, nothing at all about building real machines, the opposite was in fact the truth. The skilled workmen of his mechanical institute also helped to overcome difficulties. The first eight water piston-engines were copied from double-acting steam engines, the power being transmitted directly to the pump without the intervention of gear of any sort. Reichenbach's experience with the first four of these machines led him to develop a second model, which also gave excellent results. 'The running of the engine,' he was able to report in 1810, 'is extremely smooth, and overcomes the enormous height, never before overcome in a single stage, without noticeable exertion.'

Now came the second and still more difficult task. In May, 1816, the surveys for the new brine pipe-line were started. The water engines hitherto used were no longer applicable. But he found new solutions. The third model of Reichenbach's water engines was single-acting. Two large machines were erected. The one in Pfisterleiten overcame a lift of 294 ft., the other in Ilsank raised the brine to the top of the Söldenköpfl, the power head being 400 ft., and the pressure on the pump piston being about 43 atmospheres. The engine cylinder was of bronze cast in the salt mine workshops of Reichenhall. The machine at Pfisterleiten, after doing its work for over ninety years, was dismantled in 1904. Fortunately, the Deutsche Museum was already in existence and so the machine now stands in the great machine hall of the Museum as a worthy monument to Reichenbach. The machine at Ilsank worked for a still longer time. Built to raise normally 50,000 gallons of brine daily to a height of over 1,100 ft., it did this at a rate of working of two and a half strokes of the piston in a minute, and with an efficiency of 80 per cent. The duty was raised little by little to 114,400 gallons a day, the machine being equal to this output, making six strokes a minute. Only when 145,200 gallons daily were needed—almost three times the output for which Reichenbach had built it—was it necessary to consider a new installation. Since 1927, a Pelton wheel turbine has been used to drive a high-pressure centrifugal pump at a rate of 3,000 revolutions a minute. The old and new machines, built 110 years apart, stand side by side. Reichenbach's engine worked tirelessly from 1817 to 1927, 110 years. The visitor to Ilsank may admire it to-day as a monument of technical culture.

It is obvious that this mighty work gave its designer and builder much anxiety, for he alone bore the responsibility, and was assured again and again by his opponents, in the memoranda sent by them to the authorities, that the work could never succeed, and even if it ever got started, would be worn out in six months. Reichenbach wrote on August 19th, 1816: 'The details of so great and important an undertaking are often more difficult than the decision itself; there was any amount of choosing and rejecting before I finally came upon the simplest.' He wrote to Gauss in Göttingen, in his joy at having overcome his troubles at last: 'I came back from Reichenhall and Berchtesgaden only a few days ago; my work on the great giant water line is getting on splendidly, and I have never any doubt of its success. The idea of having built the largest engine in the world often gives one great pleasure—man can never escape from vanity!'

His brother Karl, who could call upon a number of specially trained workmen, helped him on the technical side. The pipe-line caused the greatest difficulties. Reichenbach devised a testing machine of his own, by which the pipes could be tested at three to six times the working pressure. Then came December 16th, 1817, and Reichenbach was able to tell the Chief of the Directorate of the salt works that exactly at midnight the great engine in Ilsank was supplying saturated brine at the Söldenköpfl. Then followed the joyous days of festival in celebration of the event. The King of Bavaria came to Berchtesgaden on the 20th December with the Prince and all the Court. In his presence, the great engine in Ilsank was started. As the brine poured into the reservoir, the guns (no doubt made by Reichenbach) thundered, all spectators cheered, and songs made by contemporary poets were sung with enthusiasm. The solemn official record of the occasion tells of visible emotion, unmistakable signs of delight, yes, even of the pearl-like tears of joy ! A few weeks later Reichenbach wrote to Gauss: 'This undertaking, it is true, is worlds apart from astronomy, but it is after all no shame now and then to turn one's gaze from the heavens to the common earth.' Utzschneider congratulated him heartily on the honour of being henceforward the first mechanic in the world.

The uncommon versatility shown in this man's work may be illustrated by a few more examples. He studied the question of cast-iron bridges ; he wished to make use of his water piston-engine for driving a factory. In 1820 the King made him head of the central office for Roads and Waterways, and he played an important part in all branches of the state building work. He was famous as an engineer far beyond the confines of Germany. No wonder that he was overwhelmed with requests to give his opinion on this proposal or that. We have still to mention the water supply of Augsburg, which he was commissioned by the town magistracy to construct in 1819. He further designed saws and grinding and polishing machines for marble, and of especial interest is a complete plan of his, dated as early as 1818, for lighting Munich by gas. The King gave him the order for this, and the original plans are preserved in the Deutsche Museum, but the scheme was never carried out. In 1826 it was hoped at least to light the arcades of the Court Garden by Reichenbach's plan. The Academy was asked, but the learned gentlemen would have nothing to do with the idea. It was only in 1850—so great sometimes is the interval between first plan and final fruition—that one could wander by gaslight through the streets of Munich.

Reichenbach then studied very thoroughly the plans for the Danube–Main Canal. He noted down some remarks and ideas concerning navigation, and did actual work in some departments of it. He also designed the plan of organization of the polytechnical schools of Bavaria.

His work on the steam engine was very remarkable. As we have seen, he had himself made the acquaintance of the first steam engine at Boulton and Watt's works. His aim was to use the expansion of the steam to drive the engine at high pressure and to do without the condenser which made the engine so immobile. In this case also, Reichenbach's work may be studied and admired in the Museum in Munich, and here too we see what this fine mechanic was able to accomplish, for we find pistons of his with metallic packing. His light high-pressure steam engine naturally suggested itself for use in transport. But Reichenbach was no longer able to realize all his hopes of the high-pressure engine.

In spring, 1824, the first sign of sudden strokes occurred and these frequently recurred in spite of all care and attention. A specially severe stroke carried him off on May 21st, 1826, in his fifty-fourth year. King Ludwig I had an official obituary notice published in the state newspaper of the Kingdom of Bavaria. 'As a man' (it runs) 'Reichenbach was as worthy of respect as he was great as a savant and artist; a pattern of honesty, sincerity, and German steadiness, a loving husband and father, a true friend, unselfish, cheerful and conciliatory in intercourse, ready to help and give good advice wherever he could.

'Twice happily married, he found in his family circle the sweetest recreation after his business labours, and though the early death of his only and very promising son, a boy eight years of age, bent him low and whitened his hair prematurely, his daughter was a source of great and pure joy to him. She married happily, and presented him with a grandson.

'Far removed from all snobbery and petty vanity, Reichenbach had the greatest pleasure in freely communicating to others his knowledge, experience, and methods, and his best reward was when he saw that others were fortunate in making use of them. Even from afar artists came to him to ask for his advice, and instruction, and certainly none went unsatisfied away.'[1]

This account may be supplemented by an address to the Academy given by Martius in Munich in 1859, wherein we read: 'Fiery, active, a steady, open, German man was Reichenbach, as he himself says "close harnessed and pulling for four"; he threw down before him doubts, hindrances, enemies, and enjoyed his life with his friends.'

Reichenbach's tomb is inscribed, 'His name is enough, his monument is his works.'

But in the Hall of Honour of the Deutsche Museum there is written under his portrait, presented by German machine manufacturers, the following:

'He hastened ahead of his time with far-reaching ideas. His works are distinguished by inventive genius as well as by mastery in execution. The art of celestial and terrestrial measurement owes important progress to him, German machine construction its first notable success.'

ROBERT FULTON
1765–1815

The man whose name is associated for all time with the successful introduction of the steamship came from the

[1] Here, of course, 'artist' (Künstler) is one skilled in the arts, and not in Art. [Tr.]

23.   GEORG FRIEDRICH REICHENBACH (1771–1826)
From the portrait by J. Stieler, in the possession of the
Bavarian Academy, Munich

24. ROBERT FULTON (1765–1815)
From an engraving. Photo: Deutsche Museum

county of Little Britain in Pennsylvania, where he was born on November 14th, 1765. His father came from Ireland, whither the family had emigrated from England. We first find him in 1735 as a respected citizen of Lancaster. In 1765 he wanted to go in for farming. But he had no success, and after a year was obliged to return heavily in debt to the town, where he died in 1768. His wife, whose family also came from Ireland, had to struggle with the care of her five children. She was their support and educator, and survived until 1799.

Robert Fulton was taught up to the age of eight by his mother, then went to one of the few schools available. At seventeen he went to Philadelphia, the spiritual centre of the new-born state, which had inscribed freedom on its banners, and with which the kings of the old world would have nothing to do. That time of the birth of the state made a strong impression on the boy, who always remained true to the ideals for which men in his youth had been ready to give their lives.

In Philadelphia he learned drawing and painting, for which he had a strong gift. His great fellow-countryman Benjamin Franklin had himself painted. The portrait pleased him; he recommended the young painter to his friends. Excellent prospects opened up for him. He was already able to help his mother and his brothers and sisters financially. But he longed to see more than Philadelphia and America, then so small a place, and wanted to try his luck in the Old World. At the end of 1786 or beginning of 1787, Fulton was in London, with an introductory letter from Franklin to his countryman Benjamin West, who had become a famous painter in England. His whole ready cash amounted to scarcely £40, but this fact caused little anxiety to one who saw a great life in front of him. Fulton soon got commissions. A high English peer had his portrait painted by the young American. The picture was successful, and Fulton was well on the road to following Benjamin West's example.

But he gave up all these great possibilities to turn to the art, the earliest great successes of which were in everyone's mouth, technology. Steam engines and spinning machines had him in their grip, for Watt and Arkwright were exemplars affording the richest stimulus to his imagination and creative power. The promising painter became the distinguished engineer Robert Fulton.

His first work was the design of a machine for sawing marble and other stone. In 1794 he sent a model of his machine to the Society of Arts in London, which awarded him its silver medal. In the meantime he had turned to another very promising field of technical work: canal construction. All the world was talking of canals at that time. It was hoped, before the days of railways, that they would satisfy the demand for means of transport. A boom in canal shares set in, which degenerated into a fever of speculation. Everyone wanted to get rich quickly by way of canal projects. Even when ten times the real value had to be paid, it was still hoped to make a profit. It was clear that this speculative mania must be followed by disaster. But before this crisis set in, canals must certainly have appeared to so imaginative a young engineer as a promising field of work.

In 1793 Fulton joined up with the Earl of Stanhope, to whom we owe a number of technical suggestions in various fields. Who will feel offended with youth for believing that the whole world has been waiting for its ideas ? Youth learns all too soon, how old, very often, are the thoughts that it thinks are new. This was Fulton's fate, who attacked the work with a fresh mind, without a thought of his predecessors. If he had known of them, he would no doubt have acted as so many up to the present day—maintained that his plans were quite different. What a pity that the gentlemen in the Patent Office were so frequently unwilling to believe it   First of all he invented, in 1793, a very peculiar steamboat, one doomed from the start to technical failure. Then in 1796 he was designing a dredger, in order to be able to build his canals quickly and cheaply. He devoted himself very thoroughly for six years to building and running these dredgers. He wanted to construct small canals, quickly and cheaply on the largest possible scale. He would have nothing to do with locks, which are expensive to construct and wasteful of time. He proceeded to invent the old inclined plane, on which his little ships were to be got up and down. He travelled about the country, learnt much from the English canal builders, and hoped for a position on one of these great undertakings. When his money came to an end, friends lent him some, but this source was not inexhaustible. Suffering want, he hoped for success.

He did not forget his native land. He wrote long letters to the President of the United States, George Washington, telling him what advantages his canal system would bring to America, and he supplemented these representations by his book, published in 1795 under the title *Small Canals*. Washington may have been slightly surprised to read how his young fellow-countryman proposed to cover Pennsylvania alone, in sixty to seventy years, with about 10,000 miles of canals, so as to make almost every house accessible by a waterway. Fulton even suggested linking Philadelphia with Lake Erie by canal. He obtained money for his plans from a rich American, plans which were to be the subject of propaganda in the new republican France.

In the middle of 1797 Fulton was in France; he did not guess that he would stay there seven years. He learned French and a little Italian and German, but most of all he studied thoroughly the fundamental sciences of the engineer, mathematics, physics, and chemistry. He acquired a good scientific training, which was of great value in his wide range of work as an engineer. He first set about getting a French patent for his canal system, and in 1798 a patent for fifteen years was granted to Sieur Fulton. But protection by the State was not enough. It was now a question of interesting men of influence in his canal plans. On May 1st, 1798,

Fulton wrote to General Bonaparte, who was getting ready to set out for the East and conquer the land of the Pharaohs. Fulton explains to the 'citizen general,' in fine and enthusiastic words, what great advantages will be conferred by his system of small canals, how the internal prosperity of a country and freedom of trade remove the causes of war and are able to bring about permanent peace.

Fulton himself may have had his doubts whether these paeans to peace would produce much impression on the General, for he suddenly turned, in this world filled with war and the tumult of war, to war work. He proposes to kill war by war, to conquer the freedom of the seas by a new and terrible weapon of his own invention. This weapon is the submarine boat, which is to blow up by mines and torpedoes the English fleet, then mistress of the seas. The submarine is introduced into the history of war as the terror of the strong, the hope of the weak. Here also Fulton had predecessors. Among these we may name Cornelius Drebbel, who, in 1624, remained two hours under water in his boat. But we have no further details of this. After his time, numerous proposals for submarines were made. But practical experiments led to no success.

Fulton had been busy with the submarine since 1797. On December 13th of that year he communicated his plans fully to the Directory and offered to explain his invention to a man with technical training such as General Bonaparte, whom he had heard to be a 'good engineer.' His communication tells us that Fulton had designed completely a machine which he calls *Nautilus*, and with which he hopes to destroy the whole British fleet. He has, he says, founded the Nautilus Company as a business undertaking, with which the French government is now to negotiate, for Fulton wants first to know what France will pay. The Ministry took these proposals, at the time quite fantastic, seriously. Negotiations were begun. Fulton was to get only half the sum he asked. The parties seemed well on the way to an agreement, and then Fulton received word from the Ministry that they would have nothing to do with the invention. But the inventor was persistent, and again attempted to approach the Government. He gave as his references the famous French machine builders, the Brothers Périer, Monge, Montgolfier and other well-known French savants. He only wanted to be allowed to make experiments at his own cost. 'The destruction of the English Navy will ensure the independence of the seas and France, the Nation which has most natural resources and population, will alone and without a rival hold the balance of power in Europe.'

No French Minister could be deaf to such considerations. He appointed referees, who were to give him an exact account of Fulton's invention. The report is dated September 5th, 1798. The hull of Fulton's submarine was 6·48 metres long, 1·94 metres in diameter, and 10·37 cubic metres in capacity. Under water it was driven by four-vaned screw propellers, turned by human power through toothed gearing. Fulton hoped to drive it by three men at 240 revolutions a minute as maximum, and 120 revolutions normally. The commission calculated that three men could remain six hours under water. In reality, it was found necessary later to be satisfied with three. Submersion and rising to the surface was effected by taking in and expelling water, for which purpose pumps were provided. A sail was used for propulsion on the surface. The boat was to attach to the bottom of wooden ships submarine mines, which Fulton called torpedoes, thus using the word in a different sense from its present one. For this purpose Fulton had thought out an ingenious device, the value of which, however, the referees thought could only be determined by practical experiments. Negotiations proceeded. Fulton asked 500,000 francs as reward for the first English ship destroyed by the *Nautilus*, and with this money he would built a whole fleet of submarines, in order to attack on a grand scale. His successes would enable the English republicans to make a republic of England, and that

Lᴇ

would mean the freedom of the seas and a permanent peace for all seafaring nations. France would reap the greatest advantage from this. Fulton understood in masterly fashion how to harness high politics in the service of his invention. But at first he made no progress.

His means were exhausted. One cannot live by writing letters. Fulton had to look around for other sources of income, and invented a machine for making ropes and cables. The invention was patented. He got more money for patents for improvements in panoramas, which Fulton as a painter was able to make excellently. The curious Parisians crowded to see them. In 1800 Fulton showed the burning of Moscow. This was not prophecy on his part. Great fires had occurred in the history of Moscow long before 1812. But he was not so busy with these panoramas as to forget his submarines. He is said to have applied to Holland for support for his invention. But people there had no desire to go in for experiments. He set his hopes on Napoleon, in whose forcefulness he had the greatest confidence. But again and again it was his experience that it is easier to overthrow a kingdom than a bureaucracy. The French bureaucrats could not get over their objections. The Minister for the Navy had qualms of conscience about breaking the laws of war. Even when Fulton offered to blow up an old and useless ship as a proof of the power of his torpedo, objections were raised that the debris would have to be removed from the channel. But Fulton was persistent, and finally, the experiment was allowed. On July 29th, 1800, the experiments were begun in 23 ft. of water. On August 5th, Fulton wrote from Le Havre to the Minister that all experiments had been successful. He now wanted to repeat them on the high sea. Fulton reported in detail to Monge and Laplace on his further submarine experiments. He was convinced that the hardest part was over. Many improvements, devised during the experiments, could easily be made. The practical application was now at hand. Fulton boldly attacked British ships of war blockading the French coast But they were warned, and always got away in time. He got to know Napoleon, the First Consul, personally, Monge and Laplace having introduced him with warm recommendations. In spite of the success, exceeding all expectations, of two submarines, no decisive result was obtained, the reason being that a suitable motor was yet to be invented. Three men are not enough for a muscle-power engine. Many years had to go by before a new chapter in the romantic history of the submarine could be opened.

Fulton now determined to bring the steamship into being, indeed to start regular steamship lines. Wide new perspectives opened out to his eyes, ever ready to gaze far into the future. Was it impossible to alter the fact, that hundreds of great sailing ships are often held fast in harbour by a calm or by an adverse tide ? The idea of putting the newly found power of the steam engine to service on the water was obvious. Papin had already planned it. William Symington had tried it in 1788, together with Patrick Miller, a rich Scottish banker. Later, in 1802, Symington had driven the *Charlotte Dundas*, a canal boat, by steam, but it was feared that the wash of the paddles would injure the banks of the canal. Early experiments with steamboats had also been made in France. The great French steam-engine builder Jacques-Constantin Périer tried a steamboat on the Seine in 1785. The Marquis de Jouffroy ran a boat in 1781, the paddle-wheel of which was driven by chains from a steam engine. But these experiments resulted in no permanent success. The time was not yet ripe for the steamship in Europe. Roads and canals still sufficed for the traffic.

Matters were otherwise in the United States, the New World. Roads were hardly known in Fulton's native country; the great navigable rivers were the best traffic arteries imaginable, if sufficient driving power were available. In America also, the plan of using steam had been investigated. James Rumpey of Virginia had travelled on the Potomac at the rate of over four miles an hour against the current in 1785, 1787, and 1788.

John Fitch of Connecticut, on September 2nd, 1785, had put before the American Philosophical Society in Philadelphia detailed drawings and a model of his steamboat. A year later Fitch had founded a steamship company. On July 27th, 1786, a steamboat built by him in Philadelphia made a successful cruise in the Delaware. Other and greater boats followed. In 1790 he attained a speed of eight knots with a boat which was carrying persons and goods regularly between Philadelphia and Bordentown. But there was as yet no money to be made, and the line was closed down. His friends sent Fitch to France, where he succeeded in getting a patent for his steamship, but there could be no thought of developing it in the midst of the convulsions of the Revolution and the endless wars. Fitch returned home. Here also he was unable to gain success. He died in 1798 a disappointed man, one of the martyrs of technology, to whom it was permitted to see the promised land only from afar.

Among the pioneers of the steamship in America, one of the chief to be mentioned is John Stevens of Hoboken. Already in 1804 he had fitted his ship with a water-tube boiler and high-pressure engine, which drove two four-bladed screws. This technical feat may be admired to-day in the National Museum in Washington. In 1807 Stevens undertook a successful trial voyage with his steamer the *Phoenix*. His son, Robert L. Stevens, likewise a first-rate engineer, carried on his father's work with great success. He designed the stern-paddle ship, a type still found in America, driven by an engine with a beam standing high above the deck.

The great American engineer Oliver Evan (1755 to 1819), who early had the courage to build high-pressure steam engines, also interested himself in the introduction of steam power for transport on land and water.

But let us return to Fulton.

In November, 1801, the Chancellor Robert R. Livingston, who had also been busy with the steamship, came as United States Ambassador to Paris. The State of New York granted him in 1798 a monopoly which gave him the sole right over twenty years to run boats using the power of steam or fire on all waters of the State. He had already enquired about steam engines from Watt and Boulton, but so far had not got any. Fulton was soon fired with enthusiasm for all these plans, and in 1803 the two decided to build at their joint cost a steamboat, to be tried out on the Seine. Fulton set about the task, using paddles. Since he knew the work of his predecessors, he was aware that there was nothing new in his plans. But everything depends upon the correct dimensions of the hull and the choice of a suitable engine. The 8-h.p. engine was borrowed from Périer, the boiler and other machine parts were ordered from Étienne Calle in Paris. Fulton used for the boiler a form of construction later employed with success by Serpollet. Water in an amount equivalent to the steam required is squirted into a chamber heated to redness, and so suddenly transformed into steam. But the chamber burnt through, and it was necessary to go back to tried and tested forms. Fulton was thus obliged to dispense with the high pressure of 32 atmospheres which he had planned.

Napoleon himself, ever well informed, had heard about the experiments, and reproached his Naval Minister with having informed him too late of Fulton's plan, which was calculated 'to change the face of the world.' He ordered the plan to be investigated by first-rate experts; he was to be given their report within a week; he was impatient. The newspapers gave a detailed account of a successful trial trip on August 9th, 1803. The steamship, which moved against the current by two wheels, as quickly as a quick walker, was much admired.

But Fulton, after his earlier experiences, had no idea of entering into new business dealings with France. He wanted to purchase from Watt and Boulton in England, the first and most famous steam-engine makers in the world, a good engine built to his own plans, and then introduce the steamship into America jointly with Livingston.

In the meantime, England had got in touch with Fulton by way of Amsterdam, in order to win him and his submarine to their side. Fulton was ready to destroy the ships of France, now an empire. Under the name of Mr. Francis, he landed in England again on May 19th, 1804. The Government entered into a very favourable agreement with him. Floating mines were tried: they were unsuccessful. Public opinion was against the new weapon of war: it was 'unfair and against the laws of war.' Finally, Nelson's victory at Trafalgar decided against these experiments of Fulton's. The French and Spanish forces were completely annihilated, and there was no other nation against which the new weapon could be used. The Government, however, treated Fulton very generously. He received £15,000 and was allowed to use his invention as he pleased, and to publish it. There was now nothing to keep him in Europe. He felt himself healthy and fresher in mind than ever, and since, as he writes in September, 1806, he cannot live without new projects, he determined to return to America.

On December 13th, 1806, after nineteen years abroad, he was back home in New York. His fellow-countrymen received him with every honour; they were proud of him; he was now to enter on the great success of his life. There was great work to come, exceeding all his past achievements.

He did not forget his torpedoes even in America, and offered his mines to the Government. Experiments were carried out, and in 1810 he published his experiences with torpedoes and submarine explosions. Finally Fulton once again ceased working in this field, for the time was not yet ripe.

The work on the steamship was more necessary and urgent. When we interpose here the fact that Fulton in

1811 was seriously planning to build in Richmond, Virginia, a railway with a locomotive for transporting coal in competition with the canal, we see how ceaselessly his technical genius worked at the development of new projects. Fortunately, he was able to control the flood of new ideas and to concentrate on the steamship which was to link New York with Albany. He attacked the problem with all the scientific weapons of his time. As regards the ship's hull, the question of the resistance of the water to its motion was dealt with thoroughly. The engine, the chief parts of which had in the meantime arrived from England, was considered in relation to its action on the ship and on the paddle-wheels. An attempt was made to determine in advance the speed of the ship. Charles Browne, a shipbuilder of repute, received the order to build the ship. The engine and accessories were put in by Fulton, and on July 4th, 1807, he was able to report to Livingston that all wheels were running excellently. The ship was at first given no name, the word 'steamship' sufficed, for there was only one of its kind in the whole world. It was later named the *Clermont* after Livingston's country seat.

The first experiments were begun on Sunday, August 9th, 1807. They were completely satisfactory, but there were still a few improvements to be made. The paddles were not as yet protected by boxes, so they could easily be injured, and threw up water on deck. But no one was willing to wait for everything to be finished. On Monday, August 17th, 1807, regular steam transport began in the world. With about forty invited guests on board, and in the presence of many thousands of spectators who jeered loudly and plainly at 'Fulton's folly,' as they called the steamboat, the ship entered on its first voyage. As it made its way upstream at an unheard-of speed, securely steering its way, the mass of spectators became conscious that they were witnesses of a great event. The jeers became plaudits.

Albany, 150 miles from New York, was reached in

thirty-two hours. Everywhere there were joyous greetings from astonished spectators of this unheard-of miracle. People were already talking of steamships on the Mississippi and Missouri. The steamships were to open up the gigantic virgin territory bought from Napoleon for 80 million francs in 1803. Regular voyages followed the trial trip, and a time-table was arranged. In New York, ninety travellers crowded on the little ship. Financially also, the future could now be faced with confidence. The twenty newspapers then published in New York, which at that time had a population of 83,000, scarcely took any notice of the affair. A great historical event was not recognized as such, and was submerged in the news of the moment.

Winter interrupted the voyages. Fulton planned for 1808 a complete rebuilding of the *Clermont*. A second steamship was to be built. Fulton was very hopeful as usual, and he was right.

But this success led to other people getting busy. Lawyers found work. Had the State of New York the right to grant a monopoly for the Hudson including the lower part, which is bordered by the State of New Jersey? The litigation was fought out with great bitterness, until finally the Supreme Court decided in Fulton's favour. Fulton built new ships, and also ferry boats. He followed Symington's plan and put the paddle-wheel between two hulls, in order to avoid injury to the paddles. The ships were built larger, the engines more powerful. Every voyage, every new ship had a lesson to teach, and what was learned was at once applied in practice. Fulton built altogether seventeen ships. While the *Clermont* of 1808 was 148 ft. long with 18 ft. beam, and a displacement of 182 tons, we find in 1816 ships of 526 tons, 156 ft. long and 33 ft. beam. The engine power was between 20 and 30 h.p. But Fulton was not satisfied with his success between New York and Albany. He wanted to carry the steamship to victory throughout the whole world.

In England he commissioned a well-known engineer,

J. C. Dyer, in 1811, to introduce the steamship on the basis of the American successes. The American success was recognized. But what was true for America was not by any means valid, so it was said even by famous English engineers, for the Old World. All attempts were fruitless. But a year later Bell's little steamboat was running on the Clyde, and with it European steamship transport began. Fulton wanted to confer the blessings of steamships also on Russia. The American ambassador in St. Petersburg was to get him the grant of a monopoly for twenty years for the line Cronstadt–St. Petersburg. In 1812 he proposed to introduce steam navigation on the Ganges in association with a certain Thomas Law. America, England, Russia, and India were enough even for the mental horizon of a Fulton.

His last great constructive work had again to do with war. America was at war with England. The New Yorkers felt how unprotected their harbour was. Here Fulton came in with a plan to build a steam-driven, very strongly built ship of war—a floating battery. The ship was built according to Fulton's plans, and the first steam warship in the world carried out its trial trip in June, 1815. The great paddle-wheel lay in the middle of the ship, well protected from all sides and from above. The steamer, named by Fulton *Demologos*, but by the Government in his honour *Fulton the First*, never went into action. Peace was concluded on December 24th, 1814. The performance promised by Fulton was exceeded at the trials of the ship. Fantastic rumours were in circulation concerning the enormous dimensions and powers of the guns, which almost exceeded the imaginative accounts in mediaeval books on gunnery. Fulton was still working on the construction of a new submarine when he was carried off in the midst of creative work by an inflammation of the lungs, in his fiftieth year. Robert Fulton died on February 23rd, 1815, deeply mourned by his fellow-countrymen, who with justice admired him as one of the great pioneers of engineering.

RICHARD TREVITHICK

1771–1833

In the south-west of England, in Cornwall of ancient fame, Richard Trevithick, the romantic of technology, the inventor of genius, and pioneer of high-pressure steam, was born. Two thousand years ago, men were already washing valuable tin out of the sand of the rivers and brooks of Cornwall. It was only later that the skill of the miner was applied to raising it from the depths of the earth. The arts of mining developed there and the mines burrowed deeper and deeper with success. Here also water put a limit to man's effort. The old technical appliances were no longer equal to coping with the water underground, and the mines had to be abandoned. This disaster to Cornish mining was experienced by Newcomen. In 1715 the first steam engine was built by him in Cornwall. Among the famous masters of the art in Cornwall we may here mention the Hornblowers, father and son. Joseph Hornblower set up his first steam engine in Cornwall round about 1725, and up to 1778 sixty atmospheric engines in all had been got to work.

The engineer had become indispensable to mining. He not only built new machines and set them going, but also saw to their maintenance in good running order. This service was paid for by a fixed monthly sum. So engineers travelled from one mine to another, and had the possibility of comparing and exchanging experiences. Among the most esteemed masters of the art in the last quarter of the eighteenth century we have Richard Trevithick, the father of our engineer; he was born in 1735. He married the daughter of a mineowner. After the birth of four daughters, his son Richard was born on April 13th, 1771, in the parish of Illogan. Shortly afterwards, the family moved to Penponds near Camborne, where the children went to school. But in those days the amount of teaching given was the least imaginable; schooling was finished at the age of seven or eight, and work, generally in the mines, then began.

The schoolmaster was far from satisfied with Richard Trevithick; he reported that he often played truant and was inattentive. The father also could not manage the extremely lively boy, so he gave it up, and allowed the child his freedom. Young Trevithick made thorough use of it. His High School was the mines with their numerous machines and technical works; learning here was play to him, and what he learned was indispensable in his later career. Everyone liked the boy with his blue eyes, high spirits, and good humour, and he did not merely look on but helped vigorously whenever he was able. As son of a respected master, who was known everywhere, he had the entry into all mines. He was to be found just at the point where something was not going as it ought, and he learned a great deal from this experience of errors and miscalculations. It was a great and important event for Cornwall when in 1777 the first Watt low-pressure engine was put in commission. It needed only a third to a quarter of the amount of coal used in the Newcomen engine; that is to say, the shafts could be sunk twice as deep as formerly. This was decisive for mining.

The very widely drawn patent of James Watt stood, as we have seen, in the way of engineers working on their own account at steam engine building in Cornwall and in the rest of England. The mineowners complained about the high royalties which they had to pay to Boulton and Watt in Soho, and rejoiced when one of the engineers had the courage to build his own engines, which were much cheaper, in defiance of Watt's patent. The natural result was litigation, since those in Soho had no intention of giving up their rights. Again and again it was declared there that no mineowner had ever been compelled to buy an engine. They had signed the agreement gladly and of their own free will, since it was very profitable to them in spite of the high royalty. Soho won, but what bitterness was caused on both sides by the battle ! Trevithicks, father and son, were opponents of the Watt patent, but the son finally saw that he would never get on without making his peace with Soho, and so he entered into negotiations which, however, led to no result, since Soho after all did not feel confidence in the suggestion. Murdock especially is said to have opposed taking Trevithick into the service of the firm of Boulton and Watt.

Richard Trevithick started very early working as an engineer alongside his father. It is related that the mine-owners were willing to give the young man, only eighteen years of age, orders such as they gave to an old and experienced engineer. The father raised objections, but the young man had won confidence, and never proved unworthy of it. If he had not succeeded in working with Boulton and Watt, if the power of the law had stopped him building steam engines independently of them, it was now his own affair to find a way out, a way of making a new form of engine, independent of the old one. All his life Richard Trevithick was full of ideas. But in this early period of his life they stormed in on him. Again and again he tried new ways, nothing seemed impossible to him, nothing frightened him. He had acquired great practical skill, he knew what lay within the technical resources of the day, but he understood little of the scientific aspects of the problems he was tackling. It was now his good fortune to gain as one of his best friends Davis Gilbert, a man who attained great eminence in the history of English science and became President of the Royal Society. We have many letters which passed between the two, and it is most refreshing to see how the great inventor and practical engineer again and again turns in confidence to his friend, his scientific conscience so to say, and asks him whether this or that may not be contrary to the laws of nature, of which he is ignorant; and how this friend brings his best knowledge to bear on every point, advises him to drop this or that, or encourages him to go on with his plans.

His father died in 1797, and in this year he married Jane

Harvey, who was a faithful companion to him all his life under the greatest difficulties—including financial troubles. She made allowance for his temperament, seeing in him the great engineer whose vision reached far into the future. During the closing years of the eighteenth century he was working at the idea of his high-pressure steam engine. The importance of this engine, which together with its application to various purposes, was his greatest technical achievement, may be estimated when one recollects the enormous size and weight of the Watt low-pressure engine, which worked with condenser and air pump and was driven by a small plus pressure of about a $\frac{1}{4}$ atmosphere. The framework of the engine was formed by a whole house; engine and engine-house were not yet separate entities. The driving force was the external pressure of the air. How much energy would he lose (he asks his friend) if he did without condensation, used high steam pressure, and let the steam escape into the air after use ? The answer is, one atmosphere. Trevithick sees the way open, thinks only of high pressure, intends to use 5, 6, 8 and even 10 atmospheres of steam pressure to work his engine.

James Watt's frank comment was to the effect that he ought to be hanged; using such a pressure was murder for the people who had to attend to the engine. Trevithick felt bitterly about this pronouncement of the great engineer, but he saw in him the competitor who wanted to close this new road to him. He was well aware of the dangers of high pressures, but not afraid of them; he may even have felt a sort of sporting enthusiasm about them. Naturally, he was unable to use Watt's huge box boiler with its great flat walls. He chose the only feasible form, the cylindrical. He built great cast-iron cylinders; his first boilers were most certainly made of dangerous material, especially in view of the then state of the art of casting. In the boiler there was a cylindrical fire-box with a return flue, so that the chimney and furnace door were on the same face of the cylindrical boiler.

The cylinder was built into the boiler, so that it was surrounded by steam and so kept hot. Naturally, accidents were not unknown. We know from a later date that one of his boilers exploded in Greenwich, and that the people in Soho took the greatest trouble to make known, by newspaper articles and letters to their customers, the facts of this explosion with all their horrifying details.

But the advantages of the high-pressure engine were too great for the idea of building such non-condensing engines to be given up. As compared with the great engines and boilers and condensing plant, with their huge machine houses, Trevithick built small machines in which engine and boiler were united, machines which could readily be erected anywhere. The small size of these plants, and their low weight per horse-power, astonished engineers again and again. What could be more obvious than the idea of using these small and movable machines for transport? And so Trevithick got to work on the steamboat. He wanted to use screws for propulsion. But more than this, he was the first to make a steam road car and a steam locomotive. He was already building models at home in the closing years of the eighteenth century, putting them on wheels and delighting his guests by making them run about the table and the floor. He used a spirit flame for the boiler, or put a piece of red-hot iron in the furnace of his little engine. Here also Trevithick was not the first. In 1769, Nicolas Joseph Cugnot had already built in Paris a lorry for military purposes, driven by an atmospheric engine, but this clumsy construction was not a success. And then Murdock in Cornwall had also had a little model of a locomotive running about his room, but he too had to give up working on it, because his employers, Boulton and Watt, insisted that he should not divide his energies, but only put up Watt engines and see to their maintenance. Concerning Trevithick we know, by the way, that he knew nothing of Murdock's little steam locomotive, though this is often said to be the case.

Now came a memorable year in technical history, 1800, in which Watt's patent expired. The road was open, and engineers everywhere threw themselves into the further development of the steam engine. Everyone thought he could improve it, very few succeeded. So it was now open to Trevithick to realize all his plans in this field. He no longer contented himself with the small model, but proceeded to build the first steam automobile. The question had previously arisen whether the friction of the wheels on the road would be sufficient, not when the source of power was able, as in the case of man or horse, to push against the road, but when the force of the steam was applied through the spokes of the wheels. This question had been discussed at curiously great length, but Trevithick was a master of the practical experiment. It is related that he had a farm cart loaded with stones and, taking off his coat, grasped, along with his friends, the spokes of the wheels and proved that the wagon could indeed be driven by this means. The machine was soon built. It was on Christmas Eve, 1801, that 'Dick's firedragon,' as the neighbours called it, got under way. Trevithick had not even sought out the highway for his trial, but chose a bad road with a steep hill. To everyone's delight, the car set itself in motion with mighty puffs, and now there was no holding people back; everyone who could jumped on the traction-engine, for that is what the first steam car looked like. All were delighted at the way it took the steep hill. But here again the trouble came later. The boiler could not produce nearly as much steam as was needed for the work to be done, and people were glad to be able to push the machine back home by hand after it had got half way. But everyone had the confident feeling: it works! The difficulties would be overcome. In spite of the misfortune which followed the fine start of the journey, consolation was quickly found. The overworked machine was pushed into a shed, and the company adjourned to an inn, to refresh itself on 'roast goose and the accompanying drinks.'

And all this led to its being forgotten to draw the boiler fire. The water evaporated, the boiler became red hot, and every combustible part of the machine went up in flames, together with the first garage in the world. But Trevithick had no thought of giving up his plans.

He was granted a patent for his steam engine for fixed and movable use. He joined up with other engineers for common enterprise, and in 1803 built a second steam car and sent it to London. All over England he put in his high-pressure steam engines for the most varied purposes. If he had now felt able to limit his activities to this branch, and set up a works of his own, he would have made it equal in importance to the first steam-engine works in the world at Soho. But that was not his line. He wanted to remain the independent engineer, unhampered by manufacturing on his own account. He was the customer of a whole number of smaller or larger foundries, smithies and works which perhaps, even at that time, regarded themselves as machine shops.

The year 1804 was also notable in technical history, for in this year the first locomotive in the world ran on iron rails. All over England betting was a favourite sport, and in the mining districts of Wales people were particularly ready to make the decision of technical questions even more exciting by laying heavy bets on them. A talk over drinks about the possible performance of a steam wagon in the minefield, to run over the flat cast-iron rails then in use, comparable to wooden planks, led to a bet, and Trevithick was quite willing to fulfil the required conditions. His locomotive did better than was expected, and it is said that the loser even paid gladly, being delighted at the result of the trial. But the unaccustomed load broke the iron rails, and at that time one could not imagine making the structure stronger merely so as to be able to use steam. So the engine and boiler were taken off the wheels and used to drive a hammer in an ironworks, and that was the end of the first railway locomotive.

All his life Trevithick had paid little attention to politics, but events were now of too great a magnitude not to have an effect on him and his work. Napoleon was seriously planning to invade England with his armies. This made the whole country uneasy, and everywhere the desire was not merely to organize defence, but to make the whole project impossible from the start. At this juncture Trevithick came on the scene. He proposed to send steam-driven fireships among the warships, and set the whole fleet on fire. Naturally he wanted to be there himself. But after all he did not get as far as this use of steam power. In 1805 he built two railway locomotives for Newcastle, and in the same year a canal boat with steam engine and paddles. In 1806 he built the first three steam dredgers and set them going on the Thames; and as though he had not yet enough irons in the fire, he took part in the plan to drive a tunnel, mining-fashion, under the Thames. It was an immensely daring undertaking for those times. There was a great difference between driving an adit through solid rock and making a tunnel under a river-bed, where one would have constantly to reckon with a dangerous inrush of water. He showed that his incredible energy and technical skill enabled him to do great work in this field also. Of 1,200 feet, he finished 1,000 feet. But the technical difficulties were augmented by personal difficulties with the people he had to do with. Finally the whole undertaking came to a dead end and was abandoned.

Trevithick now had time for new plans. In 1808 he built a passenger locomotive, brought it to London, and got it running in the middle of the town on a large plot of building land near Russell Square. He put a strong fence round the ground and charged a shilling entrance to see the new marvel and travel on it once round in a circle. The locomotive was described as Trevithick's travelling steam engine, its name as given on the entrance ticket was *Catch me who can*. This travelling without horses, as it was called in the newspapers, stimulated great interest. Everybody wanted to see the machine, but few had the courage to take a ride on it. We hear that great sums were bet on it. It ran for some weeks, and then a rail broke, and the whole machine went straight on and then turned over. Fortunately, the ground was very soft. The trips were then given up, for Trevithick was losing money, the gate money not being enough to pay the running costs. A tablet has been put up in commemoration of this machine.

We must further mention Trevithick's patent for iron tank ships, which were to serve for loading and unloading the great sailing vessels. In 1809 he was granted a patent for floating docks and for iron masts. He wanted to cook by steam, and he raised sunken ships by means of his tanks. In the meantime he had moved to London in order to carry out his numerous business undertakings. He was there seized in 1810 by a severe disorder, and returned to Cornwall. He also met with a heavy financial disaster. He owed it to his partners that he was not saved from bankruptcy, he whose greatest anxiety was that others should not suffer on account of his losses.

Back in his Cornish home, he turned with great success again to the mine pump. He built pumps of entirely new design with huge plunger pistons, and above all, he made use of higher steam pressure and greater expansion. He devised the cylindrical boiler with interior fire, which then became known throughout the world as the Cornish boiler, and is still used to-day in many plants as an efficient type of boiler with large water capacity. Technically speaking, the work which he did for Cornish mining cannot be estimated too highly. Trevithick took care that the engines were regularly overhauled, and finally got to the point at which the performance, expressed by the ratio of water raised to coal consumed, was published. This had a great educative value, and also appealed to the sporting instincts of the mineowners. Everyone now wanted to show the highest efficiency. It thus came about that Trevithick's high-pressure expansion engines in Cornwall, by reason of a coal consumption so low as to be frequently not credited in other parts of England, were everywhere admired as masterpieces of steam engine construction. They had an essential influence on steam engine design far beyond the frontiers of England. They made it possible to reduce the coal consumption to a third or a quarter of that attained by Watt in 1800, who himself had made a like advance as against the atmospheric engines. It has been calculated that this engine of Trevithick's saved the mineowners of Cornwall over half a million pounds in ten years. But in this also he worked for others; no financial reward came to him and his. Trevithick needed his Boulton. When we add that he used his little locomobile high-pressure engines early on in agriculture for threshing and grinding corn and sawing wood, and when we further note that he constructed in 1813 a sort of earth cutter which could move over the land, we see from this short account of his technical achievements how fertile his mind was in all branches of technical work. Again one may say, 'Less would have been more,' but he had to go storming onward, and his ideas always ranged far beyond what he was able to carry out.

Trevithick was forty-two years of age when his high-pressure steam engine led him into the greatest adventure of his life. In Peru there were rich silver mines, distant about 160 miles from the capital, Lima, and situated in the mountains 14,000 ft. up. But these mines loaded with riches were a failure, for existing technical means were unequal to fighting the water. Now the steam engine had already been heard of in Peru. Unwilling to yield the treasure to the water without striking a blow, the owners decided to send a Swiss, Franciskus Uvillé, who had been many years in Peru, to London, to seek in the land of technology the means by which access to the silver could be preserved. He did what seemed most obvious, he got in touch with Boulton and Watt in

Soho. But he was to learn that at so great a height above sea-level, a low-pressure steam engine would be very inefficient; and even if one resigned oneself to that, how could such a gigantic machine be dragged 14,000 ft. up over tracks only passable by mules ? Uvillé then saw by chance in a London shop-window one of Trevithick's small high-pressure steam engines. He bought it for £20 and went straight back to Lima with his prize. The machine was set up in the mine and worked satisfactorily. The way was now clear, and a company was formed to pump out the Pasco mines. Uvillé was then sent again on the long journey to England to find the man who had invented and was building high-pressure steam engines. But Uvillé, sent as emissary to Trevithick without even knowing his name, became seriously ill on the way. He learned on board ship that the builder of engines was Richard Trevithick, and chance would have it that his informant was a cousin of Trevithick. The ship berthed in Falmouth on May 10th, 1813, after a six-months' voyage. The Peruvian was still ill and had to stay in bed, but he at once wrote to Trevithick, who already visited him on the 20th May. Trevithick was delighted with the idea of saving by means of his engine the wealth of a whole country. Uvillé shared his enthusiasm, and translated it into terms of big orders for Trevithick, to a value greatly exceeding the sum provided for by the Company in Lima.

Trevithick was very busy. Since he himself did not make engines, he handed over the orders to his friends. No one could deliver quickly enough for him, and Trevithick promised money galore. He told everyone ready to listen of the vast richness of the mines, and that dollars and work were to be had from them in abundance. Once again Trevithick was dreaming of a golden future. The directorate of the Company in Peru was no less enthusiastic. The mineowners' company expressed the same sentiments in writing. A monument was proposed, to inform posterity of the great work of clearing the mines of water. A river of silver was now to pour out of these mines and fill all other nations with admiration. This silver would stimulate trade and bring prosperity to the whole country. It would fill the royal treasury of the beloved ruler.

In the same year, Napoleon had been banished to St. Helena. The world was again at peace, but all hopes set upon this event were, at first, unfulfilled. The world-crisis took effect everywhere, there was no trade, no money, no credit, nothing but general decay. In the meantime Uvillé had returned to America with an English technical expert. Matters had now come to the point of Trevithick having been won personally for the work on the Peruvian mines. He embarked on October 20th, 1816, with three other Englishmen. He thought to be away only a short time, and certainly never dreamed that eleven years would go by before he saw England again. New engines were constantly sent out, but not only for the mines; the State Mint needed a new plant. Trevithick fulfilled the task to everyone's great satisfaction. The output of the Mint was greatly increased.

We are also told about Trevithick's arrival in Peru. When he landed, all the bells were rung, everyone with a pair of legs was out in the streets, which were crowded with people anxious to welcome him. Men of high position in the land had travelled far so as not to miss his arrival. It was proposed to put up a statue in silver to Trevithick. But there was soon another side to the picture. Uvillé himself was jealous of Trevithick. The Englishman found opposition everywhere; it was easier for him to deal with machines than with jealous and ill-disposed people whom, we may well imagine, he did not treat all too gently, his temperament being what it was. Uvillé died in August, 1818, and another Englishman who had been making trouble for him had died a few months earlier, so that the greatest hindrances seemed to be overcome. But the revolution broke out, everywhere in South America it was hoped to throw off the Spanish yoke;

revolts had been an everyday occurrence even before Trevithick's arrival. Simon Bolivar, the Liberator, was the leader of this movement. Lima, the headquarters of Spanish military power in South America, had remained comparatively calm, but in February, 1817, shortly after Trevithick's arrival in Peru, a Spanish army had been completely defeated by the rebels. In the next year victory favoured the other side. But the Spanish were not able to keep their hold on the country permanently; in 1821, Peru declared itself independent, and Bolivar marched into it. These political events did not fail to affect the silver mines. Trevithick was helpless in face of the troops. Now it was the Spaniards, now the Liberators, who were in possession of the mines. It was just the latter who, fearing that the Spaniards might again seize the mines and use the silver so gained to strengthen their power, destroyed everything movable, and threw the machine parts down the mines. These machines had been successful, in seven years of work, in mastering the water, and now all their work was in vain. Even Trevithick's friendly relations with Bolivar were no help to him. In 1824 Trevithick left the soil of Peru, upon which he had put his foot seven years earlier filled with tremendous hopes.

The indefatigable Trevithick had not only erected and run his engines high up in the Andes, but, as a man closely connected from childhood with mining, had received again and again the strongest impressions of the natural riches everywhere to be found in the country. So he went to Chile to investigate the copper mines there, being ever full of great and new hopes. We know that he raised a Chilean warship, which had been sunk with its full complement of bronze cannon, and much else, and had saved all the valuable tin and copper. He received £2,500 for this service, and one of his friends strongly advised him to send the money to his wife at home. But Trevithick used the whole sum for fresh dreams. He had been advised to take shares in a Panama pearl-fishing enterprise, and in it lost the last penny. After this failure in Peru no news came from him for a long time. Great anxiety was felt for him, but meantime he was travelling about the country, ever in pursuit of new hopes. We find him in Ecuador where he met a Scotsman, Gerard, who shared his belief in the enormous riches of the country. Trevithick travelled to Columbia at Bolivar's request, but he gave up all profit that this connection might have brought him and proposed to open up, jointly with Gerard, the mineral riches of Costa Rica. The two studied mining there for four years. They acquired extensive mining rights of great value, surveyed the land, and acquired every sort of useful information. They planned to open up new great mines, to build settlements, construct railways, erect stamp batteries, and to carry out many other projects. They proposed to mine 250,000 tons of ore a year, and dreamed again of the golden treasures lying underground.

But first they proposed to return to England in order to raise the necessary capital for these undertakings. They were unwilling to make the long journey again round Cape Horn, but proposed to travel right across the pathless mountains, through virgin forest and desert to the Caribbean Sea on the other side, from which the way home would be shorter. This journey was, at that time, an unparalleled adventure. Accompanied only by a few persons, among them two boys who were to go to school in England, they set out, trusting to their good fortune, like their predecessors the Conquistadores of old. The party suffered loss of life, Trevithick came very near to drowning in crossing a river, but even this adventure was finally successful. After a three weeks' exhausting march, they arrived at the southern harbour of the State of Nicaragua, Greytown, completely exhausted and with torn clothing. From here they got to the harbour of Cartagena, and by a curious chance Trevithick met in the hotel there young Robert Stephenson, whom he had known as a boy, and with whose father he had so often talked over railways and locomotives. Stephenson gave him money for the voyage;

he himself was going to North America in order to see Niagara Falls. Concerning Trevithick we know that he went on to Jamaica and from there to Falmouth. He was not even able to pay his fare, and one of his fellow-travellers gave him enough money to enable him to leave the ship. Anyhow, it is said that he came back to his native country after eleven years' work without a penny. His only possessions were the clothes he stood up in, a gold watch, a compass, and a pair of silver spurs. But he still had mining concessions for a copper mine, and for rich mines in Costa Rica. He hoped to sell these concessions in England for a large sum, but his endeavours were in vain. How strong was his faith in their enormous value is seen from the fact that he rejected indignantly a cash offer of £8,000. When his friend told him that he would have done well to take the money, he was so angry that he almost threw the man downstairs.

When in 1827 Trevithick returned after eleven years from the New World to his native country, technical development had progressed. The high-pressure machine was everywhere in use; in America, in Germany, enthusiastic advocates of high pressure existed. The Cornish pumping plant and boiler had proved its value. Steam navigation had been introduced, even on the ocean. The steam locomotive had already found a place in mining; in fact, the great railway connecting Liverpool and Manchester was being built, and the steam carriage was in use in London and its environs. The iron industry had made great advances.

When Trevithick arrived in Cornwall, his fellow-countrymen gave him a great reception. Everywhere the bells were ringing, everywhere he was given banquets, the most prominent men in Cornwall could not do enough to celebrate his achievements, and they assured him again and again that without his labours deep mines would have been impossible. He was treated like a great hero, while it was forgotten that he did not possess a penny. But Trevithick had not yet lost his optimism. He could not imagine that these eulogies over sumptuous banquets would not be followed by a respectable financial recognition. Here he deceived himself; he had a great moral claim, but it could not be upheld in a court of law and so the mineowners, enriched by his efforts, did not present him with a penny. But his courage was not yet broken; he ever conceived new plans. He improved ships' guns. He wrote to his scientific friend that he had now heard that much money was being spent in bringing ice from Greenland and that he believed ice might be made artificially by the use of the steam engine. He also made journeys abroad; he went to Holland to assist in land reclamation. We also learn from one of his letters that he was in Germany, and was there interested in the heating of large rooms. He paid much attention to this problem and proposed to heat them with steam, or better, hot water. But nothing brought in money. Along with his Cornish boilers he built water-tube and tubular boilers of the most varied descriptions.

His last great plan was the building of a gigantic tower. The Reform Bill passed through Parliament in March, 1831. A great many English people believed in the coming of a Golden Age. Trevithick, too, wished to honour this new epoch and designed in 1832 an enormous column, 1,000 ft. high, 100 ft. across at the base, and 11 ft. at the point. It was to be made from 1,200 pieces of cast iron. A high-pressure steam engine of 20 h.p. was to take visitors to the top in ten minutes. This whole national monument was to cost £80,000. It would have been five times the height of the Nelson column in Trafalgar Square. This plan— perhaps not regrettably—was never carried out.

Trevithick, who in his last years worked in Dartford, Kent, in association with a young and enterprising engineer, John Hall, lived there alone in a modest inn, his family remaining in Cornwall. Here he designed his machines, and here ended the life of this great engineer on April 22nd, 1833. His associate buried him and also paid the costs of the funeral. He was interred in a pauper's grave, now unknown.

It is assumed that he died of inflammation of the lungs; his iron constitution had after all not been exposed without injury to the eleven years of intense strain in America.

Trevithick was a tall and impressive figure, 6 ft. 4 in. in height, and broad shouldered; he had a fine, well-shaped head on a splendidly built body. His bright-blue eyes and somewhat large mouth with its kindly expression were never forgotten by anyone who knew him. He paid great attention to his clothing and behaviour, and anyone meeting him in a London street would certainly have taken him for one of the most respected citizens. Full of good humour and gaiety, he could readily forget the cares of every day in cheerful company; he had a gift for expressing himself well. People loved to listen to him when talking of his thoughts and ideas, and of all there was still to be done in technical work. He had an enormous capacity for work, and plunged with all the force of his temperament into every new task. He was an optimist who did not see what had already been done, but what there was still remaining to do. He understood how to carry people along with him, and this fact no doubt brought much harm to others. But what would the world be like if we had no such pacemakers to set the times moving quickly ? His whole make-up was that of a practical man, and at the same time he was a dreamer. He forgot over his technical plans both his family and friends. He lived all the time in the future, he despised gold and goods, and yet saw in them the external expression of recognition, after which he struggled in vain. He thus enjoyed to the full after his own fashion the life for which his nature fitted him. All the mischances which it brought him did not embitter him. Shortly before his death he wrote down his ideas about his life, and with these words we will close this account:

'I have been branded with folly and madness for attempting what the world calls impossibilities, and even from the great engineer, the late Mr. James Watt, who said to an eminent scientific character still living, that I deserved

25. RICHARD TREVITHICK (1771–1833)

From the portrait by J. Linnell, 1816, in the
Science Museum, South Kensington

26. GEORGE STEPHENSON (1781–1848)

From the portrait by John Lucas   Photo: Deutsche Museum

hanging for bringing into use the high-pressure engine. This so far has been my reward from the public; but should this be all, I shall be satisfied by the great secret pleasure and laudable pride that I feel in my own breast from having been the instrument of bringing forward and maturing new principles, new arrangements of boundless value to my country. However much I may be straitened in pecuniary circumstances, the great honour of being a useful subject can never be taken from me, which to me far exceeds riches.'

GEORGE *and* ROBERT STEPHENSON
1781–1848 & 1803–1859

The introduction of the steam-driven railway is one of the decisive events in human history. We speak of a time before and after the introduction of railways, and wish to express thereby the fact that our lives have been changed fundamentally by this means of transport, which has opened up to mankind undreamed-of possibilities in the most diverse directions. The development of trade and industry as known to us to-day would have been unthinkable without the railway. But its effects extend far beyond these, and exceed, in all that we now take for granted to-day, the dreams even of the wildest optimists, who only a century ago had to face ridicule for prophecies which were soon to be far exceeded by facts.

This technical achievement was not, of course, the off-spring of one man's brain. Whole generations of engineers and clever workmen took part in its creation. But a century ago there was living, still at the height of his fame as fore-most railway engineer of the world, a man whose great powers and tough endurance were justly rewarded by the greatest success in the age when the railway was born: George Stephenson.

This famous son of the coal-miner Robert Stephenson was

born on June 8th, 1781, in a low ivy-covered cottage in the little mining village of Wylam, eight miles west of Newcastle. The father had attained to a weekly wage of 12s., and it was even in those days by no means easy to keep a family of six children. We know that the father was industrious and skilful, and that he had great pleasure in nature, in animals and plants, a taste inherited by his son. It is related that he used to tell the school children, after work was over, the most wonderful fairy-tales and stories of adventure, and hence was much admired by the young. He was too poor to be able to send his children to school. They had to start helping in the house at an early age, and earn a few pence themselves as soon as possible. George Stephenson, when a small child, had to look after cows and prevent them straying on the railway of the mine. He was proud when he was finally allowed to drive the horse working a hoist, and his highest ambition was one day to carry coals to the old atmospheric engine. And so he rose to be a stoker at the age of sixteen.

The pennies he had earned now became shillings to take home. His real school was the mine, and there he learned what there was to be learned. He was soon able to help and to take care of the engine, and when work was over he endeavoured to get the most complete knowledge of the machine and all its parts by cleaning it, taking it apart and putting it together again. Young Stephenson thus developed into a skilled worker, and also into a cheerful comrade. He loved to pit his bodily powers against those of his comrades. It is related of Stephenson, as of Trevithick, that none could throw the blacksmith's hammer as high as he.

He was already eighteen when he began to learn to read and write, for he recognized that these arts would open the doors of further progress to him. At twenty-one years of age he married Fanny Henderson, the servant of the mine-owner, and in 1803 his son Robert was born to him, who was to be his great collaborator in the development of the railway. The young father's ambition was from the first to give his son the education, of which he himself had so often and so painfully felt the need. But money was needed for that, and he had to think of a way to earn more. He first tried his hand at cobbling; he nailed good solid soles on the miners' boots, and made all repairs to the shoes of the villagers. This was no road to riches. In the meantime he had also set to work to understand clocks thoroughly, and he was soon in a position to apply his skilful hands to repairing them; in this way, putting clocks and watches to rights was soon bringing him a certain income. He told later how proud he was when he was first able to call a piece of gold his own. A journey to Scotland, in the course of which he was able to execute a number of orders, brought him what was, in his circumstances, a substantial profit. But when he came back, his father had been blinded by an accident at his work, and so what the son had earned just sufficed to support the father. He set to work again to save, and his steady persistence enabled him to put aside shilling after shilling. He was soon able to send his son to the High School at Newcastle, and it must have been an affecting picture when father and son sat together in the evenings at the thick oak table, and went together through the problems set by the teacher. In this way the father learned from the son and his teachers.

After his schooling in Newcastle, Robert had first to get a thorough knowledge of the practical work of a coal-mine. He was for three years working at all the various branches of this, and his father had then got on so well as to be able to send him to Oxford or Cambridge. But this step seemed to him too long a one. He did not want his son to rise so quickly out of his class. He was afraid of mere learning and over-refined people, so he sent him to the University of Edinburgh. But even there Robert Stephenson was only able to put up with a single term. Together with what he had learned by practical work, and with his quick grasp of things, it seemed to him enough. Many changes had come about in his father's position. He had moved from one mining district to another. He had learned everywhere whatever there was to be learned, and everywhere he had done his work steadily and carefully. In this way he had risen from stoker to machine master and then to manager of the whole technical plant of the coal-mines.

Another great technical feat of Stephenson's must not be forgotten. He invented the miner's safety-lamp, which prevented the many terrible explosions from which the mines of his district especially had had to suffer. Stephenson had already made in August, 1815, before Humphry Davy, a satisfactory safety-lamp, which he considerably improved in the course of that year. The lives of many miners were saved by his invention, and by it the mines were preserved from heavy losses.

The transport of coal from the mine to the place where it was to be used, or to the ship, caused him much anxiety. He improved the railway, he worked on the wagons, he had heard of Trevithick's steam carriage—indeed, one had come to Newcastle, and another had been ordered from Trevithick who, however, full of other problems, had not got as far as delivering it. In Leeds, the great industrial town, a machine master, Blenkinsop, had also built a locomotive. But he was one of those who were convinced that iron could not get a grip on iron. Hence he had put down a toothed rack between the rails, and had taken out a patent for the first cog-wheel locomotive. Another master, Hedley, had had more confidence in friction, and had built, like Trevithick, a small locomotive which he called *Puffing Billy*. It was put in commission in 1813. It has been preserved to us, and is now in the Science Museum in South Kensington. The Science Museum in Munich has an exact copy of it, able to run under its own steam. Hedley deserves the credit of having been the first to put into practical service a locomotive with smooth wheels travelling on flat rails.

George Stephenson observed this development with growing interest, and succeeded in persuading the owner of the
mines in the Killingworth area to make a trial with a locomotive built by him. In 1814 the first Stephenson locomotive was turned out from the mine workshops, mostly by
the work of Stephenson's own hands; he called it *Blücher*,
for all England at that time was full of enthusiasm for the
Prussian 'Marshal Forwards.' This name was a good omen;
the first step to the creation of the railway had been taken,
from then on things went forward. The first locomotive
was followed by others, more and more experience could be
utilized. The mineowners also saw the great advantages
of steam traction. But progress was still very slow.

Stephenson was not the man to make propaganda for himself and his ideas; it was enough for him to proceed step
by step. His post prevented him from devoting himself
entirely to the railway, for he had also to deal with pumping
and hoisting plant, and he managed to deal successfully even
with the oldest of these. The word went round that he was
the best machine doctor in the neighbourhood, and his
employers were quite agreeable to his helping others besides
themselves to keep their machines in order. For eight years
Stephenson's locomotives did their work day by day up
there in the North, without the slightest notice being taken
of them either by the newspapers or by the technical world.
Elsewhere the only thought at the time was for the improvement of the roads. Macadam made great improvements in
this field; he was justly given praise and fame, and received a
grant of £41,000, whereas not a shilling was given to
Stephenson. It was the time when everyone believed that
victory would go to the steam carriage running on the
improved roads. Leeds as a great centre of trade was much
more in the public eye, and Blenkinsop's machine was
known in London.

But at last Stephenson's time came. On November
18th, 1822, a fair-sized railway was opened on the Hetton

mine, not far from Sunderland, and Stephenson had to deliver the first five locomotives for it. People called them 'iron horses'; they were used only for hauling coal trucks on the flat, stationary steam engines being used for pulling them up the very heavy gradients. Stephenson had provided five such cableways. He now became known to a wider public as a man who could not only build railways and locomotives but also run them to the economic advantage of the owner.

A new problem was set him in 1823. He was chosen to build the very important railway from Darlington to Stockton, a line of decisive importance for the whole development of railways. It was to transport the coal wealth of the county of Durham to North Sea ports. The promoter was Edward Pease of Darlington. He was a coalowner, and wanted to improve transport in order to open up new markets for his coal. At first he thought only of horse traction. But when he got to know Stephenson he slowly and cautiously acquired faith in steam. The railway was the first designed for serving the general public. Pease was the far-sighted *entrepreneur* who went to work with iron energy and endurance. Smiles, Stephenson's biographer, was able to visit Pease as late as 1854, in his eighty-eighth year, and found him as full of life and mental energy as if he were only forty years old. It was men of such metal as this who brought railways into being in a comparatively short time. He related how hard it had been to get money for this railway. He had to go to his best friends and beg them again and again to do their share in getting together at least the money necessary for building the line. But permission had first to be obtained from Parliament, for it was a question of a public highway. This also was done, but only in face of great difficulties, of which we will speak presently.

In the law permitting its construction, it is stated that the carriages may be drawn by men and animals or 'otherwise.' None dared to mention steam traction. Exactly as in the case of a canal, a fixed sum was paid for the use of the road.

The track was open from morning to evening. Naturally, it was soon evident that a railway is not a canal, and the owners proceeded to take over the running themselves. It was Pease, too, who with Stephenson set up a locomotive works in Newcastle. This first locomotive works in the world was opened in 1823, and is still working to-day. It was of decisive importance, for George Stephenson, who put the management in the hands of his young son Robert, whose name the firm bears, was able to collect around him men who understood something of loco-motives and railways. That was a work which was as necessary as it was difficult, but he was successful. Many of the most important railway engineers came from this locomotive works, and became pioneers of English railways, and indeed of railways built by Stephenson and his son in distant countries, where they taught the local engineers.

The line from Darlington to Stockton aroused widespread interest. New railway projects sprang up everywhere. The most important plan of all was to link the great port of Liverpool with the trading and industrial city of Manchester by a railway. The business men and industrialists of both towns had recognized, from their own experience, the necessity for an efficient means of transport. The canals sometimes failed in winter. The textile industry had devel-oped to such an extent that cotton arriving in Liverpool from America could not be got quickly enough to Man-chester. The factories were frequently idle for days for want of cotton. So the leading industrialists got together in order to apply to the Government for permission to build this railway. All sorts of plans were made, but the greatest need was for a man able to carry out the work on his own responsibility. The Darlington and Stockton railway was studied, and it was believed that in George Stephenson the only man capable of executing the work had been found.

Courage was needed for this decision, for George Stephen-son was not at that time one of the famous engineers of the

NE

land. What was he after all but a mechanic who now
and then built a locomotive ? He was not to be mentioned
in the same breath with the great builders of roads, canals,
and harbours. But he now had to face the music in London
before the Parliamentary Committee dealing with the Bill.
These were certainly the hardest hours in Stephenson's life,
as he used to say later. There he stood, the big burly
Northerner, whose forefathers had once immigrated from
Scotland. The words of broad hard Doric came stumb-
lingly and reluctantly from the strong, well-cut mouth. The
refined and educated men in the Committee smiled at his
clumsy turns of expression. His manner of speech seemed
to Londoners rough and untaught, and he was mockingly
asked whether he was indeed an Englishman. The
opponents of the railway—chiefly those who had made fortunes from canals, and great landowners—had engaged the
smartest lawyers to be found in England, and they understood how to cross-examine Stephenson to a point at which
he at times was unable to follow. But this gives an idea of
how new the railway was, and how much energy was
required to push it forward in face of all difficulties.

Not one of the great engineers took Stephenson's side; he
had to fight his battle alone. And what absurd remarks were
made ! The locomotive would set fire to all houses near the
line, it would burn up the cornfields ! Worst of all—
and this was the sorest point with the great landowners who
were lovers of the chase—all game would leave the neighbourhood. No pheasants and no foxes would be left, and
then what would there be left to live for ? Also the noise
would be unendurable, the land near the railway would be
unsaleable. And what was to become of all the people who
were driving the stage coaches, famed throughout the world,
on the roads only recently improved, and of the many road-
side inns at which such good cheer was provided ? All that
would be wiped out by such wild projects, which anyhow
could never be realized. And then came the technical

experts, who proved quite clearly that the locomotive was an absurdity. For it had to carry coal and water with it, and it would certainly be necessary to provide every few miles great stores of coal and casks of water. If steam was to be used, there was only one way to do it; to put up at certain points great, solid, well-tried condensing steam engines, and pull the carriages along by ropes. Stephenson was asked at what speed he proposed to run his trains. His friends had begged him not to let out the fact that he believed the speed would be ten miles an hour, but to say six only. But even that appeared too high, and what reply would have been made to a prophet who predicted that in a century men would be travelling at ten times the speed then held to be possible?

Stephenson had naturally to put forward plans at this hearing, and surveys were necessary for this. Here forcible resistance was encountered. The farmers, armed with sticks and stones, drove away the surveyors and smashed their instruments. They were in danger of their lives. Stephenson had to post sentries, and strove to get the most important data secretly. It was clear that such data were not always free from error, and this fact was used to prove that he understood nothing of the whole business. He wanted to carry his line over a notorious bog, a bog which swallowed up even a stick thrown into it. What could be more foolish than to believe that one could lay iron rails over such ground, and run heavy loads over them? Ridicule and mockery were rained on Stephenson for months, and when he was asked again and again from all sides to give exact details of what he intended to do, he finally spoke words which have become classical in technical history: 'I can't tell you how I will do it, but I will do it.' The Bill was finally passed into law by thirty-six votes to thirty-five, and the work could begin. Even now every possible obstacle was put in the way, but it was finally seen that it could not be prevented in the end, and then all those who believed themselves to have suffered damage, came to court and asked for compensation, often of large amounts, for what they did not possess, and so could not lose. If the railway could not be averted, at least something might be made out of it. Here again continuous fighting went on.

The question of the means of traction was not yet finally decided. The more cautious of the promoters believed rather in the stationary steam engines recommended by the engineers; they were thinking in terms of horse traction. But Stephenson finally succeeded in persuading them at least to make a trial with locomotives. It was agreed to hold a competition, the most famous in all technical history. A £500 prize was regarded as a sufficient stimulus to competition. The locomotive was specified as having to weigh no more than 6 tons, and to haul a 20-ton load, including tender and water tank, at the rate of ten miles an hour, and to cost not more than £550. The steam pressure was not to exceed 3·5 atmospheres. The test was to take place on a straight, level stretch of line two miles long at Rainhill between Liverpool and Manchester. The locomotive was to traverse this course twenty times. On the day of the competition, October 8th, 1829, only four locomotives appeared, among them the famous Ericsson's *Novelty*. Stephenson's locomotive *Rocket* won the race. It was built in the new works at Newcastle, and had the tubular boiler still usual to-day, producing steam at a rate exceeding all previous locomotive boilers. The business director of the railway, Booth, made the suggestion of inverting the action of the water-tube boiler then under trial, by sending the hot gases through the tubes. Stephenson took up this idea and carried it out. The cylinder, hitherto vertical, was put in a sloping position, and shortly afterwards horizontal in the manner of to-day. A decisive point was the decision to lead the exhaust into the chimney, as Trevithick had previously done with full knowledge of the effect, which is greatly to increase the draught. Here again we see that Stephenson was not the inventor of the locomotive, but the great designer and constructor, who assembled the different parts in such a way as to form the most effective machine.

The success of his locomotive exceeded all expectations. It attained an average speed of over thirteen miles an hour, and its maximum speed was twenty-one and a half miles per hour. The prize was divided between Booth and Stephenson. The *Rocket* developed about 12 h.p., and a few alterations brought its power up to 20 h.p., using about 17 to 19 lb. of coke per horse-power hour. That was a great advance on previous locomotives, which developed at most 10 h.p. and used 28 to 30 lb. of coal for the horse-power hour. This battle of the locomotives at Rainhill, as it was called in England, and the opening of the railway on September 15th, 1830, decided the question whether locomotives or stationary engines were to be used on railways for good and all in favour of the locomotive.

Robert Stephenson was not able to be at his father's side in the most difficult years because he had accepted an offer to get some large mines started in Central America. He had enlisted Cornish miners, whom he found, however, very hard to manage, for they refused to submit to discipline of any sort, and thought they knew all about mining on their own account. After years of very hard work and worry he determined to follow his father's urgent call to come back to England. No one needed him more than his father. He thus came to play an essential part in his father's work. Father and son were equally highly esteemed, and the fame of the son soon began to exceed that of the father at large-scale engineering work. Robert Stephenson became the great railway engineer equipped with wide experience and the best knowledge of his time, and able to meet the great ones of the earth on equal terms. Father and son remained true comrades in the fight for the development of the new means of transport. This is one of the most beautiful pages in engineering history.

The opening of the railway by the Prime Minister, Wellington, the victor of Waterloo, took place with all due ceremony. All expectations were far exceeded, and the traffic between Liverpool and Manchester increased enormously. Exactly the opposite happened to what had previously been feared. The land along the line did not decline in value, on the contrary, its price increased very considerably. The traffic was at first taken by eight Stephenson locomotives. It was hoped to carry 400 to 600 persons daily, but the actual figure was 1,200. By the year 1835, 500,000 passengers had already been carried. In 1830, the thirty miles between Liverpool and Manchester took a good hour, an almost unimaginable speed. A serious technical reporter expressly states in his account that the ladies conversed quite coolly with the gentlemen in spite of the speed.

The building of the line from Liverpool to Manchester broke the spell. Everyone everywhere now wanted to have the new means of transport as quickly as possible. Bills for new railways were laid before Parliament in ever-increasing numbers. But the obtaining of these legal rights cost enormous sums, which were a burden on the railways from the start. To this was added the battle of the engineers. Everyone wished to give proof of his technical skill, each wanted to be more daring than the next man, and this ambition of the engineers cost the promoters much money. But Stephenson went quietly on his way. He did not let his knowledge of what was technically possible disturb his sound economic calculations. He wanted his shareholders to earn money, for only so could the development of railways be encouraged.

He and his son continued to get further great contracts for important railway lines, and carried them out to the great satisfaction of their clients. But they could not build nearly all the railways they were called upon to build. And so came finally the notorious year 1845, in which Bills for railways to the value of £44,000,000 were promoted in Parliament. In the next year the value of the lines which were to be built had risen to £400,000,000. Railway mania, it was called later. The first railways were promoted by men who were engaged in practical life and experienced on the spot the need for the new means of transport. They had tackled the problem like cool-headed business men, though with great courage, and they had been proved in the end to be right. The money thus spent brought a rich return. Dividends of 10 to 15 per cent. were no rarity.

But England had become rich through her technical industry. Many were seeking to invest money, and the great bankers in London had also finally realized that there was actually money to be made out of railways. A tremendous propaganda started, everybody was trying to get rich simply by the rise in the price of shares, quite without regard to the possibilities of the undertakings or the need for them. A railway fever was generated, which took hold of all classes of the population. Anyone who did not speculate in railway shares was looked upon as a fool. Men and women, employers and employed, high and low, the whole mass of normally steady English people was as though seized by madness. It was no one's duty to take any steps. The free play of forces, in which the people of England believed as in a divine law, celebrated orgies. Neither Government nor Parliament made any attempt at the time to interfere with the development.

Stephenson kept his head and refused to have anything to do with this development, which he recognized as fraudulent. Father and son were pestered; famous names were needed— only names !—and £1,000 was paid at the time for permission to print a 'name' on the prospectus to back its rosy promises. Here again Stephenson was right. Enormous sums were thrown away. All these limitless hopes ended in complete collapse, and it was some time before decent business principles ruled in the field of railway development. On the technical side also there were very disagreeable features. Numerous new men who knew nothing of technical work, but called themselves engineers, were pushed by the immense increase in railway work into positions for which they were entirely unfitted. Contemporary reports complain of shoddy work. Economies were made where they ought not to have been made, and the money thus saved went into private pockets; corruption reached a degree hitherto unimaginable. The result was collapse of tunnels and bridges, and a failure of the service. Years were needed before the mistakes could be made good by sound work. The newly rich who came to the fore at this time made themselves very objectionable in English society, and all the trouble was put down to the railway which, like any human product if misused, had potentialities for evil as well as good.

Stephenson, who had previously been asked to conceal the fact that he could attain a speed of twelve miles an hour, now ran his trains up to twenty and thirty, but this was not nearly enough for the younger generation. The newspapers now wrote: the locomotive can travel at unlimited speeds, why not then 100 miles an hour ? At this point Stephenson spoke a word of warning to the effect that the question was not how quickly in theory a locomotive could travel, but what speed would be of most advantage to the builder and user, and he warned against exceeding forty miles per hour. But, asked other people, is the steam locomotive as designed by Stephenson and others, really the last word in development ? Engineering now went through a curious phase. The eternal pressure of the atmosphere was to drive the trains much faster and more safely ! A great pipe was to be laid between the rails, and in it a piston was to move, connected to the carriage above through a slit. If the air was sucked out of the tube on one side of the piston, the latter would of course be driven along by the pressure of the air, and take with it the carriage to which it was fixed. That was the basic idea of the atmospheric railway, and it was actually carried into effect by a marvellous feat of engineering. How great were the hopes that were set upon it! Once more, only stationary engines at considerable distances apart were needed for working the air pumps, and the coal consumption would be much less for the horse-power hour. The locomotive, which is only a steam power plant on wheels, could be dispensed with. But Stephenson would have nothing to do with this idea, and never believed that it would lead to the scrapping of his steam locomotives. And time proved him in the right.

At first no one was ready to believe that carriages with iron wheels running on iron rails could be driven even on the level, by turning their wheels. Friction would be much too small. Experience then showed that it was possible, but it was believed to be necessary to avoid all gradients. Stephenson himself endeavoured to do without gradients as far as possible by suitable alignment, even when large detours had to be made, costly tunnels bored, and valleys bridged. This often made early railway construction very dear as compared with our present methods. In this again the young generation was sure that it knew better, and so, instead of going forward step by step, they fell over their own feet. If the maxim had previously been that railways only run on the level, the switchback system was now discovered, and it was maintained that the more hills and dales there were on the line, the better would it be for the economic running of the railway. But this fashion, too, was very short-lived; engineers cannot dictate laws to Nature.

Then came a third struggle, a very serious one: the battle of the gauges. We have seen how in the mines, wooden and iron rails had been laid on which to run the ore and coal trucks. When the change was made to steam running, Stephenson did not dream of changing the gauge of the rails at great expense. Thus the gauge used in the North of England mines determined the railway gauge for the whole world. No one had thought of working out scientifically a gauge suited to the new form of transport. No one had even considered the question. But now, when first-rate engineers, chief among them the famous Isambard Kingdom Brunel (1806–1859), set to work to build new railways, they began to consider whether Stephenson had really fixed the gauge for all time. People refused to be bound by such a standard, and there was a time when about seventy different gauges were in existence. At first numerous short stretches of line were built, without a thought that they would one day be joined up into a network. Stephenson pointed out repeatedly that a standard gauge must be adhered to, if intolerable difficulties were not to arise later. People would not listen to him, and so Brunel built the Great Western Railway with a broad gauge. It was then of course necessary for locomotives, carriages, and railway stations to be adapted to it. Brunel, who together with his father did great work as an engineer, could never have things big enough for him. He built the greatest ship in the world, the *Great Eastern*, a romantic blunder of the first order. He also wanted to have the biggest railway and locomotives, which were to excel all others. His railway from London to the West was to be independent of every other railway, completely self-sufficient, and his promoters were agreeable. But then came, all the same, connections and cross-country lines, and all trucks had to be unloaded and reloaded at great expense, and all travellers had to change carriages. That could not go on for ever, and so this railway finally repented and went over to Stephenson's standard gauge. When the locomotives were ordered from Stephenson for the first German railway, which was opened on December 7th, 1835, between Nürnberg and Fürth, they were ordered for a special gauge, but Stephenson built them just the same to the English standard, and wrote to say that it was the only practical one. So it was Stephenson who decided that the first German railway should have the English standard gauge.

Years went by, and George Stephenson began, at the age of fifty-nine, to withdraw more and more from business, leaving the field to his son, who had attained to such success in it.

But a Stephenson could not remain idle, so he bought some coal-mines and limestone quarries in his county, and built himself a railway there. But that was far from absorbing his energies, and the love of his early days now came to full expression. He laid out great gardens, and had round him all the animals he loved; horses, cows, dogs and birds were those he liked best. He took an especial pride in his hot-houses. Along with these he had a large country estate, and the greatest joy of his later years was his success in this line. He was delighted when it was said by the outside world that he grew the largest melons and the most wonderful cucumbers. But they worried him because they were crooked when he wanted to have them straight. Only when he grew them in glass tubes was he entirely satisfied with them. He recognized very early the importance of electric telegraphy for railways, and made use of it.

He thus became one of the greatest engineers of his time. He forgot the fact that he had at first been taken at less than his true worth on account of his want of early education, but long refused to go into upper-class society. However, he finally yielded to the wishes of ministers of the Crown, who had a high opinion of him, and left behind the best possible impression of his calm, assured and ripe character. He had long ago learned to talk about other things besides locomotives. In working together with his son, his intellectual interests had acquired a wide range, and though he was no match for some in the matter of eloquence, his firmly formed personality made a strong impression. He was frequently offered a title, but he refused it, because he thought that such a rise in social status would not suit him or his work. He and his son were on excellent terms with their work-people and employees. Stephenson was well aware how much he owed to these collaborators of his, and he would never have been able to do his great work if he had not had the gift of finding the right man and putting him in the right place.

He thought a great deal of practical education and training. We have one of his addresses given in the Newcastle Technical School. He never tired of recommending to the young men, none of whom had ever been as poor as he, serious work, and most of all persistence and endurance.

When on August 12th, 1848, after a short illness, he reached his allotted span, he was mourned not only in England, but far and wide outside it. He was buried in the cemetery in Chester, near his estates. His great son, who had not his father's health, only survived him by eleven years. He became still more famous in professional circles, and beyond them, because his work spread over three continents. He was looked upon especially as the greatest bridge-builder of his time. He was buried in Westminster Abbey, next to James Watt, and in the company of great generals, kings, and learned men.

The railways, which, as the English say, are perhaps the only one of their great technical achievements in which they have not yet been rivalled, spread from England over the world. We saw how the two Stephensons helped to build railways in Belgium, France, Spain, and many other countries. The last great railway at the opening ceremony of which Robert Stephenson was able to be present, shortly before his death, was the Norwegian State Railway.

In Germany, the battle for the railway was fought in the first instance by our great German industrialist Friedrich Harkort, and the economist List, who had gained his early experience with railways in America. Railway projects came into being amid furious battles and struggles on all sides. Nürnberg–Fürth, Braunschweig–Wolfenbüttel, Düsseldorf–Erkrath, Berlin–Potsdam, Leipzig–Dresden, and so on; indeed, Cologne–Minden was even suggested. But the comfortable citizens would not hear of it. Everything that was said in England against railways was repeated, but above all the question: who is to pay for all that ? Where are the people to come from to use all this costly construction, and

28. HENRY MAUDSLAY (1771–1831)

From a bust

27. ROBERT STEPHENSON (1803–59)

From a lithograph by George Richmond, 1848

29. JAMES NASMYTH (1808–90)

From an engraving by Paul Rajon after a portrait by George Reid

this terrifying speed ? The first railway was the work of the Burgomaster of Nürnberg, Scharrer, and of a big merchant, Platner. The desire was to employ a German, and in Bavaria was found the engineer Camille von Denis, who had already studied railways in England and America. But the first locomotive was supplied by George Stephenson; it was not until 1838 that Schubert built in Saxony Germany's first locomotive. Then came the great German locomotive builders, Emil Kessler in Karlsruhe and Esslingen, and above all, August Borsig in Berlin, Georg Egestorff in Hannover, Karl Anton Henschel in Cassel, and J. Maffei in Munich.

George Stephenson thus found in Germany and all other countries, again and again, famous successors, who carried on the work begun by him, and adapted it to the needs of the time in their own countries and to their economic conditions. The short lengths of railway which Stephenson was at first able to build, have become gigantic networks which cover all continents. The railway became the great customer and stimulus for all industry. The short railways became great lines with branches everywhere, forming a net with meshes of ever decreasing size; the results in all directions were many times better than those thought possible 100 years ago. The railways of the world would encircle the world thirty-two times at the equator.

But whoever attempts to survey the great development still going on to-day from the point of view of its historical origin will hold George and Robert Stephenson in grateful memory.

HENRY MAUDSLAY *and* JAMES NASMYTH
1771–1831 & 1808–1890

The machine of to-day needs for its production thousands of other machines of the most varied description. This was not always the case. How much handwork was there

not still in James Watt's steam engine ? Hammer and chisel
and file were the tools of the neat-handed mechanics, of
whom there were all too few. A forging hammer driven by
a water-wheel may have helped with the forging; a primitive
lathe, copied from that of the wood-turner, could not be
dispensed with. In such a workshop were further found
a few small drilling machines, and when steam engines were
being made, they had to have the great boring machine for
the long steam cylinder. That was the whole machine
equipment. But the more developed machines became, the
less adequate was simple hand labour. The hand worked
much too slowly and also too inexactly for the machine,
which depends upon the most accurate interconnection of all
its parts.

Again and again in technical history one sees that it is not
enough to have an idea, that it is not sufficient to work out
an invention on paper. What has been thought out and
drawn must be transmuted into realities of steel and iron.
Many good ideas have come to grief owing to difficulties in
carrying them out, and have later on come to life again when
methods of manufacture have been sufficiently improved.
This high importance of constructional methods, well known
to every practical man, is not sufficiently emphasized in
technical histories. This lies in the fact that progress in such
methods is chiefly a question of the general work of the
mechanical workshop, which forms a unit; hence the
advances made do not become so widely known by patents
or articles, as is the case in other branches of technical work.
To this must be added that people were especially fond of
keeping to themselves the progress made in methods of
manufacture, in order to derive commercial profit from their
superiority. A change only came about when, little by little,
firms specializing in the manufacture of tools and machine
tools came into existence, and took care to make widely
known the improved methods of manufacture rendered
possible by their products.

Another point was that the skilled workmen who were able to make machines with the help only of primitive tools were not by any means always inclined to be industrious. They felt how completely indispensable they were, and were fond of going on strike at the moment when they were most needed. These were the driving forces which in the first half of the nineteenth century led, first of all in England, where such enormous progress in mechanical technology was made in this period, to the development of very many machine tools, by the help of which the production in sufficient numbers of other sorts of machines was rendered possible. So it was just the engineers working in this field who had a decisive influence on technical development. The value of their achievements can only be gauged by realizing what difficulties were to be overcome. We have the diary of such a machine builder of 1760, who on an American mine had to bore out a cast bronze cylinder for the steam engine. The process consisted in the simplest form of rubbing down with emery, and they were very proud to be able to show that the diameter of the cylinder did not vary anywhere by more than the thickness of the little finger. The master adds an expression of his great joy at having thus obtained the best possible result, but that he will nevertheless think hard about ways and means of doing still better in future. The joy was justified, for they had all despaired of ever succeeding with so great a work, and it is touching to read in the diary that 'we give great gratitude to Almighty God, who hath brought us through such fiery tribulations to an efficient termination of our arduous labours.'

James Watt had no better fortune. He found in the great John Wilkinson a man who actually succeeded in boring a cylinder true to $\frac{1}{8}$ in. We further learn from James Watt that all engineers of his time held it to be quite impossible to turn a piston rod by hand so accurately as to slide through a steam-tight stuffing box, at that time an entirely novel element of construction. And what did toothed wheels look like ? We hear of machines, the many toothed wheels of which made so monstrous a noise, that everyone thought they were bursting into pieces. The machine maker attempted to remedy the trouble, but had to admit that it was impossible to do so. He said, 'I think we had better leave the cogs to settle their differences with one another; they will grind themselves in time !' But what else could be done at a time when no machines existed for cutting toothed wheels mechanically ?

At this point the engineers got to work, and in the first half of the nineteenth century brought about a Golden Age of English machine tool construction. Joseph Bramah was a Yorkshireman. Born in 1749 as the son of a peasant farmer, he too seemed destined to follow the plough, when an accident in his sixteenth year made him unfit for such work. He was then apprenticed to a carpenter, and learned to be a fine workman in wood. But he soon started inventing. He made very considerable improvements in the water-closet, then being slowly introduced, and invented the first safety-lock, which kept its place for almost eighty years, till new locks were devised in America. Bramah had in the mean-time settled in London, and he felt so sure of his lock that he offered a reward of £200 to anyone who could pick it. But in order to make these complicated safety locks with sufficient accuracy, machine tools had to be devised if they were to be made on a large scale. At this point it was Bramah's good fortune to find in Henry Maudslay an excellent collaborator. He himself then did very successful work in connection with hydraulic piston engines. He now no longer called himself a carpenter, but a machine builder. In 1795 he obtained the famous patent for the hydraulic press, a tool which is indispensable to-day for the most varied purposes. Although Pascal had already suggested in 1664 the construc-tion of such a press based on physical principles, practical success in carrying out his plan was only attained 130 years later. Robert Stephenson could not get his great bridges erected without the help of this hydraulic press, and Brunel used it to launch his giant ship the *Great Eastern*. The hydraulic press then replaced the large steam hammer for forging, and has done great work up till to-day. Very great difficulties had to be overcome in its construction and working, the worst being that no one knew how to provide the plunger with a water-tight packing able to resist great pressure. The solution of this problem was found by Maudslay. He arranged for the water pressure itself to put sufficient force on the leather packing, which was formed like the turned-back cuff of a coat, to make a tight joint round the plunger.

Bramah designed a number of other valuable machines, among them the wood planer. Indeed he worked in quite other fields, as was still possible at that time. He built great new works in the last decade of the eighteenth century. He made machines for sawing marble, and devised new methods of building bridges and canal locks. He died, famous as an engineer, on December 9th, 1814, in his sixty-sixth year.

A great number of remarkable engineers came from his workshop. We have already mentioned Henry Maudslay, who was born in Woolwich on August 22nd, 1771. His father was employed in the Royal Arsenal, and the boy had to set about earning money at an early age. He left school at the age of twelve, and then helped in loading cartridges with powder. But two years later he was put in the joiner's shop, where his father was also employed, and here he first learned to work in wood and iron. He was fond of telling in later years how greatly he was attracted by work in the smithy, and how he much preferred using hammer, chisel, and file to saw and plane. This desire was finally fulfilled, and he was soon a master of the smith's art. His co-workers admired him, and he was known in London workshops for his manual skill.

We saw how he came to Bramah in London, and played a decisive part in the great success of the latter's workshops.

But here there was at first a great difficulty to be overcome. Maudslay had not gone through the seven years apprenticeship demanded for the workshops. He offered, however, to carry out a piece of work which had beaten the other men in the shop, and he was so successful as to be then admitted as capable of working on an even footing with the others.

Maudslay had grown into a big strong man. With his height of six foot two, his round face with its merry eyes and firm mouth, the impression he made on his fellows was such that he was always chosen as standard-bearer in ceremonial processions. When he was technical head of Bramah's works he was still earning not more than 30s. a week. When he pointed out that he had now some claim to a slightly larger income, his modest suggestion was so scornfully rejected that he determined to start in business on his own account. In 1797 he opened a small mechanical workshop and smithy in London. Little by little orders came in, and his fame as one of the most skilful metal workers of England was soon so firmly founded that he was presented with harder and harder problems. He not only knew what exact work meant for machine construction, but actually loved this exact work as an expression of his whole nature. He recognized that the old form of lathe, where the turner himself had to hold and guide the tool as in woodturning, and needed great physical strength for the job, would never turn out sufficiently true work. For this reason he was already pondering, while with Bramah, the problem of how to make a self-acting lathe, in which not only the holding of the tool, but its guidance also, should be taken care of by the machine. He thus arrived at a lathe in which the support to which the tool was fixed was traversed by a lead-screw driven from the machine.

We know that this idea had been suggested before Maudslay's time in France, where there were very skilful workmen; it had already been published in 1772. But Maudslay knew nothing of this, and his solution was essentially different, for it served to fulfil very exact practical conditions; he is thus rightly regarded as the creator of the self-acting lathe, which was used for decades in all countries under the name of the 'English lathe.' It became the universal tool, which could be used for a very great number of purposes, before special machines were designed. This wonderful machine tool was now followed by a great number of other machines, which replaced step by step the laborious and rare skill of human hands. Maudslay then built for certain purposes a number of other special machines, by means of which he was able to turn out certain parts in great numbers, and in a form not hitherto considered possible.

Maudslay had very early made great efforts to improve the making of screws. At that time screws were made by hand. Small ones were filed, larger ones were worked by hammer and chisel. But that was so difficult that screws were only made use of where absolutely necessary. Otherwise wedges were employed, such as are used in wood-construction. Of the few screws made, every one with its nut was a separate individual with its own special form. One favoured one form of thread and pitch, another another form, and so no two screws were alike. The screw and its own nut had both to be marked, for there could be no question of interchanging them. When the screws got mixed up, there was trouble with a vengeance. When we think of our cars to-day, this state of affairs is beyond our powers of imagination. Maudslay saw that this could not go on. He showed the way as well, and one of his great pupils, Joseph Whitworth, solved the problem in a fundamental fashion. His name lives on to-day in his system of threads.

Maudslay was a great constructor. One might say of him as of James Watt, that he possessed the wonderful faculty of knowing what could be left out. He always arrived by a touch of genius at the simplest solution of a problem. He not only built machine tools; he was famous for his excellent steam engines built for driving factories, and above all for his great marine engines, which he constructed with hitherto unexampled accuracy for both merchant- and warships. He always set great store by practical work. Whoever could satisfy him on this score was befriended and helped by him. It is related that he laid great stress on avoiding sharp angles and corners in his cast- and wrought-iron parts. He had a feeling for the material, and knew that sharp edges such as are usual in the work of carpenter and joiner, are not to be introduced into ironwork. But it was a long time before he educated his co-workers up to using the forms he required. He used to hold out his hand to them in the workshop, and point out how Nature had joined the fingers to the palm of the hand by rounded curves, or he took the man to the nearest tree and showed him that there are no sharp corners between trunk and branches. On holidays he was accustomed to go through the empty shops with a piece of chalk from bench to bench. He looked carefully to see whether the tools were well looked after and arranged so as to be ready to the hand. He examined the work itself very closely, and his laconic remarks written in chalk on the bench or the work, by way of praise or blame, were renowned and well noted, for the owner of the whole factory was the most skilled workman in it.

But Maudslay was not submerged in his professional work. He was a friendly person who liked talking to people, without, however, allowing much interruption to his work in his own shops. He loved music, and had acquired a number of musical boxes, which were kept in an adjoining room, and delighted him by their tunes when he was at work. The fame of his work spread far beyond the shores of England. He received many distinguished visitors. We know for example that he showed Faraday over his workshop, and that the latter had the greatest admiration for what he saw. Maudslay came to Berlin in the course of his travels, having to install the machines in the Royal Mint (1830). Here he met Humboldt and Schinkel, whom he much admired. But it was the Berlin Observatory which fascinated him most of all, and his last great wish was to make himself a similar great telescope and use it in his own observatory. He died on February 14th, 1831, and is buried at his birthplace, Woolwich, in which his early years were passed and of which he was very fond. His work was carried on by his pupils, to whom he was able methodically to communicate the riches of his experience.

One of the most distinguished of these men was the Scotsman James Nasmyth. His family can be traced back in Scotland to the thirteenth century. The Nasmyths were brave warriors in the never-ending Border wars, and they knew how to value a good sword as a piece of craftsmanship. The father of James Nasmyth came from a family of craftsmen. By day he painted wagon bodies for a wagon builder, while by night he visited an art school in order to learn painting. He went to London, but returned to his home town Edinburgh, where he earned a modest but steady income as a portrait painter. The son said of his father that he could sit any saddle: he was at the same time painter, architect, craftsman, and mechanic. He was proud of his workshop, and there the son learned while young to handle tools. James was the youngest child of four sons and seven daughters. He was born on August 19th, 1808, in Edinburgh. At the age of nine he met James Watt, then eighty-two years of age, in Edinburgh, and the recollection of this meeting was treasured by him all his life. He also knew Walter Scott, and the many noteworthy friends of his father taught him much.

His schooling came to an end at the age of twelve. We know that he was no friend of the dead languages, but was interested in mathematics and natural science, and loved drawing. He loved 'the eloquence of the pencil' as he called it. A school friend brought him when only a boy into the closest contact with ironworks, and there he learned, as he tells us in his autobiography, very much that served him all through his life. He also spent some years at

Edinburgh University. When he was nineteen he built himself a steam carriage, which ran for quite a long time.

But now he saw that it was time to lay a sure foundation for the calling of a machine builder. He heard Maudslay praised as one of England's greatest builders of machines, and at once resolved to go to him. But that was easier said than done, for Maudslay had a dislike for the sons of rich fathers who were apt, when taken as practical pupils, merely to pretend to work. He wanted apprentices. But Nasmyth was able to show him drawings and sketches which had such an effect on Maudslay's sharp eyes that he even took him as his private assistant into his own workshop with its wonderful and extremely accurate tools. He started work with Maudslay on May 30th, 1829. His wages were 10s. a week, and he managed to live on that sum. Nasmyth gives enthusiastic expression to his admiration and reverence for his master. He was greatly impressed by Maudslay's love of his work, and repeatedly astonished at his intuitive sense of the material on which he was working. He also learned the meaning of accurate measuring instruments. Since all such instruments then commonly in use were too weak in their design, Maudslay had constructed a very strong one, and had thereby raised the accuracy to a thousandth of an inch.

After Maudslay's death Nasmyth remained with the partner in the firm, J. Field, and built with him 200-h.p. steam engines for a water-works. But then a strong desire for independence came to him. Field willingly lent him his aid, and allowed him to copy the best lathe in the workshop. Nasmyth first returned to his home in Edinburgh. There he set up a modest little workshop, in which the lathe was driven from a wheel turned by a workman. He then travelled around in England, and thought of settling in Liverpool or Manchester, where the railway was, which he had visited shortly after its inauguration, when the elder Stephenson drove the locomotive while his son acted as fireman. Nasmyth was now twenty-six years old and had so high a reputation that a rich banker said to him: 'I will lend you a large sum at low interest without asking for security.' Nasmyth began his work in a large inn in Manchester. Orders soon came in, the machine tools were soon fully occupied; the small smithy in the cellar was already crowded out. So he made up his mind to build a works of his own near Manchester, where the beginning of railway construction was most favourable to such development.

But Nasmyth soon had to find much fault with his workmen. They took a holiday not only on Monday, but most of them on Tuesday as well, and considered it enough to turn up to work on the Wednesday. They had drunk away their wages in the three days of idleness. Convinced that they were indispensable, they were ill-behaved when at work, and very difficult to keep in order. These facts, so Nasmyth thought, greatly contributed to the further development of automatic machines and to their introduction into the shops in spite of their high cost. For he could say of them: 'The machines never got drunk; their hands never shook from excess; they were never absent from work; they did not strike for wages; they were unfailing in their accuracy and regularity, while producing the most delicate or ponderous portions of mechanical structures.' Every new machine was the best recommendation for further orders. Nasmyth then acquired very cheaply a ninety-nine-years lease of a further plot of land lying directly on the railway line from Liverpool to Manchester, and near the great canal. He thus had no need to tie up capital in order to set up his first works.

Nasmyth, who was a great lover of nature, was well pleased with the surrounding country, and delighted in the orchards, trees, and meadows. He was greatly affected by the way in which the wonderful countryside was being ruined by the rapid rise of industry. 'We may fill our purses, but we pay a heavy price for it in the loss of picturesqueness and beauty.'

He soon got orders for steam engines; even yet it was not possible for a firm to concentrate on a few special lines of work. In 1838 Nasmyth devised the safety pouring ladle for casting metal, in which the ladle was operated by a screw and toothed wheel. His business extended, and many rich people were now anxious to put in money as sleeping partners. But he would have nothing to do with the idea. He found in Gaskell an excellent business man, whom he willingly took as an active partner and worked with for sixteen years in the closest and most friendly manner. Difficult times came along; again and again the fight with the trade unions gave him much trouble. The unions strove remorselessly for power, even in the individual works, and Nasmyth would have nothing whatever to do with the idea. When on one occasion a strike took place, he fetched sixty excellent workmen from Scotland, who arrived complete with their families, and were given steady and well-paid work.

The machines ordered from Nasmyth became larger and larger. He built locomotives, which had a high reputation; he built marine engines, and the constructors of the big iron ship *Great Britain* came and told their troubles to him. They were unable to make the huge shaft, at the ends of which the two great paddle-wheels were to be fixed; it had to be 30 in. in thickness, and how were they going to forge it? Existing hammers were not nearly powerful enough. The problem took hold of Nasmyth, and after some thought he hit upon a stroke of genius. He fixed a steam cylinder vertically on the top of a strong A-shaped frame, and had the piston-rod pointing downwards with a heavy hammer-head fixed to it. The steam was admitted under the piston and lifted the hammer, which then fell down again on the forging.

A master of the art of sketching, he immediately recorded the idea in his sketch-book. The steam hammer, that indispensable tool, was present in his mind's eye with every detail of its control gear. He proposed to build it and forge the 30-in. shaft. But then screw-propulsion was decided upon, and the propeller-shaft, which revolves at a much higher speed, could be much thinner; Nasmyth's steam hammer was no longer necessary. It was a period of decline in business activity, and no one thought of spending money on new tools. Nasmyth had also other matters to worry about, and the steam hammer was put aside for a time. Many visitors came to see him, including foreigners, and it is said that one of the great French engineers also visited his works when he was absent, that Gaskell showed him everything there was to see, including Nasmyth's sketch-books, and that the Frenchman was thus enabled to copy his hammer. When Nasmyth went to France some time later, the famous Creusot works showed him some wonderful forgings made by his steam hammer. He returned home very well pleased, for he was now able to point out to the English industry that his steam hammer was already in use on a large scale in France. It was decided in 1842 to take out a patent and build the hammer, which very soon proved itself a wonderful tool. All who saw it at work were particularly astonished at the ease with which it was controlled. It could be used for the lightest forging, or made to deliver blows which shook the entire neighbourhood. When Alfred Krupp had set up his famous giant hammer *Fritz*, it made an unforgettable impression on visitors when it was caused to descend at full speed on to a watch laid on the anvil, without doing more than cracking the glass. Nasmyth soon made use of his hammer for driving piles, and is thus the inventor of the steam pile-driver.

His business connections took him all over Europe. He travelled in France and Italy, and saw much more than the factories to which he was desirous of selling his machines. In Italy he went to Herculaneum and Pompeii; he never passed a museum unvisited, and always brought home with him wonderful sketches. He was an enthusiastic lover of technical work, saying that:

'It is one of the most delightful results of the possession of the constructive faculty, that one can build up in the mind mechanical structures and set them to work in imagination, and observe beforehand the various details performing their respective functions, as if they were in absolute material form and action. Unless this happy faculty exists *ab initio* in the brain of the mechanical engineer, he will have a hard and disappointing life before him. It is the early cultivation of the imagination which gives the right flexibility to the thinking faculties. Thus business, commerce and mechanics are all the better for a little healthy imagination.'

One of his journeys took him in 1842 to Nürnberg. Though his negotiations with the Nürnberg-Fürth railway came to nothing, this in no way diminished his enthusiasm for the old town. He calls Albrecht Dürer the greatest artist who ever lived: a universal genius—painter, sculptor, mathematician and engineer. He was for Germany what Leonardo da Vinci was for Italy. Nasmyth visited Dürer's grave and there found on a bronze tablet the following inscription: '*Dürer. 8 April* 1528 *emigravit.*' This he held to express an especially great truth, that the true artist cannot die; he does but emigrate. He also visited the grave of Hans Sachs, and admired the wonderful achievements of Adam Krafft, calling his famous sacristy a wonderful work. Krafft worked on it for over five years with two labourers, and was only paid 770 gulden for the work. A year later we find Nasmyth in St. Petersburg. Locomotives were wanted there too, but the Tsar wished to build them himself, and Nasmyth received large orders for machine tools. He was well received everywhere; specially memorable for him was his visit to the observatory, where he stayed over two months. We are again and again stirred when we see how much a man like Nasmyth sees and experiences. He also visited Sweden and inspected the famous iron mines. Machine construction in England increased continually; wherever he went he saw his own designs, often copied

faithfully without permission. But he overcame his annoyance, and remarked humorously that it was a sort of left-
handed recognition.

Nasmyth's whole mental make-up was obviously such as
to lead him, in his enthusiasm for art and science, to run a
number of hobbies, which he loved and cultivated with care.
He was particularly fond of drawing. His charming fairy-
tale pictures found many friends. Sometimes people were
unwilling to believe that these products of a glowing imagination originated in the man who created the steam hammer
and the ram. But his favourite occupation was to watch the
stars at night after the day's work, for he had inherited
from his father a love of astronomy. He had built a small
telescope in 1827, and infected his teacher Maudslay with
his passion for the stars. By virtue of his mechanical gifts
he was able to build himself ever larger and more powerful
telescopes. He had one set up in his garden, and all his
guests were invited to admire the heavens through it. From
1842 on he began a methodical scientific investigation of the
moon. He used his great gift for drawing to record what he
saw by means of black and white chalk on grey paper set
alongside the telescope. It was thus that his pictures of the
moon, so famous in their day, were produced. In 1850 he
exhibited these drawings in Edinburgh in the rooms of a
large scientific society. The famous astronomer Herschel,
Faraday, and many others were so delighted with them that
they arranged for their exhibition at the first World Exhibition in 1851. Nasmyth was given a prize and invited to
show them to the Queen and Prince Consort. Soon
astronomy became his chief occupation, much more than a
mere hobby. He also busied himself with the microscope
at that time; and he took so much delight in the science,
which his technical work had endowed with such important
tools, that he determined to retire from business in 1856,
at the age of forty-eight.

He wished to spend the evening of his life, as he called

it, in active leisure. He removed to Kent, and took with him all the material things which had become especially dear to him through the joy in his work, such as his telescope, his own tools, and many other things that he had made himself. All these treasures were given a place of honour in his workshop, which he built next to his beautiful house. At that time he wished for the introduction of the custom of burying with men the tools they most loved, as in the past the weapons of the warrior. For he had so often seen such things unfeelingly scattered to the four winds, after the death of their owners.

Much as he loved working in his workshop, much as he loved contemplating the secrets of the heavens through his telescope, he loved equally well to be in his garden. He planted his trees and was proud of his flowers. And now, having retired from business, he began a thorough investigation of the sun. Some of his discoveries received high recognition from professional astronomers. In the meantime photography had advanced so far that he was able to take direct photographs of the moon. So the years went by, until he too had to take leave of the great life of creative work which he had enjoyed for eighty-two years.

Nasmyth, the great engineer, the distinguished artist, the profound scientist, died in London on May 7th, 1890.

JOHN ERICSSON
1803–1889

Sweden has produced great engineers, whose work is with justice given one of the first places in the new technical museum at Stockholm.

We may mention here Christopher Polhem, the great mechanic and 'master of arts,' clockmaker, and canal builder, who was born at Wisby in 1661 and died in his ninetieth year in Stockholm in 1751. He produced masterpieces in the most varied technical fields, but specially in mining and metallurgy. Further, John Ericsson, who looks down upon us from his monuments in Stockholm and Washington, and de Laval (1845 to 1913), the great inventor and designer, to whom we owe, beside many other first-rate achievements in metallurgy, the milk centrifuge and the impulse steam turbine.

We will describe more fully the life and work of John Ericsson. Ericsson was born on July 31st, 1803, in Wärmland, in the centre of Sweden. His forefathers had been mining folk since the seventeenth century. They are described to us as great, strong, well-looking active men, brave and honest, faithful unto death. His father was a mining engineer. At twenty-one years of age he was already in charge of a mine as technical director. Ericsson inherited from him his enthusiasm for technical work, and from his mother, tall, slim, and beautiful, with bright blue eyes, he inherited his noble outlook and strong character. There were three children of the marriage; in 1800 a daughter was born, and in 1802 his brother Niels who—here we anticipate—entered the engineering side of the Swedish Navy. He built the new locks on the Trollhättan Canal, the docks in Stockholm, and great canals. The Swedish Parliament confided to him, in 1853, the task of laying out the chief lines of the Swedish State Railways. Niels Ericsson is regarded as the creator of the Swedish railway system. He died in 1870 in Stockholm. Sweden honoured him for his technical achievements by the grant of a title.

Little John passed the happy years of childhood among the mining machines. It is related that he began very early to study the machines, to draw them, and to ask his father and the officials to explain them to him in every detail. He began here to lay the foundation of his great engineering achievements. War came with Russia in 1811 to 1814, Finland was lost, industry and trade suffered very heavily, many rich families were impoverished, among them the Ericssons. His father, brought up in comfortable circumstances, could not bear to calculate in pence. He had to give up his post. He received further employment as an inspector during the building of the Göta Canal. The son was fifteen years old when his father died.

Count Platen became the protector of young Ericsson. He prophesied a great future for him if he would remain faithful to technical work. Ericsson entered the Naval Engineers, and had soon to decide, at the age of seventeen, whether he wanted to be an officer or an engineer. His fatherly friend, Count Platen, advised him against becoming the former, but Ericsson thought that in that time of perpetual warfare, he would get on more quickly in that profession. Tall, well set up, healthy and strong, he wanted to serve Sweden in her army, if possible in the artillery.

He learned how to handle large guns, and this knowledge was of great value to him professionally in later years. He retained all his life an understanding of military, and especially of naval, matters. Young Ericsson sought to acquire further knowledge; amongst other things, he studied geometry and surveying with a German officer of engineers. He applied himself to chemistry and mathematics, and regarded it as essential to learn English. His insatiable appetite for knowledge was remarked by all, as was his power of actually making use of the knowledge acquired in the shortest possible time.

Friends have no doubt often regretted in later years that he was not able to acquire a thorough technical training in his youth. The answer to this is characteristic of Ericsson and his point of view. He thought that what others regarded as a defect was a piece of good fortune for him. The schools would have imbued him with a faith in authority, and that would have prevented him from developing his own ideas and thinking his own thoughts. This striving to get free of what the so-called cleverest people held to be right, may be traced throughout his whole professional career. He wanted to go his own way, and he went it even when it led him wrong, as appeared later, in one of the great fields of work. It was said to be characteristic of him always to see things as they ought to be in his opinion, and not as they really were. The Viking blood in him came thus to expression. Even if he did not discover new worlds and undertake daring sea-voyages, he was again and again attracted by the hope of discovering great wide fields of work, and of journeying in unconquered country.

He was already interested, when an officer, in the hot-air engine. He thought, along with many other inventors and engineers, that it was time to scrap the old steam engine, which had done much great work. Ericsson expended, as we shall see, decades of highly original engineering work on this problem. But the laws of nature, even when we are ignorant of them, refuse to be upset. Work on this hot-air engine aroused in him the desire to go to England, the Promised Land of technology. There he hoped to carry his hot-air engine to victory. He arrived there on May 18th, 1826, but had to suffer the discovery that England was not waiting for him and his invention. The 1,000 kronen he took with him were soon spent, the engine did not get off his hands, he had to earn money. He resigned from the Swedish Army with the rank of Captain, which title he used all his life.

The rapidly growing English machine industry had good use for engineers with ideas. The machine manufacturer John Braithwaite took him into junior partnership; the firm called itself Braithwaite & Ericsson. Here Ericsson learned an uncommon amount about machine design. He worked in the most varied fields, and at this time even attempted to use compressed air for power transmission. He built boilers, refrigerators for breweries and distilleries, he designed a surface condenser which he successfully applied to marine engines. He built high-pressure boilers, and in designing ships attempted to get the engines below the water-line, in order to protect them from projectiles in case of war. A well-known feat of his was the construction of the steam fire-engine which he built in London in 1828. This brought him great success. People were astonished at the vast quantities of water which it would throw house-high into the air. His opponents objected that there would never be in any town as much water as this engine needed. But the men with the hand-engine feared the loss of their occupation through the new technical advance, and more than once they are said to have first used their hand machine to put their rival out of action by quenching its boiler fire before attacking the destructive fire. One of the first two steam fire-engines built by Ericsson was delivered to the King of Prussia at Berlin. This was the first steam fire-engine outside England and was intended to protect the Royal Palace and its surroundings. Excellent though this work of Ericsson's was, it was not a financial success.

Ericsson came to England in the middle of the railway age. All engineers were talking of the railway, and of Stephenson's bold idea of pulling the carriages by a steam locomotive instead of living horses. The first great and famous line from Liverpool to Manchester, also renowned for its building structures, was to show by a competition between locomotives which of them was the best. We know how Ericsson applied his great technical powers to this business. He took up the competition with Stephenson, and on the day of the battle, Ericsson's *Novelty* appeared against Stephenson's *Rocket*. The former pleased by its light build, and it was expected to win. But bad luck pursued it, for some parts gave way during the run, and Stephenson won. At first it seemed that this way of getting ahead quickly was now closed to Ericsson. But he was not at a loss for new ideas. Again and again he busied himself with improving the steam engine. He invented a rotary steam engine, and he did well with his marine engines.

He was now well on the way to earning money, but he

had no talent for it. He was said to be one of those Swedes who, when they have a million, know how to spend two very elegantly. He also had little taste for honour and fame in an external sense. He was consumed by the desire to carry his ideas into practice. He sacrificed without a thought his own means to this end, and, as far as possible, those of his friends. Indeed, it is reported that he actually made the acquaintance of a debtor's prison, for the laws in England concerning debt were in those days very stringent. He could not stop inventing. Three or four patents a year was the average over a long period, and in looking back to that time of his highest activity, he often said that he never made an invention which, having proved its value, was not at once claimed by others. His experience in this respect was no doubt the same as that of all other great creative workers.

However much he tried to improve the steam engine, it still remained a coal-eater with a large appetite, and so he returned to his hot-air engine in the hope of making an economical and effective source of power. A parson, Stirling, had obtained a patent for a hot-air engine in 1826. This incited him to pursue his own line. His new engines were admired also by professional experts, and once again the belief arose that a substitute had been found for the steam engine. Ericsson was at that time very near to the belief, which, however, he fought against, that energy could be generated almost from nothing—in other words, that he was approaching perpetual motion. His 5-h.p. engine, which was so much admired in London in 1830 was to show that heat, which was then looked upon as a substance, could be communicated and removed at varying temperatures. In his regenerator, consisting of a dense network of metallic wires with a great surface, Ericsson believed he could remove from the used-up escaping air the whole of its heat, and store this. The fresh air was then to take up the necessary heat from the metal. The fire was only necessary, thought Ericsson, to cover small chance losses of heat. Ericsson was

PE

not alone in falling into this error, for the law of the conservation of energy was not discovered by Robert Mayer in Heilbronn till 1857, when it was soon confirmed by Joule and Helmholtz in its full generality. But the impossibility of perpetual motion in a purely mechanical system had been postulated centuries before, though not all engineers were yet clear on the point.

The famous Michael Faraday was asked for his opinion of the hot-air machine. He said in a public lecture that he would have found it very easy to prove the impossibility of such a machine. But after Ericsson had asked him to see the machine itself before the lecture, he had to admit that it actually worked, but that he could not say why.

Another great engineering problem was presented to him. Steamships had hitherto been driven by great, slow-turning clumsy paddle-wheels. Ericsson believed that the rapidly revolving screw would be the driving organ of the future, and so he turned to designing and making them. Experiments with models showed that it was possible to make progress along these lines, and with American support he built in 1836 the first screw steamer of considerable size, with which he demonstrated on the Thames to the Admiralty the advantages which a screw steamer would have as a man-of-war.

He was not the first to think of the screw. John C. Stevens had made experiments in America in 1804 with screws, and Delisle had done the same in France in 1823. A patent for ship's screws was granted to Josef Kessel in Austria, and a trial trip took place in 1829. No advance had been made on these tentative efforts. A farmer, F. P. Smith, had worked in England at the same time as Ericsson, at the idea of introducing the well-known Archimedean screw. By chance, half his screw broke off, but Smith discovered that the result was a great improvement. Smith and Ericsson both applied for a patent, and Smith was granted it six weeks earlier.

But the gentlemen of the Admiralty took no interest in the results of the trial trip. They could not deny, it is true, that a screw could be used for propulsion, but it was asserted that a screw-propelled ship could never be properly steered. An American captain, who had become acquainted with Ericsson's work, was enthusiastic, and promised that America would show much more understanding for his work than Old England. A small screw steamer was now built, which gave fine results. It was learned on May 30th, 1839, through American newspapers that the little steamer driven by Ericsson's screw had arrived safely. It was only about 55 ft. long, with a displacement of 30 tons, was built entirely of iron, and took forty-six days for the journey from England to America. Ericsson now held that the time for hesitation was past. He gave up his position as leading engineer of an English railway and left on the *Great Western*, the pioneer of steamship lines, for New York on November 11th, 1839. He arrived in the New World on November 23rd, at the age of thirty-six, with the intention of introducing his screw for merchant and naval use. But that was easier said than done. The experts were much cleverer than Ericsson, and would have nothing to do with the new-fangled invention. Indeed there were enough old ships' captains who would have nothing to do with steam, and were convinced that steamships would soon disappear again. Ericsson arrived at the conclusion that an experienced seaman is not open to conviction.

Ericsson had married in England in 1836. He admired his wife's beauty as much as she his genius. But a lasting marriage cannot be built on mutual admiration alone, the more so as in this case Ericsson had no thought for anything but his work. His wife could not settle down in America, and was jealous of his machines. She soon returned to England in the hope that Ericsson would follow her in not too short a time. He supported her all her life, and remained in correspondence with her and her relatives, but they never saw one another again. Ericsson was a fanatic for work, and once said concerning friendship, that a friend takes up more time than a hard-working man has to spare.

He pursued his own plans. His great screw steamer *Princeton* became famous. It was a man-of-war, in which he succeeded by a peculiar design in getting boiler and engine below the water-line, to protect them from attack. The ship aroused great interest and was in service for many years. In that time he fitted twenty-five ships in American waters with his screw. America led the world in the use of the screw on its great lakes.

Again and again he returned to the problem of his hot-air engine. In 1852 he completed in New York a great ship, named after him, and fitted with what was said to be a 1,000-h.p. hot-air engine. The excitement, extending far beyond merely professional circles, was great. It was believed that the ship would not move, but it developed about 300 h.p. The engine, unfortunately, consumed at least as much coal as a steam engine. The bottoms of the hot-air chambers were soon burned through; steam engines had to be fitted secretly. Finally, the unfortunate vessel foundered on its return journey with the whole of its crew. Ericsson was richer by a very bitter experience. He concluded that his engine could not be used for large powers. But now he wanted to use it as a small motor in small ships. He pointed out how safe it was, how any child could run it, since there was no dangerous steam boiler in it. In two years he sold about 100 such engines, and soon over 3,000 were working in printing shops, lifts, docks, on ships, in mines, and in mills, and they were finally used also for running small boats. Ericsson also had at one time the notion of running a street carriage with one, but they were after all too heavy to act as automobile motors. But Ericsson's world fame does not depend upon the works of peace served by these motors, but upon his improvements in men-of-war.

The American Civil War started in 1861. Ericsson was then fifty-eight, and felt as young and full of energy as a man of forty. The Southern States possessed almost the whole American Navy. The Northern States had to create a new fleet, and the young industries of these states were called upon for unheard-of outputs. They succeeded in a short time in producing 500 men-of-war with more than 5,000 guns. But the Southern States also were not idle. It was their chief problem to keep open their communications with France and England, from which they hoped for assistance, and not to suffer any check to the export of cotton, which was their life blood. The Southern States had surrounded the fleet of the Northern States in the harbour of Hampton Roads near Fort Monroe. The South had succeeded in constructing an iron-armoured floating battery, with a powerful ram designed for the destruction of the wooden ships. The *Merrimac* had sunk three great ships of the Northerners on one day. The danger for the North was gigantic. Ericsson was ready with complete plans for a new form of floating battery, which he had early submitted to the Admiralty at Washington; a semi-submarine, hardly rising above the level of the water, and forming a sort of foundation for an armoured turret, fitted with guns of great calibre, able to rotate. He promised to construct this *Monitor* in 100 days, and he kept his promise.

But at first the order was not given, not because he and his achievements were unknown in America, but because, perhaps, they were too well known. Ericsson had already put forward unblushingly, when the *Princeton* was building, the opinion that the engineers who were building the ship and its engines knew more about it than the officers commanding them. He had dared to deny to the officers, who by their position believed themselves sole arbiters concerning all the tools of war, the right to an independent opinion as against the engineer; indeed, he had gone farther than that, and had permitted himself to form, from his knowledge of weapons, his own personal opinion concerning the practical use in war of this machine. Dealing with Ericsson was not an easy matter. Only the desperate pass in which the Northern States found themselves with their fleet, overcame even these personal resistances. Ericsson got the order. The keel was laid on October 25th, 1861, and the ship was handed over to the Government on February 19th, 1862, and went straightway to its test in face of the enemy. The price was 275,000 dollars, to be paid in instalments. The enemy was met with on March 8th. It was armour against armour. The *Monitor* was hit no less than twenty-two times, but it was master of the field. The *Merrimac* was destroyed. Ericsson was honoured as the victor, and the Government in Washington was freed from a great burden of anxiety.

It was now decided to spend 10,000,000 dollars on armoured ships. Within a week of the battle he got an order for six gunboats, similar in design to the *Monitor*. Naturally there was no lack of criticism. The *Monitor* was designed by Ericsson simply as a fighting machine, and the officers were not perhaps so very unreasonable in pointing out that living on such a ship was no great pleasure. But Ericsson thought that that was about the same as expecting a knight of old to sleep comfortably in his armour.

The great success of this armoured ship excited the world. Ericsson thought that the end of the large and expensive man-of-war was at hand. Now, he thought, the small states too would be able to afford this powerful means of attack and defence, England's rule over the waves would be at an end, the *Monitor* would bring the freedom of the seas. He thought first of all of fitting out his native country Sweden, which he had never forgotten while in America, with such fighting machines. In 1866, Sweden received the first armoured man-of-war of Ericsson's design, and the King named it *John Ericsson*. In England as well, there was the greatest enthusiasm for the new floating fort. For a *Monitor* had succeeded in crossing the ocean. The powers of this ship could now be studied in England itself.

Ericsson never tired of setting himself new problems. His work on high-speed steam engines is admirable, but he had not forgotten his hot-air engine. He now wanted to make direct use of the sun as a source of power; he designed a sun motor, and pointed out that perhaps one day when all coal had long been exhausted, the sun itself would generate, on the shore of the Nile, the power needed for driving factories.

Ericsson was all his life a solitary, who must often have made his work and his life harder by giving utterance all too plainly to his opinions. In a fight, he held attack to be the best defence, he would have nothing to do with compromise, for he was aiming at what was entirely new. When he gained the victory, he could hardly expect his beaten enemy to proceed to crown him with laurels. He himself tells how for years he lived a very strange life. He worked for fifty years twelve to fourteen hours daily, and he was proud of being able to work 365 days in the year. He was quite unable to imagine how a man could be happy without having a great deal of work to do. He bought himself a house early on in New York in what, at the time, was a good residential district. But this condition of affairs changed with the years, factories and shops were built close to him, the outlook from his windows became more and more disgusting. He went on living there in isolation among dock labourers, without even thinking of moving. No one visited him any longer, he did not know his opponents personally, and it was quite understandable that the world, when he was said in 1869 to be dead, believed it. Only professional people knew from his work that he was still alive.

Ericsson had an uncommon power of intense work, and he also began early in life to arrange his habits in such a way as to extract the highest efficiency from his own human machine. Though he had been fond of alcohol in his youth, he soon gave it up, as well as tobacco. He was a moderate eater, kept to a diet, went in for gymnastics right into his old age, and walked three miles every day. He enjoyed unbroken good health. Even in his eighty-second year, he wrote that he had still much important work to do, and hence lived like a man training for a fight. Shortly before his death he gave it as his greatest desire to carry on his work as long as he could stand in front of a drawing board. Even on March 5th he was able to go downstairs to the dining-room, eat with appetite, and talk animatedly; all he wanted to know from his friend and doctor was whether he could go on working.

On the morning of March 8th, 1889, Ericsson quitted this earth without pain of any kind. He had outlived his time, and people at first did not know which Ericsson was dead. It seemed impossible that it was John Ericsson of the battle of the locomotives in 1829, the builder of the *Princeton*, the advocate of the hot-air engine. No one would believe that the *Monitor's* builder had lived till then. He was buried in New York. But when a few weeks later Sweden asked permission to bring him back to his native land, America agreed. The dead Ericsson was taken to his native land on the American man-of-war *Baltimore*, sixty-four years after he had left it. The coffin arrived in Stockholm on September 14th, 1890. The Royal Guard gave him military honours. He was carried on the railway built by his brother to his loved Wärmland, where he was buried on September 15th in a special chapel in one of the most beautiful of Swedish cemeteries.

ALFRED KRUPP

1812–1887

In the Hall of Honour of the Munich Science Museum is a portrait in marble by Hildebrand, presented by the Verein deutscher Ingenieure. It has on it the inscription:

30. JOHN ERICSSON (1803–89)

31 ALFRED KRUPP (1812–87)
From a photograph about 1880

ALFRED KRUPP

With iron endurance, fiery courage, and constructive genius, he led the steel industry out of the village smithy to its highest achievements, to the honour and security of Germany.

The Krupp family in the little country town of Essen, which round about 1800 had hardly 3,000 inhabitants, had for centuries been one of the ruling families of the town. The Krupps were chiefly merchants. In 1732, one of their ancestors founded a firm dealing in dry goods with a capital of 615 reichstalers, and earned enough to acquire a number of pieces of land. He died in 1757. His wife, Amalie Krupp, *née* Ascherfeld, also came of a respected merchant family of Essen. She was an uncommonly energetic woman, and was the first in the line who did not want merely to buy and sell, but to produce. She made snuff, wove cloth and linen, and even dyed the material, and had started to take shares in mining ventures. About an hour's distance from the town of that day she bought an old fulling mill which was later to become, during the first period of development, one of the chief parts of the Krupp cast-steel works. Among the undertakings into which Amalie Krupp put money at that time was Pfandhöfer, which had built the Gutehoffnungshütte in Sterkrade. This ironworks eventually came into Frau Krupp's possession. There is not much to report concerning her son. His son, Friedrich Krupp, the ancestor of the industrial family of to-day, was born on July 17th, 1787. We know little of his youth. He had to work practically for his grandmother, and she sent him to the Gutehoffnungshütte. Here he first learned iron and steel manufacture. Having married in 1808 Therese Wilhelmi, the daughter of an Essen merchant, he wished to develop the Gutehoffnungshütte, which had been made over to him by his grandmother. But Amalie Krupp changed her mind. She took the works back and sold them for 37,800 thalers to Heinrich Huyssen, Franz Eberhard Haniel and Gottlob Jacobi. Thus was founded in 1810 the firm of Jacobi, Haniel and Huyssen, out of which the present Gutehoffnungshütte has developed. Friedrich Krupp returned to Essen, and there his first son Alfred, the subject of this chapter, was born on April 26th, 1812.

Friedrich Krupp first attempted to find a new field for his activity in trade. Then he was attracted by a very important metallurgical problem of the day; he wanted to make cast steel.

In England, Huntsman had made cast steel in 1740. He had had to overcome the greatest difficulties; he had to seek his first customers in France, till finally the Sheffield steel industry realized what advantages lay in this new steel of the highest quality. Huntsman had managed to keep the manufacture a secret for a long time, in order to derive full personal advantage from his great technical advance. English cast steel then ruled the roost in all works in and out of England, wherever the highest quality was a condition for permanent success. This English cast steel could be bought in Germany at very high prices. But Napoleon put an end to this state of affairs, when, in his life and death struggle with England, he proceeded to close the European continent to all English goods. The influence of this embargo of Napoleon's on the development of industry was of the greatest importance. A large prize was offered for the production of cast steel, but every merchant could readily work out the handsome profit to be earned by a successful solution. The more secret Huntsman in England kept his method, the greater the mystery attributed to it. Again and again people claimed to have discovered the secret. The problem was solved by the addition of secret ingredients. One is reminded of the alchemists when one hears accounts of these cast-steel makers of the beginning of the last century; they only differed from their predecessors of former centuries by the fact that they were trying to produce cast steel and not gold.

And then two former Nassau officers came in 1811 to Essen who called themselves 'steelmakers.' Friedrich Krupp hoped that with their help he might produce cast steel in Essen. The three of them founded in Essen in November, 1811, the firm of Friedrich Krupp. The first casting was poured in January, 1812. But it soon appeared that these officers had not the slightest notion of manufacture. In the meantime, Krupp had built a factory, in which the old fulling mill was to drive the hammer by water-power. The buildings were ready by the end of 1812, and work was begun on April 9th, 1813. Though success in making cast steel had not yet been attained, Krupp, nevertheless, wanted to manufacture finished goods. He founded a file manufactory in 1813 with nine workmen who came from Remscheid. Cementation steel was used for the purpose, but the files could not at that time be compared with English files. The attempt had to be given up.

Friedrich Krupp, in spite of his interest in metallurgical work, was not able to concentrate upon this work to the necessary degree. He loved to busy himself with a variety of things. Chief among these were services which he did to the town. Finally, his own money—he and his wife together had a fortune of something over £6,000—was spent. The Continental embargo was lifted in March, 1813, and English steel could again be imported unhindered into Germany. The incompetence of his colleagues had now become so evident that he separated from them, and it appeared as if the cast-steel factory had already come to an end after only two years. But Friedrich Krupp would not acknowledge defeat; he cut down still further the already small number of employees and borrowed money from his mother. Just at this time the Prussian Colonel of Hussars Nicolai came to Essen with warm recommendations from the Prussian Office of Mines, provided with funds, and in possession of a patent granted to him by Prussia for the manufacture of cast steel. Friedrich Krupp then resumed manufacture once more under the name of Nicolai and Krupp. But the disappointment which quickly followed was still more bitter. Two orders were obtained, but no cast steel could be made. Nicolai had to leave the factory, which was shut down. The question of proprietorship was only finally settled in 1823 in Krupp's favour by a legal action carried through three courts. Nicolai was condemned to pay all costs, but Krupp did not receive a penny, for there was no money to be had. Events of this sort made his financial position worse and worse. It is true that Krupp was at last able, on September 15th, 1816, to make cast steel by his own process in the factory, now finally his by process of law, but it was difficult to find a market for it, and Krupp again tried to start producing finished goods. He forged tools, drills and lathe tools. Krupp steel was especially famous for its natural hardness. It was therefore used by preference for leather-working tools which could be used without first being hardened. These tools were Krupp's first marketable product.

A specially important line was the making of dies for minting coins. In this he was supported by the Mints in Düsseldorf and later in Berlin. Up to 1818, 40,000 thalers had already been put into the factory, and as the yearly turn-over was 3,000 thalers, with a very small margin of profit, the works with its ten hands could hardly be called a very profit-able business. Relatives regarded the undertaking as hope-less, and were no longer ready to sacrifice good money on its behalf. Finally, only Krupp and his wife believed in the future. But even they could not at the time foresee for how exceptionally long a period the financial difficulties of the firm would continue. In 1817, the Prussian Government was applied to for an interest-free loan of 20,000 to 25,000 thalers. It was desired to enlarge the factory considerably, but the application was refused, like so many others for small but desperately needed sums sent in the course of years to Berlin. This happened even at a time when it was considered in

Prussia, then under the guidance of the great industrialist Beuth, to be one of the most important duties of the State to support men of ability who needed money.

At that time, all clever people in Essen looked upon the end of the undertaking as inevitable. Finally, Krupp's father-in-law once more gave his help. The new buildings were finished. A new furnace building was put up in 1819 near the coal; alongside it was built a small and modest dwelling-house for the factory manager. There was no working capital. No one would lend any more. Even the old suppliers would give no more iron; indeed, orders had often to be refused because it was impossible to buy iron. The decision was come to in Prussia to erect a State steel works in Neustadt-Eberswalde, though this soon came to an end again. All the same, even in Essen other people were proposing to manufacture cast steel.

Where were workmen to be got? Alfred Krupp said later that he took them from the plough and the hearth. It was a question of training these men. The old band of the first Krupp workmen had untiringly supported the firm through all its difficulties. But the position became more and more hopeless. In 1823 the end seemed to be at hand. Friedrich Krupp had for years been ill from time to time. The works had frequently to be shut down because there was no money to carry on. Most of the workpeople had to be dismissed. The turnover was now only one-third of what it had been a few years back. But the mother strove again and again to help. She sold her land, called in her loans, stood security for her son, and often helped him out, when difficulties were greatest, by a few thalers. Anxiety for the future became more and more oppressive; there were a daughter and three sons to be provided for.

It was now decided to give up the house in Essen. The family moved to the works itself, to live in the humble house built for the manager, and hoped that the country air would do the sick man good. There Friedrich Krupp lay ill, for eight months until September, 1825; his son Alfred, at school in Essen, was the only consolation of the embittered and suspicious man. The son had to leave school at Easter, 1826. He was to learn the secrets of cast-steel manufacture. The father taught the son what he knew, and what he himself was no longer able to show, Alfred Krupp learned from the few workpeople who still remained. On October 8th, 1826, the founder of the cast-steel works died, but not before the town had had to remove his name from the list of taxpayers. The works were shut down. The wife took over the inheritance. No raw materials were to be found in the empty buildings, furnaces were cold and hammers were silent, no one would give the firm a thaler. But Alfred Krupp's mother, Therese Wilhelmi, persuaded her well-to-do father once more to help. The great Alfred Krupp used later to speak of his mother with the utmost respect and reverence, saying that she had endowed him with her industry and endurance, which had brought him success. She added to her industry the greatest economy; no item was too small to be considered. This heiress, Frau Therese Krupp, informed all business friends of her dead husband that the eldest son had received from his father the secret of making cast steel. Alfred Krupp, who had already, at the age of thirteen-and-a-half years, had to represent his father at legal hearings and in dealing with customers, took over the management of the cast-steel works. His grandfather Wilhelmi and his uncle Schultz became his instructors in business methods, and found him an apt pupil with an extraordinarily quick grasp.

Alfred Krupp in 1826 set about building up afresh the work of his father, at a time when his former school-fellows in the same class were striving to penetrate the secrets of Greek. In later years, Alfred Krupp wrote of this year: 'We inherited from our father no fortune, no knowledge, and no name. The manufacture by the old process brought no profit, and nothing was retained but the site and the empty buildings.' To this were to be added eight workmen.

Shortly before his death, he once more wrote out the names
of the seven faithful men who had helped him in 1826, and
added: 'making with Alfred Krupp eight men.'

In actual fact, the fourteen-year-old boy stood shoulder to
shoulder with these men; his extraordinary ability was early
recognized. At that time the manager of the Mint at Düsseldorf addressed him by letter as the 'Factory Owner Alfred
Krupp,' and treated him as a grown-up and knowledgeable
director. The business began to revive again. There was no
working capital. Buying a load of iron was like spending a
fortune. Clay and graphite were bought only in the smallest
quantities from the shops in Essen. Krupp often recollected later that when in those days a crucible broke
during a melting, it was almost like bankruptcy. Alfred
Krupp was the best of his workers. He knew all about furnace work and forging. He trained new people and taught
the smiths, showing them how cast steel should be treated.
But the factory owner could not be content with that. He
was also the business man, who had to see that the sales
increased. So young Krupp set out on Shanks's pony through
the valleys of the surrounding country, visiting all the forges,
rejoicing when Krupp cast steel was already known. Mean-
while, the old and experienced smiths seemed to like the boy.
They talked of their experience, of what they needed, and
Krupp would always bring back home one or two orders.
When, now and then, after such a day of hard work, he came
home with orders for 25 thalers' worth of steel, there was
great rejoicing.

He understood perfectly how to deal with customers.
His first principle was absolute honesty. If mistakes had
been made, he admitted it at once. But then he endeavoured
to explain to the practical men in what these mistakes consisted, and how they could be avoided in future. His
customers concluded from this that Krupp knew how to get
ahead, and they very soon learned to value the high quality
at which he was aiming. 'Low-class work goes against the

grain with me' was a saying of young Krupp's, and he remained true to it all his life. In his *Reglement*, which he regarded as so important, the first sentence runs: 'The first and most important principle to be kept in mind is, that the Firm is to manufacture the finest and most perfect products possible.' Again and again he impresses on his colleagues: 'The quality of our work, impartially considered, is what will bring us work.' A further principle in his business dealings was that of guaranteeing the tools he supplied. He undertook to replace free of charge any piece not fulfilling requirements. He thus gained a high degree of confidence from his customers.

However, this guarantee frequently caused him much anxiety, for more than once the iron delivered to him was not up to standard, and good cast steel cannot be made from bad iron. The Mints, which were very important customers of his, suggested to him that he should manufacture hard steel rolls, which could not be obtained of sufficiently high quality in England. In 1828 he made a decisive advance in this direction. Along with tool steel and leatherworkers' tools, he was now also making steel rolls. But money was needed for all this, and money was practically unobtainable. Krupp had to depend on himself. He went methodically to work to raise the quality of his wares. His object was to raise their money value. While the steel production increased between 1827 and 1833 by only 50 per cent. in weight, the value of the products increased by 125 per cent. A hundredweight of cast steel in rods brought in only 25 thalers; in the form of rolls it was worth about 125 to 250 thalers.

Krupp's experience with the cast steel which he delivered to other firms to be worked up by them forced him to take up the manufacture of finished goods, for again and again he found that his good steel was spoiled in other workshops by bad hardening or wrong treatment at the hands of persons not sufficiently conversant with the material. This development from producing a raw material to manufacturing finished articles from it was repeated again and again throughout the 125 years of the firm's history up to date. But tools and machines are needed for manufacture. He had no money to buy them, so he had to make them himself. In the rolling mill he built the simplest possible form of lathe—using wood as his chief material—and a simple grinder. This was the beginning of his great activities as a designer, which were too long forgotten as compared with his achievements as ironmaster. Krupp could now inform his customers that he could deliver ready hardened and ground rollers, and with the healthy optimism necessary to great accomplishment he added: 'I can now make any cast steel roller, however large.' Here he was anticipating developments by a very long way.

Every step forward called for new equipment. Again and again came the never-ending battle for money. One must know how to help oneself, and one may learn how to get results of the highest class by use of the most primitive machines. But a producer of goods has to find a market for them. The business was in need of further development from this point of view, and so Krupp undertook in 1832 his first long tour. He went up the Rhine to Bonn, Coblentz, Wiesbaden, Frankfort, then the seat of the Hessian and Suabian gold and silver industry; he came to Stuttgart, Heilbronn, Hanau. He everywhere visited the mints; he got acquainted with the Rhineland leather industry, which was an important market for his tools. In the winter he visited the Berg-Marck industrial area. Two years later he was again in South Germany, and from there he went for the first time to Berlin. Alfred Krupp has said that during these years he was his own bookkeeper, coke-breaker, and night watchman. But he was still more. He was turner and smith, grinder and hardener, and commercial traveller as well. There was nothing which he did not have to attend to. He was obsessed by his task of increasing the property

confided to him. He was always thinking of his problems.
He did not forget them while working; he did not forget
them while eating and drinking; they kept watch by his
pillow at night. Add to all this that he was not a healthy
man. He suffered from shortness of breath and continual
headaches, but he always conquered even these natural disadvantages. He kept on his feet by virtue of his firm belief
that he would succeed. But for this faith, life would have
been unendurable for him. But how short, compared with
long periods of deep depression, were the hours in which he
dreamed his dreams of the future, intoxicated with the
greatness of the task he had undertaken.

What were his experiences on these journeys ? He
learned the needs of his customers. But he also learned by
his personal experience all about the miserable state of the
Germany of his day. Take only one example, the coinage.
In South Germany gulden were in use, in North Germany
thalers, in the West some seventy varieties of foreign coinage
were used in trade. Then he got to know how bad the roads
were, such that large loads of goods could not possibly be
transported economically before the days of the railway.
It was a great piece of good luck for the cast-steel works
that the Customs Union, and the first German railway, both
came into existence at the same time.

But though Krupp now succeeded in increasing his sales,
he had to tell himself on his return to Essen that he simply
could not execute his orders with his existing plant. Every
success in the one direction brought with it new and heavy
anxieties in the other. In Essen, the few machine tools had
been driven by man-power. In the fulling mill, an hour's
journey from his works, there was water-power, but it was
not always available. The water in the two reservoirs was
used up in a few hours. Krupp has later told us how often
he used to gaze longingly upstream from the pear-tree in
his garden, to see if the miller was not at last opening his
penstocks, so that Krupp could work his hammer. The large

4-cwt. hammer was not powerful enough for most work. Heavy work had to be carefully packed in hot ashes and taken laboriously to Sterkrade, to be forged by other people. That cost a lot of money, and often was not successful.

A mechanical workshop was needed. In 1832, Krupp built his first workshop; the upper rooms of the hammer building contained the grinding and turning shops. The machines were driven by long ropes from the water-wheel. Even now the lathes were of wood. The struggle with water was a hard one. The works were idle for months in dry summers. Water was short just when the hammer was most needed, and it soon became clear to Krupp that it was impossible to continue without steam-power. If he could only have a 20-h.p. steam engine, he believed he could 'turn out an enormous amount of work.' But where was the money to be found ? The works suffered continually from shortness of cash. On pay-days friends and relations had now and then to help out with a few thalers. On top of all this came a serious attack of inflammation of the lungs, which left Alfred Krupp physically weak for months.

But even in these hard times his courage never deserted him. 'I wish I could breathe my courage into others; it is not recklessness, it is based on confidence.' He succeeded in breathing this faith in final success into his relative, Friedrich von Müller, who in 1834 put 10,000 thalers into the firm as sleeping partner, and so provided funds for extensions. At that time the owner of the works was twenty-two years of age, and the way in which he regarded this turn of fortune in its effect on himself is characteristic. He went to his doctor and asked to be told the full truth regarding his weak health. He had previously written to him: 'I have much mental work, have to think and contrive a great deal to employ fifty men properly in my works, so that I am hardly able to sleep at night.' The doctor consoled him, and his health did actually soon become so much better that he was able to tackle new problems with energy keyed to the highest pitch. In 1835, he ordered his steam engine, costing 5,000 thalers, from the Gutehoffnungshütte. This beam engine, which at 25 strokes a minute gave 20 h.p., is to be seen to-day in the Museum at Munich, a venerable relic testifying to the modest beginnings of the Krupp works.

Now began great work in designing. Alfred Krupp drew and sketched. His own extensive practical experience enabled him to design the machines which were to help the output to be expanded to an undreamed-of extent. The machines have long ago perished, but many of these brilliant sketches have come down to us, and arouse our admiration for the great designer in Alfred Krupp. The new plant soon began to tell. In 1849, the production of steel had increased from 9,000 lb. to 280,000 lb. Eighty men were already being employed. The sales were doubled. Eighteen thousand thalers had been spent on building. Fresh capital was needed. Again an application was made to the Government; again there was a refusal. Again von Müller helped with a loan of 6,000 thalers. And now some staff was engaged. His brother Hermann Krupp, born in 1814, was working very keenly in the business at the age of twenty-one; the elder sister and the younger brother did counting-house work. Hermann Krupp travelled in South Germany, and succeeded in making new and valuable business connections.

In 1835 the direct connections of the firm with foreign countries began, after a few dies only now and then had been delivered to Greece and Holland. In four years the turnover was multiplied tenfold, three-fifths at that time going abroad. The prophet has least honour in his own country. It was hardest for Krupp to make progress in Germany. The land was all too divided, both economically and politically. People in Germany were poor, and Krupp insisted on his prices. He was no huckster, and he told everyone who would listen that a good roll was never too dear. In 1838, Krupp himself went abroad. He visited first France, then England. He was away from Essen for sixteen months. He had great success in Paris. He had early recognized the value of a knowledge of foreign languages, and had quickly become fluent in French and English.

But he was no less urgently needed in the business. Orders were falling off. Anyone who had Krupp material did not need to order again for a long time. A Krupp cast-steel die would strike 230,000 coins without serious wear, other makes of material hardly 25,000. The old customers were well pleased, and had no thought of sending new orders. The position was difficult when he returned to Essen from his long journey, but he went to work again with unimaginable tenacity and patience. 'Getting there is a question of will alone.' That was no empty phrase for Krupp. He believed it, and the greater the obstacles, the greater became his passionate desire to overcome them. 'The worse the times, the less can we take things easy, the more we have to get busy.' 'The worse it is now, the better it will be later.' 'Now, at it twice and thrice as hard !'

His confidence was rewarded. A year later we find him travelling. In Berlin, he got the largest order so far for rolls, to a value of 5,000 thalers. He was only a short time in Essen. He went from Berlin to Warsaw, to Saxony and Silesia, to Hungary, and often to Vienna. Here he got a large order, worth about 25,000 gulden, for machines and rolls, and this very success was destined to plunge him into the worst of trouble. He had accepted in his contract such severe conditions that, as he only realized later, he could not possibly fulfil them. Hence he was refused payment when he had done the work. He remained in Vienna, and the works in Essen declined more and more. He finally appealed to the Emperor, and he decided in Krupp's favour. Before this decision was given, collapse was at hand in Essen. But credit was again successfully obtained, and it was mainly the growth in export business that saved the situation. In 1843 the three brothers were again working together in Essen. The youngest, Friedrich, showed great technical talent, but was wanting in tenacity. This difference in outlook led to Friedrich Krupp finally leaving the firm altogether in 1848. The second brother, Hermann Krupp, found a great new field of work in Vienna, built up on the spoon roll. A method was worked out for the mass manufacture of spoons by the use of suitably engraved rolls. Together with a member of the old Düren firm of Schöller, which had removed to Vienna, Krupp built a factory in Berndorf near Vienna, because water-power was to be had there. The manufacture was begun in 1845, but more than seven years' hard work, and an expenditure of over 100,000 gulden were necessary before there could be any talk of profit. From September 1844 onwards, Hermann Krupp was working in Berndorf. He and his son Arthur Krupp, the 'Austrian Krupps,' made out of the little Berndorf works a great world firm. Essen was able to carry out orders for this plant in 1840–45, at a time of industrial depression.

Alfred Krupp strove again and again, in all sorts of directions, to make use of his cast steel. He felt himself a pioneer in the use of the highest class of material. Thus he was in the forties, already making springs, and even whole machine parts out of cast steel. In 1843 he forged the first rifle barrels. In 1844 Krupp offered the Prussian Minister of War a cast steel gun tube for the first time. It appeared as if the period of greatest difficulty was over. Krupp built between the original family house and the old furnace building a second modest house, and here a son, Friedrich Alfred Krupp, was born to him in 1854.

A new time was at hand. Locomotive and railway were beginning to change fundamentally the form of industrial life. In 1835 the first railway, only a few kilometres long, was opened from Nürnberg to Fürth. A few years later, it was possible to travel by train from Dresden to Leipzig, the first German line of any considerable length. Short lines from Berlin to Potsdam, Brunswick to Wolfenbüttel, Düsseldorf to

Erkrath were in existence. Longer stretches were already
planned; in the West the railway between Cologne and
Minden attained a special importance, and this railway
needed iron and steel, locomotives and carriages, workshops.
Hence the rise of the railway was the cause of new machine
works being put up everywhere.

One hundred years ago, the works of Borsig in Berlin,
Schickau in Elbing, Hartmann in Chemnitz, and Maffei in
Munich were founded. Success was being attained in
Berlin by Freund, Egells, and Wöhlert. The railways were
everywhere a great source of orders, and the trade in raw
materials increased to an undreamed-of extent. Alfred
Krupp turned his attention to railways and steamships as an
outlet for his products. In 1848 the Bonn–Cologne railway
had taken the first piston-rods from Krupp, and the Cologne–
Minden railway had had the first axles in the same year. This
was the start of a great development. But in those days, cast-
steel rolls were still the chief product. Krupp travelled a
great deal. Again and again he went to England, for whose
people and their attainments he had the greatest respect. He
travelled France and Holland. He succeeded in greatly
increasing his turnover by foreign orders. But bad times
came along again. The audit of December 31st, 1847, showed
a heavy loss. What he had built up in twenty-one years of the
severest labour seemed lost. Krupp's mother was now advised to sell the works to her eldest son. If it was to be saved,
it could have only one master. The brothers and sisters
agreed. A deed of sale dated February 24th, 1848, made
Alfred Krupp sole owner of the cast-steel works.

'Start small, hold out in hard times, strive for big things,'
Krupp's own slogans, had again to be his guide. In 1848, the
Essen Chamber of Commerce decided that Krupp's cast-steel
works were having a harder struggle than any in the difficult
industrial conditions. Only the workpeople were still holding out, even in this revolutionary epoch. Krupp insisted
on paying wages just as if everything were going as well as

possible. Krupp had to find wages for seventy men, and no one, not even the banks, thought of supporting him. Alfred Krupp had once more, in those hard times, to go from one acquaintance to another and borrow money in small amounts at high interest. But even that did not suffice, and so he decided to take the final step. He ordered his foreman to melt down the whole of the family plate, which still remained from days of prosperity, in the top room of the factory. The bars of silver were taken on Krupp's thirty-sixth birthday to the Mint at Düsseldorf. He used the money to pay his men's weekly wages. Krupp said twenty-eight years later, referring to this step: 'Money was not to be had for bills, and then I had spoons and jugs and spurs and medals melted down; and as by a miracle it happened that from that day onwards we had as much work and money as we wanted.'

A profitable order for spoon rolls had come in. There was work again, and now things actually started to go ahead with giant strides. The railways became the largest buyers of Krupp cast steel. In 1852 Krupp set up his first rolling mill with a 100-h.p. steam engine. Order after order now came in for carriage axles. A new workshop had to be built. At first eighty, but very soon 300 men were employed in it. The first lathes for wheel tyres, for heavy crankshafts, were purchased, the first hydraulic press for pressing-on wheels was installed. But Krupp very soon had once more experience of the fact that it is not enough to offer a new material for sale. Many failures had to be put down to wrong treatment. He therefore resolved to increase more and more his output of finished axles. His axles were renowned everywhere. In Vienna Engerth, in Switzerland Riggenbach, in France Polonceau were special admirers of Krupp material. Borsig and Wöhlert in Berlin ordered the first heavy crankshafts for locomotives from Krupp in 1852. Krupp was fully represented at the first World Exhibition in London in 1851.

Krupp wrote of this exhibition in the Crystal Palace:

'Our things are well placed and attract a notable amount of attention. I am waiting on tenterhooks for the other things. I hope that the cleaner of the two large castings will be forged over without delay and sent here. The English have a 2,400-lb. casting here with the label MONSTERPIECE, and a long description of the magnificence of the piece and the difficulty of producing it; none of it is forged, and so there is no proof that it is not cast iron. I said that we make castings like it every day. I would like to send it to grandfather. . . .'

At the end of May the great casting arrived from Essen, 4,300 lb. in weight. 'Our exhibit is almost more admired than any. All princes present, including the Queen of England and Don Miguel of Portugal, have enjoyed staring into our shop-window.' At that time Friedrich Harkort, the great German industrialist, visited the exhibition in London. He was enthusiastic over Krupp's block of steel. 'No Englishman can do the like' was his view. At the exhibition in Paris in 1855 Krupp showed a block twice as heavy as the London one. This block weighed 5 tons; in 1862, eleven years after the first exhibition, the second London exhibition saw a block of 20 tons weight, and in 1873, a 52-ton block of Krupp cast steel was shown at the Vienna exhibition. Poured from single crucibles, such a block calls for military discipline in the workers, of a kind hitherto unknown. In 1857, the number of workmen employed had passed the first thousand.

The old steam hammer was naturally inadequate for feats of this description. So Krupp determined at the end of 1858 to build a gigantic steam hammer with a fall-weight of 600 cwt. This was intended for making the largest ships' propeller shafts, and steel blocks in weight up to 50,000 lb. Krupp was the designer and builder of the hammer, which he called *Hammer Fritz* after his son, and which became one of the most popular machines that ever on this earth slaved with its limbs of iron and steel for man's purposes. The construction cost 600,000 thalers, and was carried out during the years 1859 to 1861. *Hammer Fritz* was later rebuilt to take a fall-weight of 1,000 cwt.

This hammer was another case in which Krupp was far ahead of his time. His best friends thought he was suffering from megalomania. No one understood him. It remained the largest in the cast-steel works. It was in service for half a century, and only in recent times did the more effective hydraulic forging press replace the faithful old servant. *Hammer Fritz* executed its last forging on March 4th, 1911. Unfortunately, it has not been preserved to us as a monument to great ability and unconquerable faith in the future. It went through the blast furnace, and its iron lives on in other forms.

Its first great task was the cast steel block of 20 tons for the London exhibition. At that time all the world was talking of Krupp and his cast steel. A famous Frenchman saw in Krupp the incarnation of the onward march of Germany's industrial power. People began to believe not only in Krupp, but also in German technology and industry. Krupp's successes strengthened Germany's all-too-feeble self-esteem. It encouraged her people to great new undertakings. Hitherto England had been regarded as unconquerable in the technical field; now Germans began to believe in their own powers. Anyone familiar with history might now cast his mind back to the fifteenth and sixteenth centuries, when Germany led the whole world in firearms, mining and metallurgy, and many another field of work.

Men of action such as Alfred Krupp led the Germans out of dreamy Romanticism along the road of creative work into another province of human activity, full of the equally high romance embodied in all great technical achievement.

Alfred Krupp arrived at one of his greatest technical and economic successes when he succeeded in making large wheel tyres of cast steel. Extraordinary technical difficulties had to be overcome. Krupp's ability amounting to genius, and his persistence, carried him to victory; the trade mark of the three rings, still used by the firm, became the symbol of brilliant upward progress in the fifties and sixties. Money began to pour in on Krupp, and true to his slogan, 'The Present for the Future,' he used the money for successful pioneer development of artillery. New works were continually going up. Every great success brought with it great new anxieties. At that time Sölling, the tried friend of the Krupps, took a very black view of the future. 'What use to you are these great works and numbers of workmen, where every new brick and every fresh man adds to your worries and get you more deeply involved. Do start at last to derive some advantage from all your work and trouble, for it is high time that you did so.' But none of these friends understood Krupp, who was never satisfied with successes. 'A business in which I was working could hardly be too extensive; I should not feel at home in a small one.' His tenacity conquered. To it alone, he was convinced, he owed all his success. 'Many would have already taken alarm ten times over, and have despaired. But I stuck to my purpose with tenacity.'

In the sixties, the age of steel for railway lines began. Krupp had been the first to introduce into Germany, in 1862, Bessemer's great English invention.

In the new stage of Krupp's development which was to make him the Cannon King, he had to prove in a still higher degree his genius, his tenacity, his faith in the future. Krupp had already attempted in 1836 to make rifle barrels of cast steel. On March 1st, 1849, the Prussian Ministry of War received two cast-steel rifle barrels which had been forged over a mandrel without a weld. At the same time, Krupp offered also to make field-gun tubes out of cast steel. The Ministry was completely satisfied with the existing rifle barrels, but a cast-steel field gun would be tried. The tests which were made in the following years were uncommonly favourable to the excellence of the new material. But the price was too high. Krupp knew that he was on the right road. At the Great Exhibition in London in 1851, a Krupp 6-pounder excited much admiration. At that time the Prince of Prussia, later King Wilhelm, desired to become acquainted with this genius, this Herr Krupp. On July 16th, 1853, the future German Emperor visited the works in Essen for the first time.

The cast-steel gun everywhere excited the greatest attention. The French Government invited Krupp to build a cast-steel works in France. Krupp declined. Russia made advances to him. But the first large orders came from Egypt. Every fresh experiment showed that there was no substitute for cast steel. In 1859, the Prussian King ordered rifled 6-pounder guns to be introduced, but there could be no question of profit for Krupp, and the firm could not live on honour and recognition. He declared that he could not think of going farther with the manufacture of guns unless he were given profitable orders. But he nevertheless soon determined to push forward again with development. This involved doing more than supplying merely the material; he had to turn out finished guns. But the military authorities would not hear of such a thing. They saw in Krupp a useful manufacturer of cast steel, but as artillery experts they could not imagine that a civilian could make guns, and even entertain his own opinions about them. But Krupp wanted to introduce his own design of gun with his new material, and he succeeded in doing so. He thus came to making gun-carriages, and to manufacturing ammunition. The activities of the Krupp works were extended at an ever-increasing pace. Krupp himself took a leading part in the work of detailed design. Many of his sketches are a proof of this. Every great exhibition gave evidence of his progress. When his guns had to be tested, he was always dependent upon military authorities who did not want him. Again he determined to be independent. He needed his own range for testing, and this demand gave rise to more head-shaking and disapproval. It was put down as a piece

of impertinence on his part, and the direct necessity of this
testing-ground for development was not recognized.   In
the Franco-Prussian war of 1870–71, Krupp guns proved
their excellence. He had shown great foresight, and made
his own contribution to the victory of Germany.

In 1865, a suggestion from Russia opened up a new
chapter in the development of steel gun tubes. In place of
the massive cast-steel tube, tubes or hoops shrunk over a
centre barrel were introduced, and again a great work
of construction had to be carried out in a few years. Russia
was the first to recognize these hoop guns and to place
large orders for them.   But the German professionals
still went on trying to use bronze as a gun material. Krupp
was of the opinion that this metal was out of the question; it was all right for decorative purposes and medals,
but not for modern weapons of war. The fiercest battles
had to be fought with the Berlin authorities.   Krupp's
staff were often ready to despair, but Krupp, with sure
instinct, again and again took the initiative, and found
his way to the highest persons in the State. Roon, Bismarck,
and the German Emperor had to listen to Krupp's views
stated by himself, and he understood how to win the
highest in the land to belief in his ideas, a fact which, however, did not make the work of his staff any easier in dealing
with less highly placed authorities. 'I have made it my
principle since my youth, to put all my weight and power
into grasping a thing—never to be content with half
measures.' And in fact there were no half measures about
his fight for his gun. 'We don't gain our ends by silence, or
by doing nothing, but only by energetic and determined
fighting.' He wanted a fight; it stimulated him. 'I prefer
ten worthy opponents to one who simply obstructs.' He
was never in want of foemen worthy of his steel.

Krupp himself was not without faults, and it may be
that, especially when an old man, his excessive obstinacy in
sticking to an opinion once expressed was often of no

advantage to the cause he had at heart. All the same, taking things as a whole, it was just this tough fighting spirit which gave him victory. Matters became especially critical when it was proposed to introduce English guns into the Navy. Krupp asked for tests of his guns under equal conditions, and he won the competition in the Tegel range in 1868. One present at these trials said later: 'The jubilation was incredibly great. I have never seen such joy, such jubilation, among professional men.'

The opponent of the gun is armour. The battle between gun and armour is one of the most exciting chapters in technical history. The Krupp firm played a great part in this development also, and for its beginnings we have to go back to the time of Alfred Krupp. His son was the one who later undertook the task of large-scale development; the firm of Krupp took over in 1893 the works founded in Magdeburg by his great opponent Hermann Gruson, and also, three years later, the Germania Shipbuilding Yards in Kiel.

But this has taken us beyond Alfred Krupp's life work. Anyone working, as he did, on a gigantic industrial scale, far exceeding all previous development in this field in Germany, had to provide for further extension of his operations on the same scale. Alfred Krupp acquired metal and coal mines, purchased together with other firms great Spanish ore deposits, the harbour of Bilbao had to be enlarged, railways were built in far countries. Blast-furnace plants were set up, and everywhere the great things he did were only the beginnings of still greater developments which came after him. He followed with the greatest interest all events outside his own field of work, at least in so far as he could make use of them for his own purposes. He began in 1871 to set up the first Martin steel plant; he evinced the greatest interest in Siemens regenerative heating. In 1863 he got in contact with Friedrich Siemens, and conceived the greatest admiration for the achievements of the brothers Siemens. 'When Siemens promises something, he is the man for it.' In 1869 the first Siemens-Martin furnace was started up. Here again the process was kept a strict secret.

Krupp had experienced too acutely that money is the heart's blood of industrial undertakings not to warn his people again and again to be economical. 'The designer's greatest achievement is simplicity, cheapness, combined with solidity. To build luxurious workshops and sheds is merely to give the world a show, paid for with the heart's blood of the purse, and is the cause of the ruin from the start of so many works.'

Krupp was for decades his own architect. An old fore-man has described how Krupp went about new building construction. He himself paced off a certain distance, and then looked around. If he thought the distance was not sufficient, he went farther, and then said: 'Dig here.' The plan of the building was thus quickly settled.

But the best raw materials, the most perfect machine tools, the roomiest shops and work places do not suffice for the production of high-quality work. Here again it is the man behind the gun who wins the battle. Every under-taking is dependent upon their abilities, their personal devotion to the work, upon their loyalty and trustworthiness. 'Sound men, sound principles, justice, kindness, must rule among us, then everything will go well and ever better.'

The social services, started by Alfred Krupp and carried on by his successors on the largest scale, have become as famous throughout the world as the firm's products. Krupp started work with seven men. At the Centenary of the cast-steel works, all the Krupp works together were employing more than 70,000 persons. The workers were to earn good wages in them. 'The workman is to earn with us the maximum that the industry can offer, or we give up an industry in which people have to go hungry.' The works were for Krupp never simply a money-making concern. He had an inward conviction of the great moral value of work, and he liked to talk of the factory as a great social unit, which had in the first place to minister to the well-being of all who belonged to it.

The worker has a claim for more than wages, and Krupp saw clearly that even high wages would be only too quickly eaten up by a rise in the cost of living, and especially of rent. He said in 1874: 'The worker has never earned such high wages as at this moment; so it is not small wages that make him dissatisfied, but the small enjoyment purchasable by his money, high rents and high cost of food.' This clear view of the facts led him to build houses; he founded a great co-operative institution, which was to have in the first place the purpose of 'supplying the least-paid workman, who has to live on the minimum, with his needs at as low a price as possible.' He created, as early as the fifties, a sick- and pension-fund, and in 1872 he writes: 'A special object of our care must be to provide institutions for the care and support of the children, and to offer adults opportunity for instruction, education and entertainment.' Here also Krupp's successors developed on the largest scale the institutions already founded by Alfred Krupp.

Fate was once more to face Krupp with a great and severe crisis. This was in the dangerous *Gründerjahre* (flotation years), which were followed by a great collapse. At that time his friend Sölling wrote to him: 'I have the greatest confidence in all your creations, only I beg you not to forget the financier in the manufacturer; the one cannot succeed without the other.' When an enormous recession of business followed in all branches, Krupp had to raise short-term loans under onerous conditions. The heaviest sacrifices were necessary to make good the neglect caused by the fact that in this department intelligent foresight, upon which he otherwise laid so great stress, had been wanting. The Royal Prussian Sea Trading Society put itself at the head of the banks and gave Krupp a loan of 30,000,000 marks.

But soon large orders for war material came from abroad, and very considerable orders for rails from America, so that the loan, to be amortized by 1899, could already be paid off at Krupp's death in 1887.

An undertaking such as Krupp's, often greatly threatened by crises, had naturally attracted by its brilliant rise the widest attention of the money market. Again and again he was approached with a view to letting himself be 'floated' so as to increase his financial basis and save him from his worst worries, and again and again he refused on principle, using on more than one occasion the words: 'I would rather die than entrust my undertaking to an anonymous mob of persons.' 'I am not a speculator on the stock exchange, but a manufacturer,' and he would have nothing to do with those so active at the time, who 'as parasites in armchairs make use by means of limited companies of the sweat and intelligence of others to line their own pockets.'

Alfred Krupp did not regard the building up of his undertaking, and all the great deeds which we have been able to follow only in outline here, as the end of his work. He knew that he, too, would in the end have to pay his tribute to Nature. He could hardly have hoped, in view of his bodily weakness in earlier years, to reach his sixtieth or seventieth year, but he desired the work he had created to live long after him, and to go on growing. He found a successor in his son. One of his chief tasks was to instil into this son, who had to spend much of his time as an invalid in the South, the necessary fundamental ideas for carrying the business on after his own death. In his old age it appeared to him to be by far his highest task to gain for his undertaking first-rate intelligences and, just as important for him, first-rate characters. So now he became the great educator, writing in his own large hand more than any of the great technical creators; his writings would fill many volumes. Here, however, his conscious determination to confine his energies to his own undertaking led to his hardly giving a thought to influencing wider circles of the whole nation.

Only his strong desire that his work, come what might, should live on after his death, explains Alfred Krupp's belief that he could lay down written and final laws for the future.   This man with so keen a sense for all that is living, with so masterly an ability to seize the moment and make it serve his purposes, believed that through the code of rules which he called the *Reglement*, he would be exerting power fifty years after his death as though still walking among men.   He who was so completely a part of his work that he would never hear of any honour being given to his own person, desired to make his work secure for all time.   He writes with reference to his laws in 1872: 'I must be certain that in 25 and in 50 years, no disorder of any sort, resulting from evil will, shall be possible.   The *Reglement* must point the way to future procedure, and every case must be foreseen, every duty and every right in every position.'   And in another place he says: 'I wish to leave behind me a great and harmonious whole.   I am devoting my remaining strength, my last wishes, to this purpose.   As compared with this high aim, money has in my eyes a completely subordinate value.'

He began to withdraw himself methodically from all details. Only in decisive cases, when he believed that the course was being lost, did he grasp the helm again energetically.   He wanted to convince himself in his lifetime that all would go well in the business without his interference.   'My sole personal contribution to management is to supply the intelligence, energy, and reputation, and it is to this that my efforts are directed.'   And further: 'The sooner I regard my own role as completely superfluous, the better I shall be pleased.   I am longing for the label "dispensable." I have the single desire to see myself so replaced that I can retire any day without being missed, and everyone should have the same desire. If close co-operation and the running of the business depends upon one man's life, the whole is always in danger.' How much greatness there is in this man's striving, who had every right to say of himself that he was working for the future, and not for the present.

On July 14th, 1887, Alfred Krupp died at his country seat *Auf dem Hügel* which he had himself created.

We honour in him not only the instructor of his own workers; he became for us Germans one of our great educators. Many of his aphoristic sayings embodying his experience of life sound to us to-day like words of ancient wisdom. They preach, in the first place, courage. He knew how much final success depends upon not letting oneself be 'got down.' Kindness and humanity were fundamental characteristics of his. He knew that everyone makes mistakes. 'Anyone who works makes mistakes, I make some. Who works much, makes more mistakes; only he who keeps his hands in his pockets and does nothing, makes no mistakes.' He was lenient with such mistakes; only when he came up against easy ways, lethargy, want of energy, did he take energetic steps.

When at the height of his life, he loved to recall the hard times he had had to go through. He determined that the modest little house should remain standing as long as the works lasted. His successors were to look upon this memorial, the origin of the great work, with thankfulness and joy: 'The house and its history may give courage to the timid, and confer tenacity on him, it may warn against despising small things, and preserve against arrogance.' And along with the house, his own recollection of his hardest struggles should be an education in confidence. For these were times in which, often working whole nights through, he struggled along for twenty-five years with the cares of the harassed father of a family, and often lived only on potatoes, coffee, butter, and bread, without any meat. 'My last recollection of the past is this long-threatening danger of shipwreck, and the overcoming of it by endurance, hard living, and work, and that is what I would like to say to every young man who has nothing, is nothing, and wants to become something.'

Again and again he puts in the forefront the moral value of all work. Work for him is not the means to become rich, but to gain inward satisfaction, in the consciousness of having made use of one's talents for the benefit of all. All that he attained was to be the means for further striving. For he expresses the conviction: 'Nothing exists, no work of man, which is not capable of, and in need of, endless improvement.' In this way all that he did became for him a moral duty, and the greatest thought that any man in creative work could conceive, is written on his monument in his own words: 'The object of work should be the common good. Then work is a blessing, is prayer.'

HENRY BESSEMER

1813–1898

The name of Henry Bessemer stands written in shining letters over one of the most important chapters in the great history of iron and steel. The genius of Bessemer produced mild steel for the first time, and thus led to an hitherto un-heard-of production of iron of high quality, without which the further development of technology would have been un-thinkable. Thus far, this great invention arose out of the needs of progressive development, although contemporaries of the invention were not yet able to detect the connection.

The life story of the inventor is no less remarkable than his invention. Bessemer's father was born in the heart of London. His parents emigrated to Holland and took their eleven-year-old son with them into the adopted country, where he became a machine manufacturer, and built the first steam engine in Holland. The grandparents went ten years later to Paris. Here young Bessemer succeeded in improving the microscope so notably, that the French Academy of Sciences made him a member in recognition of his achievements. He found work in the French Mint, in the plant of which he made important improvements. The effect of the French Revolution led to his wishing to return to England. This was easier said than done at the time. Bessemer finally succeeded in reaching London with his pockets full of worthless paper money.

There he had to start again from the beginning. His powers and industry enabled him to make such progress that he was able to buy a house and garden in Charlton, then a village not too far from London. Here this greatly gifted engineer and mechanic became the father of a son, Henry Bessemer, born on January 19th, 1813. The father did not content himself with living only for his garden, with the beautiful tulips which he had learned to love in Holland. He very soon felt the need for activity of a technical sort. He started a type-foundry, producing types which attracted attention by their artistic qualities. Also, the excellent qualities of the type-metal were soon greatly appreciated.

Young Bessemer grew up in this environment. He quickly learned what the simple village school could teach him. The life around him was a more important school for him. He was familiar with the work in his father's factory, and at home in the local mill. Every machine, every handicraft was the object of his close attention. Head and hands were trained simultaneously. He loved every one of his faculties. Nature was a kind teacher for him from his earliest youth. His schooldays were soon at an end. His father could easily have continued his education at one of England's higher schools, but the son begged to be allowed to go his own way, free of any school. The father was agreeable. He fitted up a workshop for his son, and bought him one of the lathes made in London by Holtzapffel, and very much in favour at that time.

In the meantime, his father's business had become so extensive that he decided to transfer it to London. Young Bessemer was at a turning point in his life. Looking back on it later, he said of this period in his life that everything that he could turn his mind to seemed possible to him. It was only a question of not allowing temporary disappointments to weaken his resolution.

Bessemer, now seventeen years old, six foot tall, full of youthful energy, with a highly sanguine temperament, left the village for the metropolis. On March 4th, 1830, he saw the giant city for the first time; a new world opened up before his eyes. *The Arabian Nights* had told him of no such marvels as those by which he was now surrounded. But he also felt alone for the first time in his life; no one knew him in the great city. He also knew that he had learned none of the regular professions, but he felt on the other hand that Nature had gifted him with the power of invention, which he would be able to put to good use.

Bessemer started first on one thing, then on another. He bought plaster casts from Italian hawkers, reproduced them in cast metal, and coated them—before the days of electro-plating—with a thin layer of copper. Above all, he was highly successful in making casts of natural objects, plants, etc. These casts gained admiration in many quarters.

At that time it was discovered that many revenue stamps which had to be put on documents, and were simply embossed on paper, were being forged. Bessemer made these forgeries so excellently by means of his easily fusible alloys, that the Director of the Stamp Office, to whom he showed his products, was greatly alarmed. But Bessemer at the same time proposed a process for making such forgeries impossible. The twenty-year-old inventor's lesson was learned; the State was saved large losses, but did not dream of giving him any compensation, for he had failed first to patent his invention. He then developed for a velvet manufacturer a method of impressing different patterns on velvet. He made a type-setting machine for Young, one of his friends, and he even designed a type-casting machine with all the latest refinements, but neither this nor the setting machine could be used on account of the opposition of the workpeople.

Instead of making lead pencils by sawing graphite into strips, he made them, as they are made to-day, by pressing a paste of graphite powder through a die. He sold this patent for some hundreds of pounds. It would be impossible to give here a list of all Bessemer's patents. The list in his Autobiography numbers 117, and he tells us that he paid more than £10,000 in fees.

Bessemer was not only an inventor of genius, but also a highly industrious worker. He became engaged to the daughter of his old friend Richard Allen, and spent his evenings mostly at his father's home, where his two sisters kept house, or at the parents of his fiancée. He had the courage to marry at the age of twenty-one, and went to live near his place of work. His aim was now to make an invention which would not only bring him honour, but put him on a firm economic foundation.

A chance pointed the way. His sister asked him to make an inscription for the cover of an album containing her paintings of flowers. Bessemer, delighted with his sister's work, thought that only letters of gold were good enough for the inscription. When he obtained 'gold' powder for the purpose, he was surprised at the high price. He found out at home that there could be no question of its being gold; it was made up of tiny thin scales of glittering bronze, for which he had to pay, under the name of gold powder, about 200 times the actual cost of bronze. The high difference in price tempted him to investigate the matter thoroughly. He at once got to work most industriously. He built a machine and made some powder, but it did not fulfil its purpose. He went on with the work and found out how to produce an equally good product, naturally at a much lower price. How was he to secure to himself a reward for this mental labour? He saw that the ordinary way, that of patenting the invention, was of no use here, because the finished product gives no indication of its origin by hand or by machine. In view of the large financial success which seemed possible, his machine would certainly be imitated, especially abroad, and he would lose the fruits of his labour.

Only the greatest secrecy could lead to the desired result. He not only designed a completely new machine, but carried out in a masterly manner all the detailed workshop drawings of the individual parts. These parts he had made in Manchester, Glasgow, London, and Liverpool, a well-mixed selection at each. None of the machine shops which had to work on them could gain any idea of the finished machine, or even of the purpose of any of the parts. He insisted on great accuracy, and finally the finished parts were delivered at his house, behind which he had built a new factory without windows, with only top light. Since Bessemer was clearly conscious that only a very few men, completely faithful to him, could be employed on the work, he designed the machine to be as far as possible automatic in action. His assistants were the three younger brothers of his wife, and he ensured that they did very well out of the business. Only he and these three ever entered the works. The man who had to see to the 24-h.p. steam engine worked outside the actual factory, the driving shaft of the engine passing through a small hole in the wall.

Bessemer saw quite clearly the difficulty of the position. Would the individual parts, produced in so many different factories, fit one another ? Would the machine he had designed at the drawing board work in practice ? He was completely conscious of the dramatic climax at the moment when the machine was first set going. If his plan succeeded, he might become rich, and be able without anxiety to proceed to other work. If failure were the result, his money, his labour, and the money of his friends were lost. But the machine did its work, and Bessemer had now achieved the financial independence for which he longed. He was business man enough not to throw his new product on the market too cheaply. The margin between cost and selling price was still very high, and everything depended on his keeping his process secret, which in fact he did for over forty years.

He now began to think of making his way of living more agreeable. He bought a horse and carriage, and took a fourteen-years lease of a country house at Highgate. Here he built a great conservatory, acquired cows and horses, played cricket on summer evenings, and when he walked on his lawns was reminded of his birth-place, Charlton, where he had lived a happy country life as a boy. He called his new property Charlton House.

The public offer of a prize led him to work in another technical field. A process was needed for a much more effective way of pressing the juice out of sugar cane than the method then in use. He studied this problem methodically, sent for sugar cane from the colonies, made experiments, and built a machine which was so successful, that the Prince Consort handed him a gold medal for his hydraulic press.

His great pioneer work went on. He later made use of the principle of his sugar-cane press to form brown coal into briquettes, which were treated with superheated steam. He made steam ventilators for mines, and showed very effective centrifugal pumps at the Great Exhibition in London in 1851. He then began to work at glass manufacture. He admired Fraunhofer's work, and wanted to do as well. He studied the problem in the most thorough fashion, and at last arrived at a very remarkable furnace for making optical glass. Here we find the furnace already mounted on trunnions, an idea to which he returned in his pioneer invention in iron founding. Far ahead of his time, he designed a machine for rolling plate glass.

In all this work, he was greatly helped by the interest he had had from youth upwards in the most diverse technical processes. In his autobiography he emphasizes the nature of his experience. He had found, he said, that even a small amount of knowledge of a great variety of technical matters had been of great use to him. From his earliest youth, he had always had to learn at least something of all the different industries with which he came in contact. He was always uneasy when there was talk in his presence about an industry of which he knew nothing. This knowledge, joined to a very good memory, helped him greatly in his work. All this work and invention in the field of machine manufacture was not followed up further by him. He took out no patents, and the great plate-glass works which he planned were never built. It was too hard a task to state his own ideas to others in such a way as to get them to put up large sums of money. He could not himself carry them out alone. Anyone else, therefore, might have made use of them, and yet, as Bessemer proved, not a single works, in England or abroad, ever made use of them. And he regarded this as perfectly explicable, since for him it was an axiom that the inventor must nurse and tend his invention like a mother her child. If he does not, there is nothing to be done with it.

The Crimean War, which had powerful political repercussions in the world of those times, also gave rise to new technical problems. Bessemer saw in them possibilities of new and important work. The military were calling for longer shells and better guidance of them in the bore of the gun. The English artillery at that time had no rifled guns. Bessemer allowed the highly compressed gases in the smooth bore of the gun to escape tangentially past the projectile, and in this way produced rotation. He wanted to make experiments, but the English military authorities refused their help, and so he had to make a gun himself, and Napoleon III, who took a great personal interest in the development of artillery, allowed him to make experiments on the range at Vincennes. Bessemer describes vividly in his autobiography how these experiments represent the beginning of the invention which made him world-famous.

After the experiments, Bessemer was sitting round the camp fire with the officers, and the one who conducted the experiments said that while they had certainly turned out very satisfactorily, he hardly thought that cast-iron guns would stand the strain. The problem thus became: Can one make guns of a substance sufficiently resistant to such heavy projectiles? This remark sank into the inventor's mind. He was still without any idea how to proceed, but it was clear to him that such a material would mean a new epoch in the iron industry. This idea got a firm hold of him. He saw a vision of riches and fame as a reward for solving the problem. If he failed, he had only time and labour to lose. He knew at the time no more of iron works than any engineer who has at some time been in an iron foundry or a smithy. But that fact Bessemer looked upon as a special advantage. 'I had nothing to unlearn. My mind was open and free to receive any new impressions without having to struggle against the bias which a lifelong practice of routine operations cannot fail more or less to create.'

These disadvantages of long experience and habit are again and again emphasised by him in his autobiography. At another point he says, 'How often it has occurred to me, and how often have I expressed the opinion that, in this particular competition—as in many previous cases—I had an immense advantage over many others dealing with the problem under consideration, inasmuch as I had no fixed ideas derived from long-established practice to control and bias my mind, and did not suffer from the too general belief that whatever is, is right.'

The experiments in Vincennes were carried out on December 22nd, 1854. In the same month, he was busily engaged at home trying to find the new iron he was seeking. On January 10th, 1855, he applied for his first patent for improvements in the manufacture of iron and steel. Three weeks after Vincennes, the first step had been taken.

Bessemer's aim was to find a material of similar properties to wrought iron and steel, such as to allow of its being cast in the liquid state in moulds or blocks. When Bessemer was thinking of the troublesome and tedious puddling process by which wrought iron was produced, one readily understands how fully convinced he was before he solved the problem that with its solution a new epoch in iron production would begin.

In his first experiments he went back to Réaumur's work. The English engineer Fairbairn had already attempted to produce high quality cast iron by melting pig iron in a cupola with wrought-iron scrap. Bessemer had first to attempt to get higher temperatures, and to avoid contamination of the metal by the fuel. He had undertaken a whole series of experiments which had taken him forward step by step. In his first experiments, melting pig iron with scrap wrought iron in the reverberatory furnace, he had very closely approached the Siemens-Martin process which to-day plays so large a part in iron and steel production, and he often wondered later whether he had been right in abandoning the reverberatory furnace before all possibilities were exhausted. Bessemer was able to make very good use, in his experiments with the reverberatory furnace, of his extensive experience of glass making.

While he was going on step by step, William Siemens, as he tells us in one of his lectures, was working at about the same time with his brother Friedrich, only a few houses away, on the reverberatory process, and had got it essentially perfect. He too needed seven years before the invention was fully ripe for practice.

A new direction to his experiments was given by chance. Bessemer had observed that in melting the pig iron, some pieces of iron remained incompletely molten at the edges. He attempted to bring about melting by supplying more air, but that also failed, and he then proved by means of an iron rod that the unmelted lumps were hollow. The air blast had transformed the surface into wrought iron, which has a considerably higher melting point. The inner parts, which had not been exposed to the air blast, had melted at

32. HENRY BESSEMER (1813–98)

33. SYDNEY GILCHRIST THOMAS (1850–85)

Photo: Deutsche Museum

the existing temperature of the furnace, and run out. This observation, hardly noticed by the iron founder because so familiar, led Bessemer to try to convert pig iron into wrought iron merely by blowing air through it.

He now devoted himself with all the concentration of which he was capable, to developing this line. He blew air through an iron pipe into a 10-lb. mass of cast iron melted in a crucible, and in half an hour the cast iron was converted into wrought iron. The decisive question for him was now whether the cast iron, without addition of further heat, would be kept sufficiently molten, even though its melting point rose, by the heat produced by the combustion of the carbon and silicon in the air blast. He therefore made a new apparatus, in which he could treat as much as 7 cwt. of molten cast iron. As long as the silicon of the cast iron was burning, the process went quite quietly. But when the carbon started to burn, there appeared the shower of sparks and huge flame which delight everyone who sees the process for the first time. But this stormy reaction was of no service to the inventor. Only when the pear-shaped vessel, now so familiar as the 'Bessemer converter,' was developed, with the blast led through the bottom of it, was the problem solved. It could be turned over on trunnions so that the contents left the bottom free, and the blast could then be cut off without the molten iron running back into the air ducts.

When Bessemer in his old age wrote his autobiography, he described in vivid phrases this great experiment, which was to decide his destiny. He awaited the result uneasily. He was employing an experienced iron founder on the work. When everything was ready, the man asked: ' "Where be going to put the metal, maister ?" I said: "I want you to run it by a gutter into that little furnace," pointing to the converter, "from which you have just raked out all the fuel and then I shall blow cold air through it to make it all hot." The man looked at me in a way in which surprise and pity for my ignorance were curiously blended, as he said, "It will soon be all of a lump".' But all went well as Bessemer had foreseen, and only one great anxiety remained for him: 'Would the ingot shrink enough, and the cold iron mould expand enough, to allow the ingot to be pushed out?' He had to wait eight or ten minutes, and then the block was slowly pushed out by hydraulic power. Bessemer, writing at a time when the facts are well known, fears that it may appear tedious to go once more over the old ground. 'But it is nevertheless impossible for me to convey to my readers any adequate idea of what were my feelings when I saw this incandescent mass rise slowly from the mould; the first large prism of cast malleable iron that the eye of man had ever rested on. This was no mere laboratory experiment. In one compact mass we had as much metal as could be produced by two puddlers and their two assistants, working arduously for hours with an expenditure of much fuel. We had obtained a pure homogeneous 10-in. ingot as the result of thirty minutes' blowing, wholly unaccompanied by skilled labour or the employment of fuel.' It was thus possible to use, without human labour, silicon and carbon as fuel, and in this way to arrive at the mass production of iron and steel of high quality. But was this glowing block really malleable iron? The excited Bessemer could not wait for experiments. He called for an axe and struck at the edge of the block. The edge went in deep, without causing the iron to crack—it was no longer cast iron.

But Bessemer did not want to live, as he puts it, in a fool's paradise. He wanted to know at once how this work of his, these ideas, struck other people. He asked the famous English engineer, George Rennie, to pay him a visit and see his process. Rennie was full of enthusiasm. The invention was so important, he said, that the secret must not be kept back for a single day. Bessemer objected that the process had not been worked out to an economic success, and he would like to delay publication until he could show a commercial success on a large scale. But Rennie would not give way, for, as he said, all that remained was to work out details, a matter of which any experienced ironmaster was capable. But the whole principle was, he saw, an indubitable success. No fuel, no labour, no puddling, no forging, great uniform masses of malleable iron could be produced in a few minutes. Rennie was so enthusiastic that he asked Bessemer to give a lecture at the yearly meeting of the British Association, which was to meet at Cheltenham on August 13th, 1855. Rennie was President of the mechanical section of this meeting. Bessemer pointed out that he had never given a lecture or written a paper for a learned society, but Rennie said: 'If you will only put on paper just such a clear and simple account of your process as you have given verbally to me, you will have nothing to fear.'

He gives a humorous account of a little experience. When he was sitting at breakfast with one of his friends, an ironmaster from Wales, Rudd, came to the table and said with a smile, 'Clay, I want you to come with me into one of the Sections this morning, for we shall have some good fun.' The reply was: 'I am sorry I am specially engaged this morning, or I would have done so with pleasure.' 'Oh, you must come, Clay,' said Mr. Rudd. 'Do you know, there is actually a fellow come down from London to read a paper on the manufacture of malleable iron without fuel? Ha, ha, ha!' 'Oh,' said Mr. Clay, 'that's just where this gentleman and I are going.' They went all three together to the meeting. Bessemer was very kindly received by Rennie, who pointed out in a few words the extraordinary importance of the lecture. Then Henry Bessemer began to talk about the production of iron without fuel. At the end he received the enthusiastic thanks of the meeting.

At the discussion, the first to speak was the famous James Nasmyth. He took in his hand one of the small, completely decarbonized bits of iron, and exclaimed with warmth,

'Gentlemen, this is a true British nugget.' He spoke enthu-
siastically of the novelty of the process, and pointed out how
he himself, in one of his patents, had been on the same road.
But he had made only one step in that direction, Bessemer
had run far ahead of him, and he would now tear up his
useless patents. The ironmaster from Wales, who, not
knowing Bessemer, had spoken of the fun to be expected, was
the second speaker. He offered Bessemer his great ironworks free of charge for further experiments. But the *Times*
reporter asked Bessemer for his manuscript, and next day, on
August 14th, Bessemer's account appeared in that world-
famous journal. It naturally aroused the greatest interest.
But Bessemer still thought that his first idea, to await
commercial success, was the right one, for this premature
publication caused many opponents and adventurers to get
busy with the invention. The fact that 5 tons of common
cast iron could be converted in a few minutes into liquid
steel seemed to them like the Philosopher's Stone, which
was able to change lead into gold. All these people wanted to
share his success, and strove to get round his patent. But
Bessemer was a very good hand at drawing up a patent, and
had covered himself in all directions. A few days after the
appearance of his paper in *The Times*, distinguished engineers
and ironmasters came to visit him in London and study his
process. Licences were discussed, and very remarkable
business negotiations were opened up. Only a few weeks after
his lecture, Bessemer had received £27,000 in royalties.

Work with the Bessemer process was begun everywhere.
But the results were disastrous. Bessemer had used for his
first small-scale experiments iron very poor in phosphorus.
It was now evident how difficult it was to obtain such iron in
large quantities. The converter having a siliceous lining, the
phosphorus remained in the iron and made it useless for
every purpose. Every day new reports of failure came in.
The newspapers got hold of this fact, the whole process was
described as the dream of a mad enthusiast, which sensible

men in the trade had never believed in. Once more hosannas were followed by execrations. A newspaper wrote that Bessemer's invention had flashed like a shooting star over the metallurgical firmament, only to end in a shower of sparks followed by complete darkness. Bessemer himself was naturally taken aback, but he maintained that he never for a moment lost faith in the invention. He went to work methodically. First he got Professor Henry, a distinguished chemist, to investigate the various qualities of raw iron. He sent for charcoal pig iron from Sweden. The price of this was such that he still made a profit out of his steel made from this material. But people were still far too much under the spell of the great disappointment to make any more experiments with the Bessemer process, and so he decided to set up his own steel works in Sheffield, together with Allen and Longdon. Here he was successful in making pure iron with any desired content of carbon. Bessemer tells with justifiable pride of the great commercial success of this works. It earned in fourteen years twenty-seven times the capital invested. Every shareholder received in this period a dividend of almost 600 per cent.

This works enabled Bessemer to show how his process could be carried out commercially on a large scale. It was now a problem of making use of British ores low in phosphorus. In this success was obtained. At the second great exhibition in London in 1862, Bessemer was represented by a great number of objects made from his steel, from razors to cannon. In the same year too, the first Bessemer steel rail was laid, and the railway became one of Bessemer's largest customers. In the same year his steel was first used for shipbuilding. On the Continent Krupp made use of the Bessemer process in Essen in 1865, and in this year the first Bessemer works were set up in America. The success of the London exhibition was very great.

So successful an invention is never left unattacked as regards the patent rights. But Bessemer was a very

Sᴇ

energetic fighter, who well understood how to stand up for himself. His aim of making himself and his family economically independent by an epoch-making invention was attained. But he was far removed from selling his soul into bondage to money. He resolved, in 1869—when fifty-six years of age—to free himself to such a degree from his great success as to be able to live his life undisturbed by compulsory daily labour. However, a Bessemer could not be idle, and so he attempted once more to solve a great problem. He suffered very badly from seasickness; a voyage from Dover to Calais could reduce him to despair. A particularly bad crossing caused him to make up his mind to put his whole technical powers to work in the endeavour to find a remedy. Once more he became an inventor on the grand scale. In 1869 he built a large circular saloon which was able to turn in all directions. He had a large flywheel as a gyro-stat, and arranged counterweights so that the whole circular saloon, with the people in it, did not follow the motion of the ship. This uncommonly ingenious construction, which revealed not only the inventor, but also the skilful engineer familiar with all the mechanical arts of his time, was first tested by Bessemer on small models, and then in a full-sized channel steamer which bore his name. When this work began he no longer had a drawing office. He went back to the drawing board himself, and, gifted draughtsman that he was, made all the constructional drawings. The steamer was built at a very considerable cost. He devotes a whole chapter of his autobiography to this work. But the steamer was dogged by misfortune. It twice collided with the pier at Calais, and was badly damaged. Bessemer was most anxious to make it clear that this had nothing to do with his construction. In five minutes he had lost £34,000, and these few minutes had robbed him, so he thought, of one of the greatest successes of his long professional life. He wanted to render sufferers from seasickness a great service. But the practical realization was denied him, and this was a great blow to him as inventor and engineer. But feeling his responsibility towards himself and his family he was too clear-headed a man of business to stake the whole fortune he had earned on further experiments.

Continuing his technical work, he fitted up for his grandchildren a new form of diamond-cutting plant. Like Nasmyth and other great engineers, he was a lover of the stars, and built large astronomical telescopes. He also conceived a furnace constructed with concave mirrors, so as to use the heat of the sun. He was no longer concerned with taking out patents and earning money, but worked at these things for the sheer joy in technical matters. His house, land, and garden in Charlton had been exchanged for a much greater and more wonderful property on Denmark Hill. This house with its farm, meadows, and garden lay so near to his heart that his children looked upon it as an inseparable part of their father's life. He took the greatest joy in the internal decoration and furnishing of his house, and was always seeking new departures in the taste of his time. This joy in constructive work extended also to the homes of his children. He was always glad to be able to help them in this respect, and find an outlet for his own sense of beauty. Living the happiest of lives with his family, he attained the age of eighty-five. He was able to witness the further great advances made in the iron and steel industry, and to recognize them by the Bessemer medal which he endowed for the Iron and Steel Institute.

He died on March 15th, 1898. When one surveys Bessemer's life history, one sees that a self-willed nature, which is unwilling always to accept the advice of the superior person, is often the precursor of great achievement. To standardize heads such as these, to limit them, and to discourage their dislike of unthinking assent, is to waste the most valuable heritage of a nation.

SYDNEY GILCHRIST THOMAS
1850–1885

In 1869, Bessemer had retired from business. He was to be granted a long evening to his life. In his retirement, he was able to witness the enormous development of his process in the seventies, the great success of his young compatriot Sydney Gilchrist Thomas, who by lining the Bessemer converter with basic material, removed the great obstacle in the way of the Bessemer process, its limitation to ores free from phosphorus. Since ores containing phosphorus are ten times more common than those free from it, this invention was of the greatest importance, especially for Germany.

Ridding iron of phosphorus was a problem on which the iron and steel experts of a great number of countries were working most industriously, but once more it was an outsider whose genius solved the problem in the simplest possible manner. Sydney Gilchrist Thomas was born in April, 1850, in Canonbury (Battersea), London. He wished to enter the medical profession. His father died just as he was about to begin his studies, and he had to provide for his mother and sister. He became clerk at a London police court, and was able to devote himself to his beloved science only in his spare time. His preference was for chemistry, and when a professor was telling his audience about the great problem of the dephosphorization of iron, the young clerk suddenly saw his life work in front of him. He studied methodically all that had been published about the experiments hitherto made. He wrote many articles for a technical journal about questions of iron smelting and learned a great deal himself by this work. In the person of his cousin, Percy C. Gilchrist, an ironworks chemist in Wales, he gained a collaborator with practical training, who carried out for him the fundamental experiments.

The first patent was granted in March, 1877. In March,

1878, Thomas, now twenty-eight years old, gave a modest account of the results so far obtained to a meeting of the Iron and Steel Institute. He showed that his results agreed with the theory on which his work was based, and that one might hope that the technical difficulties had been overcome. But how could so young a man, known to no one, have been able to do more than the most famous men in the profession ? With somewhat weary resignation, his short account was listened to. At the end of the sitting the incident was long forgotten. But Thomas was not to be deterred. He went on with his experiments, and found a complete solution of all difficulties. Important new patents were taken out in 1878 and 1879, and a year later no one could deny the great success that had been attained.

Thomas received, as the highest distinction possible from professional circles, the Bessemer gold medal, which was handed to him by Bessemer himself. Riches came with world-wide fame, but neither in any way affected his love of science or the essential modesty of his nature. Serious disease soon threw a shadow on his life. Travelling in warm countries was not able to arrest the consumption from which he was suffering, and he died quietly in Paris, at the age of thirty-four, on February 1st, 1885.

WERNER VON SIEMENS
1816–1892

Engineers first began in the nineteenth century to make use of electricity on a large scale for technical purposes. In this way they conquered a new and great field of work. First the electric current was used successfully for the transmission of news. But in the last third of the century, powerful currents began to be used for the provision of light and power. The electric current soon penetrated all branches of technical work, and had a decisive influence on their development.

One of the great electrotechnical pioneers of Germany was Werner Siemens, who rose to world fame in his province of work. We see in him the great inventor, the learned investigator, the great engineer, the daring industrialist, the far-sighted organizer, and last but not least the warm-hearted master, who had a powerful influence on his contemporaries as a 'source of abounding genius and kindly realism.'

The greater the man, the stronger and more evident become the links joining him to his environment, and allowing him to exert a directing influence far beyond his time. The life of the individual is closely bound up with ancestry and posterity, by cause and effect, with all the process of events. Great men live in their influence and their thoughts far beyond the end of their earthly existence, and thus become a valuable possession of their nation, and we ought to learn to cultivate the memory of them to an increasing degree.

The Siemens family has been at home in the heart of Germany for centuries. The history of the family takes us to the old town of Goslar. The ancestors can be traced back without a break to 1538. The Siemens were farmers, but were already taking part in commercial ventures; they ran oil- and corn-mills, and also mines. Soon some members of the family took to the learned professions, but the chief profession remained agriculture.

The father of Werner Siemens, born in 1787 the youngest of fifteen children, was a farmer. On December 13th, 1816, the fourth child, Ernst Werner Siemens was born on the estate of Leuthe on the Benther Berg near Hanover. Here Werner Siemens passed the first happy years of his childhood. But the father, a passionate friend of a great and strong Germany, felt less and less at home in the 'Royal British Province of Hanover,' as the land of the Lower Saxons was called at the time. To this was added the necessity for increasing his income to meet the demands of his increasing family. So he exchanged Leuthe for the Domain of Meuzendorf in Mecklenburg-Strelitz.

The time soon came when a career for Werner Siemens had to be decided upon. A learned profession was excluded, for languages would be needed for it, and Siemens was no friend of grammatical rules. He sought for a practical profession allied to science and mathematics, and thus went into technical work. But at that time technical work meant chiefly civil engineering. The engineers who built roads, bridges, canals, and harbours, or were employed in leading positions, received at least some meed of respect as compared with the honour paid to the learned. The Berlin *Bauakademie* would have been the place for training, but the profession was too dear for the parents. In the meantime, Werner Siemens had already replaced the study of ancient Greek by mathematics and surveying, and his teacher in these subjects, a former Prussian officer of artillery, advised him to enter the Prussian Engineers' Corps. He would learn there, he said, about the same things as at the *Bauakademie*.

So at Easter 1834, Werner Siemens, seventeen years of age, started on his march to Berlin, to the city that was to become his home. He went on foot through the sandy Mark with youthful joy in his heart, to meet a great future. But he learned from the chief of the Engineers that they had not been waiting for the seventeen-year-old boy from Mecklenburg. Everything was full up; he was told to go to the artillery; the officers would receive just as good training there as in the Engineers. So off he went on foot again to Magdeburg, for there was no railway in Germany in those days. Here also the prospects were at first very poor. Only four applicants out of fifteen could be taken, explained the commandant, and he would take those who did best in the examination. But Werner Siemens passed. The King of Prussia by a special Order in Council gave him the right as a foreigner to serve in Prussia, and his father bought him free from military service.

Werner Siemens learned to appreciate strict Prussian military training. But it was the technical side of the profession which gripped him most strongly. He was transferred in the autumn 1835, to the United Engineers and Artillery School in Berlin, and there he was able to acquire methodically both scientific and technical knowledge. Werner Siemens looked upon these first three years in Berlin as laying a foundation for his whole life. The cheerful comradely intercourse with men of his own age, and the stimulus of distinguished teachers assisted his studies, to which he applied himself with enthusiasm. Every free hour was devoted to mathematics, physics, and chemistry, which he called his favourite sciences.

In autumn, 1840, he was transferred to Wittenberg, and in this time produced his first successful invention. He became acquainted with the work of Professor Jacobi—at that time in Dorpat, later in St. Petersburg—on the new subject of galvanoplasty, and he wanted to coat articles not only with copper, but also with gold and silver. 'To my unspeakable delight,' he writes in his autobiography, 'the experiments were surprisingly successful. I think it was the greatest joy of my life when a German silver teaspoon, which I connected to the zinc pole of a Daniell cell and dipped in a beaker filled with a solution of hyposulphite of gold, while the copper of the cell was connected to a louis d'or as anode, became changed in a few minutes into a spoon of purest shining gold.' He experienced for the first time the profound satisfaction of the discoverer and inventor. He sold the rights of the process to a Magdeburg jeweller, who had hastened to the Citadel on hearing a rumour of the wonderful event, for 40 louis d'or, which enabled him to go on with his experiments. He got time for this in Magdeburg. He was soon transferred to Spandau to the firework department, for his superior officer was now convinced of his special gift for technical work. Here also he did successful work. But his following transference to the artillery workshop in Berlin was specially important for him, for there he was able to continue his studies methodically.

Siemens' life in Berlin, in those years when he settled down there, was unusually stimulating. Beuth, the great Prussian industrialist, the Westphalian Egells, who had founded there a great machine works, and above all Borsig, with his reputation extending far beyond Prussia, were all there.

Another group of great importance for Siemens was formed by a number of young scientists who founded the Physical Society in 1845, Siemens being an active member of it from the start. While in this circle he was in search of scientific stimulus. He also frequented the Society for the Advancement of Industry, founded in 1821 by Beuth, and the Polytechnic Society, founded in 1839, in order to get acquainted with the technical side of industry. Receiving and giving ideas, he regarded the work of these societies as of great value for his development. But Werner Siemens always readily recognized also how greatly his path in life had been smoothed by his career as an officer in the military and bureaucratic Prussian State of those times.

Werner Siemens, whose parents had less and less to spare for the education of his brothers and sisters, had to help in this. He therefore sought with ever-increasing energy for new ways to get money by working out new ideas. The Technical Deputation in Berlin had granted him in 1842 a patent for a process for dissolving gold by the galvanic current in the wet way for the purpose of gilding; the duration of the patent was five years. He succeeded in negotiating the patent financially in Berlin. His brother William helped him with the work. Werner thus got the idea of sending his brother to England, in order to negotiate the invention there. William asked no less than £3,000, and succeeded in getting one half of this. This was a gigantic sum for the brother, who was struggling with debt.

This lucky deal raised visions of mountains of gold in the brothers' heads; William, on his return from England, was no longer content to live in so modest a place as Magdeburg. He soon returned to England, which became his second home, and at the same time an extremely important member of the world-wide Siemens group. He wanted to negotiate a whole lot of new inventions. But the two brothers soon recognized that speculation in inventions is not the surest way to get on in the world. Even Werner, who had taken six weeks' leave in order to help his brother, and went to England in 1844 for the first time, could not compel success. But he came back to Berlin via Paris full of new stimuli.

Ever new plans and ideas in overwhelming abundance came rushing into his mind. The danger of dissipating his energies, of losing himself, became very great. But the mental freshness and elasticity with which he took up the thousands of suggestions, weighed them, and passed them on, is remarkable.

He was interested in the hot-air engine, which at that time was creating enormous excitement in the technical world. Success was not obtained, but interest in these ideas then led his brother Friederich to the regenerative furnace, an invention of first-rate technical importance. William wanted to form a large company to build railways in Germany, but Werner regarded railway speculation as too daring. 'Much experience is needed for it, if one is to be certain of not making a fool of oneself.' Werner was busy trying to make use of guncotton, invented by Schönbein in Basel, for military purposes. The problem seemed solved, but then, as so often happens, great difficulties began to crop up. There could be no thought of replacing gunpowder generally by guncotton; but the latter was excellent for blasting. Anyhow, Werner in this way gained his end, which was to remain in Berlin. Werner and William were already considering at that time the possibility of using guncotton in an explosion engine, and they hoped to make engines so small in weight that by their help 'the never-to-be-forgotten flying' might be possible.

Werner Siemens' numerous technical investigations had naturally led to his having close connections with first-rate mechanics in Berlin. In the technical societies, and the workshops of machine builders, he soon learnt the problems of electric telegraphy, then just coming into being. He also learned that the General Staff was having experiments carried out with a view to replacing optical telegraphy by electrical. The very difficulties to be overcome now took hold of Siemens. He found satisfactory solutions for them, and was able to make his invention, by simple devices, clear to the young mechanic Halske, whom he had met at the Physical Society, so that the latter was ready to use his technical powers for the problem. Werner Siemens hereby took a step nearer to the first great task of his life. He became a technical pioneer of telegraphy.

Anyone who desires justly to estimate the achievements of men who have pointed out new technical paths, must attempt to forget a great deal that is taken for granted to-day. Miracles cease to be miracles when they become everyday affairs, and what at one time set the hearts of the greatest inventors and discoverers beating more quickly, is finally taken over as a matter of course into the school curriculum. Hence only history can give us a measure by which we can make a just estimate of great achievements.

The nineteenth century is remarkable for a leap forward in the development of transport. Mankind is learning, in a manner never before dreamed of, to conquer space. Steamships, railways, and telegraphy become the emblems of the new age. We have to remember that it took fourteen days for the news of the death of Frederick the Great to get from Potsdam to Karlsbad, where Goethe at the time was taking a cure, and that the people of Berlin only learned of the taking of Paris in 1814 nine days after this event in world history. How great had to be the change in the world, when the transmission of news was successfully revolutionized by electricity. The electric telegraph has made a small town of the world, in which one may learn at once what one's neighbour is doing.

Distinguished men had worked in this field before Werner Siemens. The famous Göttingen professors Gauss and Weber had been the first to set up a permanent telegraphic connection in Göttingen.

The electric telegraph aroused interest, in the first place, in railway and military authorities. The first great German railway, Leipzig to Dresden, had applied to Göttingen in 1836 for information concerning the use of the telegraph for ensuring safety on railways. In Berlin, the Prussian General Staff was keenly interested in its use for military purposes. Already on July 15th, 1846, Werner Siemens was writing to his brother about his telegraph. Here again he was ahead of his time. Great difficulties had to be overcome, but he recognized that there was a life work of a very promising character in the problem. He was tired of inventing all sorts of things, and was longing for fundamental work, for a great goal to aim at. On December 14th, 1846, he wrote to William that he was determined to make a solid career for himself in telegraphy, either in or out of the army. Werner Siemens was thirty years old. 'One must after all try finally to get a firm footing somewhere.' He threw himself into the work with fiery zeal. He gave lectures on telegraphy to the Chief of the General Staff, and to the Polytechnic Society, and was able to report that 'my principle has proved an excellent one, and I have every hope that it will beat all others.' He was able to send about forty letters a minute. But he was very soon writing: 'the first instrument is useful as a rule only for one's own study, a fact I have very good reason to know ! Don't let us rush matters, we must go ahead slowly.'

This apparatus had not only to be thought out, it had to be made. Here also Siemens was resolved to be independent.

The mechanic Halske, two years older than himself, was ready to start a works with him. He was to manage it, Siemens was to see to building the lines and dealing with the outside world. In 1847, the world-firm of Siemens and Halske came into being. For the time being it was decided to manufacture only needle telegraphs, sounders for railways, and wire insulated with gutta-percha, using the gutta-percha press invented by Siemens. On October 11th, 1847, Werner Siemens was able to report that he had found a house and workshop at No. 19, Schönebergerstrasse. This undertaking begun in a small and modest way was to become in course of time one of the greatest in the world.

Tireless industry is necessary to apply scientific methods to great technical purposes, and to overcome the great difficulties inherent in new technical development. All great creation of a new form is art. Without imagination, great creative work is unthinkable. Imagination is not the special property of poets and artists. Imagination in technical work is a subject well worthy of discussion, but it seems self-evident that the men who turn fairy tales into reality must have the imagination possessed by those who tell the fairy tales. Imagination is the power of foresight, of recognizing possibilities of development. From this springs the courage to overcome difficulties. There arises a firm belief in the great future of an idea, without which it is not possible to achieve great things. But imagination has to go hand in hand with critical understanding in order that phantasy may not degenerate into the fantastic. Hard facts prevent him who is intent on working out an idea in a practical form from overestimating the value of the mere idea.

Werner Siemens' life history conditions the attitude which he takes up towards invention and inventors. 'Ideas in themselves,' he writes on one occasion, 'have only a very limited value. The value of an invention lies in its practical realization, in the mental labour put into it, in the work and money spent on it.' And in another place, 'It is a long and hard road from a successful experiment to a useful and well-tried mechanism, a road on which ninety-nine per cent of inventions break their necks.' And again on another occasion, 'Inventive activity will only be useful and sure of success when working in close connection with manufacture, for the purpose of solving questions actually presenting themselves for solution. A spontaneously made invention may of course in rare cases be directly successful, but that is just about the same as winning a large prize in a lottery On the other hand, innumerable able and talented persons come to grief over inventions which are not firmly founded on practical work.' 'Useful and valuable inventions,' he writes, 'are not made in the way described, but are the result, forcing itself unsought upon one, of ripe experience and tireless labour, resting on the firm ground of interrogating nature by experiments conducted with a knowledge of natural laws. . . . "Genius" fights its way out, if it only sticks to the paths of conscientious work and keeps free from illusions. The illusion of invention is the great enemy of sound progress and of the inventor himself, and it seems to me a useful task for the writer to combat it, and to warn people against chasing after inventions !' He himself took up this task, and in answer to numerous enquiries from strangers concerning the exploitation and valuation of inventions, he always gave expression to this idea with extraordinary conscientiousness; he was again and again angered at the way even very able men strove after inventions for which he felt it impossible to promise success.

At one place in his memoirs, he gives an extremely vivid description of the joys and miseries of inventors, when he writes: 'When a law of nature hitherto only dimly sensed suddenly appears clearly out of the mist, when the key has been found to a mechanical combination long sought in vain, when the missing link in a chain of thought fits neatly into place, the inventor has the uplifting emotion of a mental victory won, which in itself is full compensation for all the hardships of the struggle, and raises him for a moment into a higher sphere of existence. True, the delirium of joy is not for long. Self-criticism usually quickly finds a dark spot in the discovery, which makes the truth of it doubtful, or at least limits it greatly. A fallacy is revealed by which one had been deceived, or else, as is unhappily almost invariably the case, the fact appears that only an old thing in a new form has been discovered. Only when strict self-criticism has left untouched a sound kernel, does the real hard work of developing and carrying out the invention start, followed by the struggle, in which most come finally to grief, to introduce it into scientific or technical life. Thus discovery and invention bring with them hours of the highest enjoyment, but also hours of the greatest disappointment, and of hard and fruitless work.' In his letters to his brother he writes: 'The instinct for investigation is a curious business. It acts like a passion, overcomes all hindrances, and suppresses with fury all other interests. A successful experiment brings more joy than the winning of thousands.' The final conclusion of his memoirs is put by him into the following words: 'To make one's future by invention is hard and bitter work, that has taken but few to their goal, and has been the downfall of innumerable people.' This all leads to his attitude towards inventors themselves, who, as already remarked, approached him again and again, and whose ideas he attempted conscientiously to test, as far as was possible for him, in regard to their practical value.

But imagination is also essential to large industrial undertakings. It is particularly fascinating to watch him allowing his imaginative ideas to range over unlimited possibilities. Scarcely does he start to interest himself in the electric telegraph, scarcely has he put together his first primitive apparatus, before he sees, as though by some power of clairvoyance, all possibilities in concrete form. The thing desired becomes reality.

A sharp rejection on his part of criticism which he

regarded as unjust led to a break with the Prussian Telegraph Administration, and forced him to seek other markets. His destiny took him to Russia. The Crimean War called for the quickest possible transmission of news from St. Petersburg to the theatre of war. The immensely long lines necessary in this case led to a rapid and brilliant commercial impetus for their maker, who had to build the first great overland lines in the world.

Siemens learned to measure the world in terms of 'telegraphic distances.' His ideas very soon ranged over all parts of the inhabited earth. He thought of China, Africa, America, and Australia, but amid all this making of plans he never forgot to fulfil the duties of the day. He was never one to let the bird in the hand go on account of the one in the bush. But his lively mind needed a view of wide horizons. It was a recreation for him to look into the future. The joy in new things gives his spirit that wonderful elasticity which he was able to retain into old age. It is true that anyone who measures the deeds of great men only by the money values gained or lost will find much to blame in his case, and it will not be hard to find proofs that by a stricter limitation of his energies to a narrower field, he might frequently have done more than he did. But in that case Werner Siemens would not have been Werner Siemens, and it is just this power of enthusiasm for new tasks, this yielding to the grip of new ideas, that brings him nearer to us as a human being, and also makes his life so valuable for the future of our nation. The efficiency of the working of great human minds is not to be measured like that of machines.

But let us turn back to our short account of his life story. At thirty-three years of age, on June 12th, 1849, Werner Siemens took leave of a military career after fourteen years of service. He did not find it easy to go, but the careers of a Prussian officer and of a Berlin industrialist could not be rolled into one. New and great technical problems were being continually thrust upon him. His technical scientific work took him beyond the day's work. The business soon extended far beyond the frontiers of Prussia. He was helped in Russia by his brother Karl, the English branch was upheld by William Siemens. Werner Siemens went through the war of 1866 in full recognition of its meaning for Germany's future. Thus was promoted the longing for a united Greater Germany. 'This high mood,' writes Werner Siemens, 'made itself felt by increased activity in all fields of life, and was not without its reaction on our commercial work.'

A number of pieces of military technical work, among which was an electrically steered boat carrying explosive charges, fall in that period. But he rightly puts in the foreground his work on the dynamo; he had, in 1855, invented the H armature, one of its most important constituents. The dynamo was born in a telegraph works. It was first built by instrument makers, and the machine constructor of the time found it hard at first to get accustomed to seeing in this physical apparatus a real machine. On January 17th, 1867, Werner Siemens gave in the Academy of Sciences in Berlin his famous lecture 'On the transformation of work into Electric Current without the use of Permanent Magnets.' He closed his remarks with the prophetic words: 'The technical means are now available for producing electric currents of unlimited strength in a simple and cheap manner anywhere where power is available.' He added modestly, 'This fact will probably be of some importance in several fields.'

The letters of the brothers during the first year of the dynamo tell us much that is significant regarding the beginning of that great invention. Hopes were chequered by disappointments. Siemens found helpers, one of the most distinguished being von Hefner-Alteneck. First the current was to be used for electric lighting. Soon a 'really terrible lighting uproar,' as Werner Siemens called it, began to occur everywhere. The glow-lamp came from America. Edison created this new system of electric lighting, and

Werner Siemens recognized quite clearly its great future. 'The glow-lamp will probably soon kill all others and open up to electricity a much greater field of application !' Cheap and high-quality manufacture was the chief thing. The manufacture was started on a large scale. Very soon plans were on foot for lighting large towns by electricity. 'With the glow-lamp all is now possible.' Work now began on a great scale for the introduction of electric lighting.

But Werner Siemens did not stop at that. He very early saw that the transmission of power was the most important field of work in connection with electric current, and this estimate led to his pioneer work on electric railways. How far Siemens saw into the future may be judged from a letter of Professor Reuleaux, who tells in 1881 how Siemens was already talking to his friends at the Paris Exhibition in 1867 of the fact that railways in big towns could now be electrically driven, how one would send enormous electric power from the brown coal districts to Berlin; while the electric railway, in which he had believed from the start, was described by him in every detail. But many years had still to pass before 1879, when at the Berlin Industrial Exhibition, it was possible to ride in an electric train for the first time, and it was not until the beginning of the twentieth century that the electric overhead railways specially recommended by Werner Siemens could be realized.

Werner Siemens took no less interest in electrochemistry, and paid the greatest attention from the very first to the telephone. But his technical work was not confined to the electrotechnical side. Together with William, he went into iron production on a large scale. Specially characteristic of the mental vigour which was Werner Siemens' up to the last, was the way he took up the Mannesmann rolling process, which he promised would bring about 'a real revolution in rolling.' He was driven into this new work not by the desire once again to earn great wealth, nor from a desire for further increase in his firm's field of power, but solely for the satisfaction of working at a great new piece of technical progress. The peculiar, the completely new attracted him. Werner Siemens provided large sums of money. They were sacrificed, only to have the final conclusion emerge that the enormous hopes at first set on this process could not be realized. This technical achievement, like many others, was not spared a long period of growth.

A characteristic quality of Werner Siemens, which received expression here, was his activity and above all his tenacity in carrying out his plans. No need to be afraid of difficulties! They are there to be overcome! Fighting is his life. Worries make him, as he says, more industrious. 'Anyhow I believe,' he says, 'neither in ill fate nor in damnation, but only in wise and foolish action. Don't let us have everywhere the fatal words "It won't go." "I can't" is almost always the most that can be said.'

This sticking to what had been started was often by no means easy in the pioneer work in which he was engaged. A heavy price had to be paid for experience before success was attained. His contemporaries called this the Siemens obstinacy. It is true that once in his life he was brought up against a wall that could not be scaled, and he found it uncommonly hard to have in the end to turn back; in some cases he preferred to leave the turning back to his successors.

It is obvious that a man of Siemens' genius possessed a markedly strong temperament. Mommsen says somewhere in his classical biography of Caesar: 'It is self-evident that Caesar was a passionate man, for there is no genius without passion, but his passion was never stronger than himself.' Though anger might boil up in him very suddenly this temperament was joined to a firm determination not to do wrong. In the evening of his life, it was his especial satistion to be able to say that no outburst of anger had ever betrayed him into acts which he regretted later.

Werner Siemens was no man of compromises. When once one of his brothers thought that he could read reproaches between the lines of one of Werner's letters, the latter wrote to him, that if he must read between the lines, he should read only good there. 'I'm plain spoken when I'm rude.'

Very characteristic of him is his inward sincerity, his standing up for his opinions regardless of the consequences to himself. The latter was of course easier for him at the height of his success than at the beginning of his career, when he threw down his glove before Prussia, feeling that an injustice had been done to him.

This inward sincerity, which was a part of him, led him to do battle against some trade customs of his time. He attacked fiercely the belief, current at the time, that it was necessary to pass off good German wares as French or English, in order to be able to sell them, and that only bad mass-produced stuff could be openly sold as German. Never, he maintained, would German industry be successful along such lines. Germany must go in for work of high quality. At that time the opinion was widely held that machine work must in itself be and remain worse and less valuable than hand work. Whenever the opportunity arose, in lectures, in conversation, and in writing, Werner Siemens opposed this view. For this reason he attempted very early on to introduce modern machine tools into Germany, and he laid the greatest stress on the training of his work-people in special work. Werner Siemens gave his closest attention to the creation of a German patent law. He had already put forward a draft at the beginning of the sixties, which contains the foundations of the German law as it finally matured. He pointed out that in the state of affairs before the German patent law a premium was actually put upon the use without payment of the ideas of other people. But that, he said, was equivalent to an inward untruth, a lie, which no nation could permantly endure, if its moral health were not ultimately to suffer. He pointed out in detail what consequences had resulted in this way.

This inward honesty, this pride in getting ahead only by virtue of his own work, determined his position in commercial relations. In spite of all his technical and industrial daring, he energetically refused to have anything to do with what he called speculation. Making money without working was repulsive to him. Making money was not to him the object of existence. A mill that grinds out gold for one even when one is asleep, had no interest for him. 'No capitalistic speculative projects,' he writes in 1865 to his brother Karl, 'are suited to our nature or experience. We are not business people, we are inferior in that line to any common moneybag.' It is not his ambition to take the lead in business and commercial affairs. But he strove to keep the leadership in technical matters in his own hands and those of his family. He did not desire the reputation of a brilliant business man—which without doubt he was—he only wanted to be a pioneer in the technical sphere. He wanted to maintain and extend the confidence already given to him in technical questions. This confidence, which he enjoyed in full measure, was a source of great pride to him.

Werner Siemens was well aware that the success of his work was in a large degree dependent upon the excellence of the colleagues he was able to gather round him. His brothers were his closest colleagues. But besides them, he was fortunate to gain the services of a great number of distinguished men for the works which he created. He was always ready joyfully to acknowledge their achievements, and he often utters the warning that one must put up patiently with the darker side of the characters of great men, for without co-workers of high quality, one cannot accomplish one's tasks. 'My practice,' he writes, 'of treating all capable people in private intercourse as if they were my equals, and of discussing with them business matters in which they are concerned just as though they were their affairs as much as mine—a practice which as far as that goes is no merit of mine, for it is natural to me—has always proved to be very effective.' And in another place he says, 'Good organization is better than doubling dividends.' Again in another place, 'I see in the business a financial property only in the second place, it is for me an empire which I have founded, and which I would like to leave intact to my posterity, in order that they may continue to work in it.'

He had the good fortune to live to see his incessant creative activity come to success, and to foresee the further great development of it. Public acknowledgment of his success was not wanting. It is a unique fact that the three brothers were given titles in three different countries: Werner in Germany, William in England, Karl in Russia.

His fundamental recognition of the value of technical progress determined also his attitude towards the representatives of technology, the engineers. He frequently expressed the view that engineers should be at the head of his undertakings; they must naturally also have some commercial and administrative training, but the technical training is indispensable. He also required his electrotechnical staff to have a good general foundation in machine design. It is true that he advised the creation of special chairs for electrical engineering at the technical colleges; but his conviction that electricity was destined to conquer all technical fields led him to require all students to attend lectures on electrical engineering. 'Don't specialize too early! One's views are narrowed. Professional work supplies the necessary special knowledge. It would be a mistake to start specializing already at the technical college.'

He laid special stress upon a thorough knowledge of science and mathematics. He regretted that he himself had not devoted enough attention to higher mathematics. He saw in science the foundations of further technical progress. Physics and chemistry are to be thoroughly studied. But one should not imagine that one may stop learning on leaving school.

As a counterweight to the practical technical and industrial questions which filled his long day of work, he sought the company of men of science, who for their part received much stimulus from the close connection between scientific research and practical application, of which Siemens was the incarnation.

Siemens was likewise deeply conscious, as a result of his whole view of life, of the necessity for scientific research. He thus became the creator of the Physikalisch-Technische Reichsanstalt, which finds worthy collaborators in the institutes of the Kaiser-Wilhelm-Gesellschaft; it fulfils the purpose of the National Physical Laboratory in Great Britain. Its aim was to provide, independently of academic instruction at universities, well-equipped laboratories for scientific work by free research workers. Germany should make it her endeavour always to be a pioneer in science. Therein lay the foundation of further industrial development and so of that position as a world power which Siemens desired for Germany.

It is refreshing to see how firmly the man who founded a firm with world-wide power was rooted in his own people. The foundation of the State is the family. Werner Siemens always starts out from the family. It was not for himself but for his family that he desired to be the founder of an enterprise like that of the Fuggers. That was the dream of his youth. His life-work brought its fulfilment. His close relationship to his brothers is characteristic of his view of the family; it is also characteristic of the heavy responsibility which, thanks to the education given him by his parents, he accepted without question.

His early home life imbued him with the longing to see his German Fatherland united. It was his good fortune to live to see this dream fulfilled.

In the Hall of Honour of the Munich Museum, Werner von Siemens is given a place among the great men of science and technology. Under a marble bust of him by

Hilderbrandt, presented by the Verein deutscher Ingenieure, is the inscription:

'At once a man of science and an engineer, his was one of the first inventive minds to make the electric current serve human ends.'

But his great monument is his works, his life, as he describes it so vividly in his memoirs which he wrote in March, 1889. In them he gives us a testament, a demand, which is also a directive for our own time: 'It is not in possessions of any kind that now and in the future the forces upholding the State are to be found, but in the spirit which inspires and fructifies them. In order to preserve the State from impoverishment and decay, we need to-day the well-planned co-operation of all great intellectual forces, the preservation and development of which is one of the chief tasks of the modern state.'

NIKOLAUS AUGUST OTTO *and* EUGEN LANGEN
1832–1891 & 1833–1895

The internal combustion engine has attained in our time an undreamed-of importance for the motor car and aeroplane. Innumerable motors of this sort are working on land, in the air, and on the water. They provide energy for the greatest variety of purposes. The lives of Otto and Langen take us back to the early history of these motors.

The explosion engine may be traced back to the gunpowder engines which, as a result of Guericke's pioneer experiments on air pressure, came into existence at the end of the seventeenth century, in the attempt to make use of the external pressure of the air in the service of man. In the eighteenth century we find in English patents ideas concerning a gas turbine and an oil engine. But the solution was

34. WERNER VON SIEMENS (1816–92)

35. NIKOLAUS AUGUST OTTO (1832–91)   36. EUGEN LANGEN (1833–95)

first found in the nineteenth century. In the fifties a clock-maker, Christian Reithmann of Munich, invented an internal combustion motor, without, however, having any commerical success with it. An atmospheric gas engine built in 1857 by John Cockerill in Seraing, was also a failure. The French mechanic Lenoir was the first to produce a gas motor which did work, and began to come into practical use. The first practical gas engine was made as much as possible like steam engines then existing. Lenoir created great excitement. Once more the word went round that the steam engine had reached the end of its development. Steam, 'a hearty and obstinate fellow,' was said to be dying, to be on the point of giving way everywhere to a new form of prime mover. All newspapers printed exaggerated prophecies concerning the great future in store for the new source of power. It was said to be going to need only about 16 to 20 cub. ft. of gas per horse-power-hour, and would certainly have been able to deal a fatal blow to the steam engine of the time as regards its consumption of fuel.

A sheet of newspaper, filled with the most rosy prophecies of this sort, fell by chance upon the table of Nikolaus August Otto, and set going in the head of that young and modest small tradesman a train of thought that was to lead to great success.

Otto was born in the small town of Holzhausen in Nassau on June 14th, 1832. The boy grew up in humble circumstances; his father was a farmer and posthouse keeper. He went to the elementary school in his native place, and then to the secondary school in Langenschwalbach. He left school at sixteen, and his parents determined to put him into business. We know little of this period of his life. He was for three years in a merchant's office in Nastetten, and then went to Frankfort as an assistant, and from there he went to Cologne, which was to become his second home. He found modest positions in various firms of merchants, and no one yet—himself least of all—thought of the great future which was to be his. Here in Cologne, in the summer of 1861, at the age of twenty-nine, he got the first accounts of the Lenoir gas engine. The lyrical prophecies concerning its future excited him. Here was unexplored territory, and just as in the days of the great voyages of discovery, new pioneers were again and again incited to adventure by fantastic accounts of the riches lying in new and unknown countries, so in the history of technology, we see the same important part played by prospects of fame and riches.

Faith in a great future is necessary if all the hardships and disappointments which are the inevitable lot of any successful inventor, are to be overcome. Otto's whole mind was always directed to a single aim, that of inventing a gas engine capable of competing with the steam engine. His friends soon recognized how firmly this idea had taken hold of him, they feared for his future and advised him to concentrate on his profession. But Otto became more and more deeply involved in his scientific and technical studies. He had already had interests of this sort in his school days, but the amount of scientific material available to him was very small as compared with our present store. He read what he could get hold of, above all, he thought over his plans. His friends called him the 'thinker' (*Grübler*). He could get little positive information about the Lenoir machine. He went his own ways, built himself a small model, and at this point began to learn how long is the road from the idea to its realization. Though the experiments were a failure, he learned from them, and then had a real mechanic build him a small experimental machine. At the end of 1861, this little machine was finished, and was already working on the four-stroke cycle. Otto was near, with this first experimental machine, to the method of working upon which was founded the vast expansion of motor construction in the whole world at a later date. He had already recognized that the mixture must be compressed before ignition, that the explosion must occur at the dead point, and that intake, compression, and exhaust can be performed in one cylinder. But the explosions were at that time so forceful, that the method had to be given up for the time as hopeless.

But Otto wanted to produce a practicable small motor—he held on firmly to this purpose. He now sought to attain his ends by other means. He returned to the idea of the atmospheric explosion engine; the external air pressure was to do the work, and the explosive gas mixture was to create a partial vacuum under the piston. In this way the Otto atmospheric gas engine was produced, for which patent protection was obtained in England, Belgium, and France. Prussia refused protection to the 'petitioner.' But the way from this little experimental machine, even though it had run satisfactorily for some months, to a commercially practicable small prime mover, was a long one. At this point the Cologne engineer Eugen Langen joined him, and became of the greatest assistance to him.

The Langen family came from the Berg district. Its ancestors were village schoolmasters. One of their descendants changed his profession in 1816 for that of a commercial assistant in an old Solingen firm. He went ahead rapidly and worked his way up to a leading position in the industrial history of the Rhineland. In Cologne, a fifth son, Eugen Langen, was born to him on October 9th, 1833. He was very carefully educated, and had a decided taste for science but none for the dead languages. His final school report was not exactly brilliant. Langen only got a 'very good' for gymnastics. At seventeen he went to the Polytechnic in Karlsruhe, an institution ranking very highly among the schools of Germany. In Karlsruhe he was fortunate in finding teachers —chief among them being the Austrian Redtenbacher—who knew how to arouse the enthusiasm of their pupils for technical work. Langen repeatedly referred in later years with much gratitude to Redtenbacher's great personality. Langen looked upon it as great good fortune that he received in Karlsruhe a thorough grounding in mechanics and physics.

This solid foundation enabled him to become at home in all the new fields of work which in later life he had to develop.

During the holidays, and after his studies, Langen devoted himself with burning enthusiasm to practical work, and he testified later to the great value to him of this part of his work. Here also he got to know working men, and he was later renowned for his good understanding of his workers, and for his personal relations with them. He became aware of the great importance of the mentally developed, capable, and work-loving trained man for all industrial development. He very soon found occasion to make use of his great gifts as an inventor. He made fundamental improvements in furnaces, and did pioneer work in sugar manufacture. He made long journeys to Spain, England, and France in connection with his work as an engineer, and what he saw and learned there was of great value to him professionally. He followed as an engineer with the greatest interest, often far outside his own range of work, whatever was new and patentable in technical work. But Langen already knew while a young engineer how great an effort is necessary to travel the road from the idea to its industrial exploitation. His experiences were embodied by him in a little rhyme which he was fond of repeating:

> 'Be inventing ever
> An "inventor" never;
> Only work brings bread
> By which children are fed.'[1]

When Otto in Cologne was at that time eagerly seeking a man who could help him to carry out his inventive ideas, it was an obvious step to put him in touch with Langen. These two men, whose names will be linked for all time with the history of the internal combustion engine, made one another's personal acquaintance in February, 1864. Langen grasped the importance which a serviceable small motor would have

[1] 'Erfinde stets, doch werde kein Erfinder,
In Arbeit such dein Glück, sonst darben die Kinder.'

in industrial life; he saw also how far people yet were from this goal. But difficulties stimulated Langen. He determined to found with Otto a gas-engine firm. Above all, they wanted to sell as well as possible the patents which had been obtained. But it was soon seen how difficult it would be to fulfil this wish, and they realized that business prospects lay in selling not patents, but marketable engines. On March 31st, 1864, an agreement was signed by which the first gas-engine works, Nikolaus August Otto and Company, was founded. Langen was a shareholder, liable only to the extent of the 10,000 thalers which he put into the firm. Otto made over his patents to the Company, and was paid the expenses incurred for these to the amount of 541 thalers, 3 groschen. But Otto had spent altogether 3,000 thalers on his experiments, for he had had to borrow. These debts were also paid for him. As he now had to devote the whole of his energies to the new firm, he was allowed to draw 70 thalers a month from its funds for his personal needs. Such was the modest beginning, modest also in a financial sense, of a great development.

Langen also took a successful part in the further constructional development; he succeeded in overcoming the great difficulties connected with the transmission of power to the shaft by means of a remarkable design. The gas engine required much more accurate machine tools than those available at the time. Also, the skill of the workmen then obtainable in Cologne was far from sufficient. It almost seemed again as if the day of the gas engine had not yet dawned, as if it was not yet possible to carry out technical constructive ideas in iron and steel. Langen found it each time more difficult to raise more money for the work. He had married at the age of twenty-one, and his first son was born while he was doing his military service in the Cologne Pioneers. His family grew, and one may readily understand that his first thought was to provide for it. But finally, faith in the gas engine conquered once more, and at last an engine could be sold; but then the war of 1866 broke out, and no one could tell what was to come. The idea now came up that the atmospheric engine should be given the widest possible publicity by showing it at the Paris Exhibition in 1867, the place where Lenoir and Hugon had already aroused so much excitement with their gas engines. Langen was carrying on a regular correspondence with his former fellow-student and friend of his Karlsruhe days, Professor Reuleaux, who had now become a celebrated man. Reuleaux valued Otto's engine highly as against that of Lenoir on account of its much smaller consumption of gas and lubricating oil. Besides, he regarded it as being more reliable in its running. However, there was much about it that was capable of improvement. At the Paris Exhibition, fourteen French gas engines were shown, which were praised because they greatly resembled the steam engines of the time. Then there was the little atmospheric engine from Cöln-Deutz. It made a very loud noise with its piston shooting upwards by an explosion. The complicated mechanism worked out by Langen for the transmission also failed to give much satisfaction to experts. The jury hardly took any notice of this machine till Reuleaux, as German juryman, demanded very insistently that the machine should at least be tested. The test produced a great surprise. Otto's machine used hardly a third of the gas consumed by the French machines. That meant to say that small industries now had at their disposal a really cheap prime mover. These experiments caused the jury to award Otto and Langen the gold medal, while Lenoir had to be satisfied with the silver medal.

This decision aroused great attention; the whole technical Press reported it. Enquiry after enquiry, especially from France, came to Otto and Langen. Up to the end of August, 1867, twenty-two gas engines had been ordered: '22 machines, all of which go out as feelers into the world, no two to the same place,' Langen wrote at the time to a friend. Otto engines were now already going abroad, to Vienna, Budapest, even New York. Otto thought that they could have accepted three times as many orders if they had been able to deliver. But now money had to be found for the necessary extensions, for it was proposed now to employ fourteen men and nine boys.

Again and again the fact appeared that the firm was working at a loss. In spite of the great success at the Paris Exhibition, the whole undertaking was again in danger. There was still no question of a profit, and new sacrifices were necessary in the hope of making one later. Langen once more seriously considered whether he should give up the gas engine, and he also corresponded on this question with his friend Reuleaux. The latter found the right words to strengthen Langen's courageous determination to hold out. This historically interesting letter of February 2nd, 1868, runs: 'What I desire and beg is that you should hold out, if the financial position allows of it, which of course I cannot judge. After all, matters have reached a point at which this machine has won out. A great success has been obtained. If you give up what has been won, the profit is gone as well as—fame, to put it shortly. Sacrifices have always had to be made for the ideal in the history of development in all branches. They alone lift one to the position accorded by contemporaries and posterity to those who have made great gifts to the world. When I lecture on, write about, explain the history of the steam engine and other machines, your engine occurs to me a hundred times, and I feel for you the respect due to one destined to be of those who by industry and self-sacrificing exertion have finally produced something of great excellence, of use to all and earning the gratitude of all. Imagine yourself living fifty years after our time, with the gas engine flourishing as in our day the steam engine ! Think of that ! Are you still hesitating ?' There was now no further question of hesitation; Langen raised more money, a new firm was founded in which Langen's name had first place. It was now decided to start the works in Deutz near Cologne, and it is there building internal combustion engines to-day on a great scale. It was thus that, in 1869, the gas engine was given its own home. The Franco-Prussian war of 1870 brought new unrest and uncertainty, but its favourable conclusion for Germany gave her industry a mighty impetus. It was now decided to turn the firm into a limited company, in order to enlarge still further the working capital. On January 5th, 1872, the 'Gasmotoren-Fabrik Deutz Aktiengesellschaft' was founded with a capital of 300,000 thalers in 1,500 shares.

Langen saw clearly that the new factory would have need of a first-rate engineer with large manufacturing experience. He succeeded in acquiring the services of Gottlieb Daimler, who later made for himself an immortal name in the history of the motor car. He was given a considerable share in the profits, and all his conditions were agreed to. Langen wrote to him at the time: 'Not because of your signature, but because I think that the right field for your future work is with us, do I hope that the bridge over which you could go back into the old camp is broken down behind you.' Daimler, a Suabian, brought with him another young engineer, Maybach, who developed in Deutz into a first-class engineer. Daimler understood how to make use of every advantage in manufacture; again and again he came with new ideas and improvements designed to lessen the cost of construction. At the same time, prices were successfully raised, and the time had come at last when a profit was being made.

Otto was still working on the business side along with Daimler. He had had a raised platform built in the middle of the works, still a small concern. There he sat and kept the books industriously and conscientiously like a well-trained bookkeeper. He was happy to be able to observe from his perch the busy activity around him. But his heart was in that corner of the works where he had partitioned off an experimental room, safe from prying eyes. The habit of cogitating over new ideas, the tenacious pursuit of all sorts of improvements had become a necessity for him.

He now attempted to make a methodical study of other inventions in his own line. Machines which showed signs of being competitive were bought, and carefully investigated in the works. The desire was to learn if the claims made for them were fulfilled. It was thus that the firm's excellent museum was founded.

Daimler understood how to develop mass production. Up to October 1st, 1872, 700 small gas engines had been built. It was felt to be a nuisance that the gas engine was always dependent on the gas works, and so a search for other forms of fuel soon began to be made. Reuleaux suggested at the time to Langen that he should make use of petroleum residues. He had made in Vienna the acquaintance of a certain Marcus, who was making gas from these residues. In 1875 engines had already been driven in Deutz on benzene. As soon as success was obtained in running engines on liquid fuel, it was possible to think of using the internal combustion motor in vehicles. Langen had already attempted, in 1872, to drive a tramcar in Liége by a gas engine.

The great disadvantage of the atmospheric gas engine very soon proved to be its low power. It was hardly possible to go beyond 3 h.p. What a business would be possible, if this drawback could be overcome ! Otto himself was continually busy with new constructive ideas. He returned to his first notion, and now succeeded in building a horizontal four-stroke engine, which was protected by the famous patent No. 532 of August 4th, 1877. The construction was further developed; new patents were added. The next step was to design and build a marketable engine. Langen thought quite rightly that the machine should be made with the greatest care. A letter of date November, 1876, tells us that the 8-h.p. machine had run for the first time, 'so elegantly and beautifully that it would have given an angel joy to watch it.' It was now hoped to displace steam engines completely in towns by gas. But development did not stand

UE

still; again and again the call was for more work to fulfil the increased demands made on the machine in the matter of output, reliability, and economy.

The great success of the gas engine set other engineers working in this field. The patent for 'Otto's new motor,' which covered both four-stroke and two-stroke working, was soon felt to be an impenetrable obstacle. This pioneer invention thus experienced the same fate as others, the patent was attacked, and the leading men were hard put to it to defend their claims. A great patent action was fought with Gebrüder Körting in Hanover, which attracted attention for years afterwards in much wider circles than those of the firms actually concerned. It is obvious that the opponents of the patent went most carefully into the historical development of the invention. In France there was found a publication of which only a few copies had been printed, and of which no notice had been taken. Even the little modest machine of Reithmann, the clock-maker of Munich, came in for a certain degree of fame. These struggles were uncommonly bitter for Otto and Langen. Otto, the inventor, regarded his personal honour as attacked. The claims of his opponents seemed to him to be an attempt to rob him of his property in his ideas. The patent was upheld in England, but the chief claim was quashed in Germany in 1886.

People were free to build gas engines, all sorts of constructions were out on the market, most of them to disappear very quickly. The gas engine works at Deutz had now to keep its position in its own field of work in competition with other firms. The great energy of its leading men enabled it to fight in free competition, and to keep its pride of place in the industry. New tasks were not wanting. Above all, there was the problem of running engines on liquid fuel.

Marine engines were built, it was hoped to fit locomotives with internal combustion engines, and the motor car was also considered. But it was not given to Otto and Langen to live to see this great development. On January 26th, 1891, Otto died, one of the great German technical pioneers, whose tireless industry had produced fruits of permanent value. He was personally extremely modest and retiring, and sought always to avoid all external marks of respect as far as possible. The spirit of true comradeship with his collaborator remained unbroken to the last. 'He was always my best friend,' he said on the day of his death. Eugen Langen survived his friend by only four years. Death took him on October 2nd, 1895, after a short illness, out of the wide circle of his activities. We have seen how his work as an engineer and industrialist reached far beyond the internal combustion motor. He founded with Guilleaume in the early electrotechnical days a works for electric lighting installations, which he linked up with J. S. Schuckert in Nürnberg. It may be recollected that the idea of the suspended railway, such as was realized in Barmen and Elberfeld, was his. He also put his great powers of work freely at the disposal of the community, he always was a willing adviser of his town, and, as President of the Verein deutscher Ingenieure, he placed his services gladly at the disposal of his professional colleagues. He was also an active member of industrial and commercial societies. He exercised with Werner Siemens an important influence on German patent law. He was a firm upholder of German colonial expansion.

In Munich, in the Hall of Honour of the Museum, there are bas-reliefs of Otto and Langen. The inscription is as follows:

'To the great inventor and celebrated engineer, the world owes the first decisive advances in the field of internal combustion engines. In collaboration, they laid the foundations of the enormous industrial application of explosion engines, which resulted in the development of the motor car and aeroplane.'

When Henry Ford some years ago visited the wonderful Museum in Deutz, he and his companions contemplated thoughtfully 'Otto's new motor.' He asked his American collaborators to look with reverence at this humble little engine, for it was the father of all the innumerable motors driving Ford cars in the world to-day.

GOTTLIEB DAIMLER *and* WILHELM MAYBACH
1834–1900 & 1846–1929

Motor-driven vehicles of all sorts are travelling to-day in vast numbers on the roads of the world. Their number is estimated at nearly forty millions. In the United States, there is one motor car to every five members of the population. The power-driven vehicle provides work and bread for millions. Millions live by motor traffic and all that goes with it, from good roads to the production and distribution of oil and fuel. The motor car is an inseparable element of contemporary history. It is waste of time to search for its 'true and first inventor.' The automobile of our day is the product of whole generations of first-class engineers. In technical work, no Athene ever springs, complete in every detail, from the head of Zeus. And this development is a matter of hardly half a century. The end of the nineteenth century brought the first successes, very modest as compared with to-day, but only in our century has the motor car acquired the importance so obvious now to all of us. This success is due to the step-by-step development of the internal combustion engine.

The engineer Gottlieb Daimler, who as we saw did so much for the success of the Otto gas engine, was the creator of the high-speed explosion engine. The first decisive experiments were carried out in the south-west corner of Germany by three German engineers. In Stuttgart-Cannstatt, Gottlieb Daimler was working with Wilhelm

Maybach, while in Ludwigshafen-Mannheim, Carl Benz was engaged in the same quest.   But long before Daimler was born, men were thinking of driving vehicles by motors. In 1769, an artillery officer from Lorraine, Nicolas Joseph Cugnot, had already built a power-driven carriage at the cost of the French Government.   He had as little success as the many inventors who followed him.   English engineers then succeeded, early in the nineteenth century, in developing the steam carriage, but the railway, developed simultaneously, drove it from the field.   Hence when Daimler was born, the first chapter in the history of power-driven road carriages was closed.   It was the explosion engine that led to the revival of the automobile.   In the fine Technical Museum for industry and trade in Vienna, there is a carriage built by Siegfried Marcus in 1875, driven by a benzene motor.   After a few trial runs, the Viennese police forbade its use 'on account of the great noise.'   The inventor, busy with other ideas, made no further attempt at the commercial development of his machine.

On March 17th, 1834, a second son, Gottlieb, was born to Johannes Daimler, a master baker, in Schorndorf near Stuttgart.   He went to the public elementary school, and then for two years to the 'Latin School,' for the father wanted to make his son into a municipal employee with the right to a pension.   But young Daimler would have nothing to do with the idea.   His friend was the son of a master gunsmith, and so he much preferred the life of a gunsmith to that of a clerk in an office.   Gottlieb Daimler was apprenticed for three years to the trade of gunmaker. His *Gesellenstück* (the piece of work by which he graduated as a journeyman) consisted of two double-barrelled pistols with wonderfully chiselled steel mountings.   In his work he was continually practising drawing.   He had so great a joy in making pictures, that he drew not only machines, but also plants and animals.

Daimler then continued his training first in Stuttgart and

then in Alsace, where he was chiefly concerned with machine-tool construction. He had saved money, and so was able to go to the Polytechnic in Stuttgart from 1857 to 1859, an institution out of which the present Technical High School has developed. In Stuttgart he made the acquaintance of Friedrich Voith of Heidenheim, Max Eyth, Adolf Gross and many other famous engineers. Ferdinand von Steinbeis, who did such great service to the development of the industry of Württemberg, enabled him by means of a grant of money to work for years abroad, especially in England, as mechanic, foreman, and manager. When he came back he worked finally in Württemberg as manager of the workshops of the firm of machine builders Bruderhaus in Rentlingen, at that time highly esteemed.

It was here that he made the acquaintance of his future collaborator, Wilhelm Maybach, who was born on February 9th, 1846, son of a master carpenter in Heilbronn. He became an orphan at ten, and was taken into the orphanage. Young Maybach wanted to become a machine builder. Endowed with manual skill inherited from his father, very gifted at drawing and mathematics, and uncommonly industrious, he became the youthful collaborator of Gottlieb Daimler, who was twelve years older. When Daimler later took over the management of a concern in Karlsruhe, he engaged young Maybach a year later, in 1869, for his drawing office. Daimler, as we saw, went from there to Otto and Langen in Deutz. There he worked for ten years as technical director, from 1872 to 1882, at the design and construction of the Deutz gas engines. He also took Maybach, an unusually gifted engineer, with him to Cologne. Daimler while in Deutz became acquainted with the foreign connections of the firm, especially those with France, a circumstance of great value to him later.

At the beginning of the eighties, Daimler had to decide whether he would continue, at the age of forty-seven, to be employed by others, though in a leading position, or whether

he would start on his own account.   The financial means for
the latter course were provided by the great success of the
Deutz motors, of which he had a full share.   In 1882 he
decided to leave Deutz.   Wilhelm Maybach again went with
him, this time back home to Cannstatt, and here Daimler
put up a very modest little workshop near his place of resi-
dence.   He took Maybach in, giving him an interest in the
business, and they set to work to put Daimler's ideas concerning high-speed motors to a practical test.   A bell-founder
made to Daimler's designs the first experimental high-speed
motor.

Otto had been proud in his time to get his atmospheric
engine to do 80 to 90 revolutions per minute in place of 30.
At the beginning of the eighties, the new 4-stroke machines
ran at 150 to 180.   In Deutz, it was scarcely possible to
touch 250 before the ignition began to fail to work accurately.
'The ignitions are all jumbled up,' they used to say in Deutz.
Benz tells us that in his first car, in which he used electric
ignition, he managed to get up to 250 to 300 revolutions.   So
Daimler's high-speed motor running at 900 revolutions was
ahead of everyone.   But high power with minimum size and
weight was the condition of success with the motor car, and
later, in still higher degree, for flight.   Daimler's fundamental
idea was so to develop his high-speed motor as to be able to
use it to drive any vehicle on the roads.   Daimler first built a
wooden cycle.   With this, in the garden of his Cannstatt
house in November, 1885, the first 'motor ride' took place.
In 1886 a four-wheeled Daimler carriage was already seen
about Stuttgart and Cannstatt.   The highest speed attained
was about 10 miles per hour.

About the same time, Carl Benz in Mannheim had made
2-stroke gas motors, and had made benzene motors which he
built into a tricycle.   With these he began his life work, so
important for the development of the motor car.   But
Daimler was not thinking only of road carriages.   In the
same year that the first Daimler automobile was run, his

high-speed motor also drove its first boat. The motor was steadily developed, important patents were obtained. Daimler's chief aim was to mass-produce his high-speed motor. Just as to-day we are able to fix on any boat an outboard motor, so it was Daimler's idea at that time to mechanize any vehicle in the simplest possible way. But Maybach thought that the motor with the chassis ought to be designed to form a single machine unit. Daimler, starting from his idea of using the motor on any wheeled vehicle, pressed all the time for the maximum of simplicity. Maybach's constructions were at first much too complicated for him. But soon the demands put upon power-driven vehicles were increased to such an extent that carriages built to be pulled by horses were totally inadequate. The development from the carriage with added motor to the motor car as a machine was forced upon him, the chief agency being sport.

Daimler and Maybach were hard-headed Suabians, and the three decades of their co-operation were not characterised by unbroken harmony. There were hard fights over many technical questions. Matters often moved too slowly for Daimler. He wanted to manufacture at a profit. Time after time when development was going with a rush, Maybach wanted to add one improvement after another. But again and again, the two men managed to agree on a middle course.

The motor car made but slow progress in Germany. It was France that played the decisive part in the development of the Daimler car. French engineers had a high appreciation of the German achievements. The connections with Paris formed by Daimler when in Deutz could now be used very profitably. He was in Paris with his family for years at a time. The great advances made first took their full effect in France, where sport brought about a rapid development of the automobile. The first international motor race took place on July 1st, 1894, on the Paris—Rouen road. Out of 102 starters, only fifteen finished; a Daimler car was the winner. This attained the hitherto unheard-of speed of about $15\frac{1}{4}$ miles an hour. Daimler received all the first money prizes—80,000 francs. Quite apart from the money, this great achievement became known all over the world; success in the race was the best propaganda. While the French were filled with enthusiasm for this race between power-driven vehicles, professional circles took up a curiously cool attitude. It was noted in 1898, that in Germany motor-driven road vehicles were regarded by the great public and by many engineers simply as toys not worthy of serious attention.

On November 28th, 1890, the Company *Daimler Motoren-Gesellschaft in Cannstatt* was formed, and became one of the greatest producers of motor cars. The power of cars increased steadily. While it had been hard to decide to build one of 9 h.p., users were already asking for 12 h.p., and next 30 or even 40 h.p. was called for. Daimler and Maybach would at first have nothing to do with such demands, but it was their customers who gave the orders, and whose wishes had to be fulfilled, however exaggerated they seemed. Hence in 1900 a new car was built in Cannstatt, which approached the modern motor car much more closely in external appearance. This car was to compete in the great races in the new century. The name given to it was 'Mercédès.'

But Gottlieb Daimler was not to live to see the great success of the first Mercédès car in 1901. In later years he had been prevented by illness from working with the others at full pressure in the firm, although he followed to the last, every development with great sympathy and often contributed valuable suggestions to the new plans. He died on March 6th, 1900, at the age of sixty-six. It was not his lot to see his great pioneer work develop its full results. Wilhelm Maybach, however, was to continue to play a leading part in motor-car development for another twenty-nine years. He died at the age of eighty-four in Cannstatt on December 29th, 1929.

Gottlieb Daimler had recommended his motor in 1897

to the military authorities for use with airships. He
was closely connected with Zeppelin from an early date.
He also took an interest in flying, but was shy of giving
signs of this interest in public. He thought that he had
created more than enough excitement in the streets with his
automobile, and didn't want people to think him quite mad
as they would if he admitted he was thinking about flying.
But a Daimler motor was put into an experimental airship
built by a Leipzig book-dealer, Dr. Wölfert, in 1888. And
when Maybach left the Daimler concern on April 1st, 1907,
he was chosen by Count Zeppelin to direct the construction
of airship motors. When the Count himself took up the
manufacture of motors in Friedrichshafen, the son Karl
Maybach, who had been his father's pupil, was called to the
responsibility of directing the work. He was also able to
continue his father's work in motor-car design.

Gottlieb was, as we have seen, successful as a machine
designer in a great number of different places and in different
fields of work. He had the great power of foreseeing development and of exercising a formative influence on it. In later
years he was regarded only as the fortunate inventor. But
he well knew how high a price in trouble and work the gods
demand for success, and when a woman once visited him and
begged him 'to teach the art of inventing' to her son, he
answered that the boy must do what he did. He worked for
fifteen years from five in the morning till eight at night,
with half an hour's interval at midday. This great power
of application was characteristic of him. And it was just
his experience of practical work that was the decisive factor in
his success.

We know little of his personality outside his work. He was
a sturdy, undersized, compact figure, not very adroit in
dealing with strangers. One could not say that he had a
ready tongue. Only among those working with him was he
able to express his thoughts very clearly. He lived in closest
contact with Nature. In Deutz he was a fruit-grower.

37. GOTTLIEB DAIMLER (1834–1900)
From a portrait by F. E. Klein

38. WILHELM MAYBACH (1846–1929)

39. RUDOLF DIESEL (1858-1913)

He founded institutions for promoting fruit-growing in Württemberg. He had a large glasshouse near his first workshop.

The Rheinische Automobil-und Motorenfabrik Benz & Cie. in Mannheim developed into a keen competitor of the Daimler concern, but they are now merged in one to-day. The two rival inventors never met while alive, but their names are joined in that of the new firm Daimler-Benz.

How modest were the beginnings made by the hard struggles of Daimler, Maybach, Benz, and many first-rate engineers who came after them! They were followed in Germany and all the great industrial nations by engineers who continued the work with success, and their united efforts led finally to the achievements which we take almost for granted to-day. Every year, innumerable new motor vehicles carry persons and goods over new roads in all the lands of the earth.

RUDOLF DIESEL

1858–1913

The end of the nineteenth century saw the development of a new internal combustion engine, based on a method of working giving a thermal efficiency never before reached. Here again decades of work were necessary before the new motor could take its place in the world's power production as an ever-ready aid on land, water, and now even in the air. The new motor, which is known to-day the world over by the name of its inventor, was invented in Germany, and brought to a high state of perfection by German engineers. The name Diesel has become a technical term understood everywhere.

Rudolf Diesel was born on March 18th, 1858, of German parents in Paris, and received his early education there. In

1870, when the war broke out, the parents went to London and sent their eldest son to be brought up by relatives in Augsburg.   Here Diesel was first introduced to technical work at the celebrated Augsburg School of Industry, where he prepared for his entrance as a student into the Technical High School at Munich.   It was his good fortune in Munich to have Schröter and Linde for his teachers, and under them he acquired the scientific groundwork necessary for the great work of his life.   Here, too, he received the impulse which led to his years of travail which resulted in the Diesel engine. Linde had explained in Munich, 1878, to the students to whom he was lecturing on thermodynamics that the steam engine only converts 6 to 10 per cent. of the heat of combustion of the fuel into effective mechanical work, but that, according to the Carnot cycle, much higher efficiencies should be possible within certain temperature limits.   Many professors have stated this piece of scientific knowledge to thousands of hearers year after year.   People reconciled themselves to the fact.   Diesel wrote in the margin of his lecture notes, 'Study whether it would not be possible to realize the isotherms in practice.'   Twenty-five years later, Diesel wrote, looking back over the years: 'At that time I set myself my problem! That was not yet an invention, not even the idea for one.   From that time, the desire to realize the Carnot cycle ruled my life. I left school and went into practical work to win a position in life for myself.   The idea pursued me perpetually.   When the question of the high steam consumption of the old atmospheric engine began to haunt James Watt, the creator of the steam engine, and the latter finally came to birth after decades of painful struggle, we find in James Watt's correspondence the following sentence: 'I have to think day and night of the engine.'   Nothing really great has ever been created without this obsession by a driving idea.

After a very stimulating period of practical work with Gebrüder Sulzer at Winterthur in Switzerland, Diesel went as engineer to Linde's flourishing concerns.   He represented the firm first in Paris, later in Berlin. From 1895 onwards, he devoted himself exclusively to developing and applying his motor.

Incessant thought about the problem he had set himself, supported by many experiments of the most various sorts, led Diesel to publish in 1893 his book on *The Theory and Construction of a Rational Heat Engine, to replace steam engines and present-day internal combustion engines.*

A great promise, a great programme. The invention, at the time existing only on paper, began at once to create excitement in the technical world. The theory was right, the practice was impossible. Criticism was mainly destructive. But three men whose opinions carried weight, Linde, Schröter, and Zeuner, pointed out that the fundamental inventive idea was right. The Maschinenfabrik Augsburg and Friedrich Krupp declared themselves ready to test out Diesel's invention, the first patent for which had already been granted. They shared the cost of equipping a joint laboratory in Augsburg, of which Diesel took control, with the object of proving that his invention could be developed into a practical, marketable engine. There now began for Diesel the 'work and pain of inventing.' It is most thrilling to read in Diesel's own words, in his book published in 1913, how this struggle was carried on. How near together lay ecstatic delight and desperate misery !

For Diesel it was not the mere notion, but the idea realized practically, that made the invention. Hence the success of these experiments decided the fate of his life's work. The battle between the idea and the physical world had to be fought to a successful conclusion. The ideal Carnot cycle could not be carried out as stated. Diesel writes in 1913: 'Only a small part of our soaring ideas can be imposed upon the physical world, the finished invention always looks quite different from the ideal originally formed in the mind, but never fully realized. Hence every inventor works with an enormous wastage of ideas, projects, and experiments. Much has to be attempted, if little is to be realized.' 'Hence, every inventor must be an optimist.'

Diesel succeeded in obtaining in his motor, by previous mechanical compression to 30–35 atmospheres, the highest possible temperatures necessary for his process. It was not possible in existing gas engines to compress the mixture of air and fuel so highly, since the result would be premature spontaneous ignition. Hence Diesel devised the plan of compressing only the air necessary for combustion, and then, at the end of the compression stroke, gradually injecting the fuel in a finely divided form into the highly heated air in which it was burnt. The result was a degree of efficiency in the utilization of the heat of combustion far exceeding that hitherto attained in heat engines. But how many years of tireless tenacious engineering work were necessary to overcome technical difficulties which often seemed insuperable ! Diesel describes in detail in his book six series of experiments, which lasted from 1893 to 1897.

In 1897 the first great chapter in the development of the Diesel motor was closed. Professor Schröter had carried out experiments on the motor in Augsburg on February 17th, 1897, and had reported to the firms that the mechanical efficiency at full load was 75 per cent., 34.2 per cent. of the heat being converted at full load into indicated work; and he furthermore certified that the motor in its then form was already a marketable machine. Professor Schröter then introduced the motor to the engineering world in an enthusiastic discourse delivered to the general meeting of the Verein deutscher Ingenieure in Cassel on June 16th, 1897. He expressed the hope 'that this motor may prove itself to be the starting point of a development of great value to industry.'

Now began the second chapter in the history of the Diesel motor: its introduction into practice. Diesel was already able to make royalty agreements in Germany and most foreign countries on the basis of the first Augsburg machine,

which now has a place of honour in the Munich Museum.
Fortune showered a rich financial harvest on the inventor,
and it may be regarded as characteristic of his way of thinking that when he became one of Germany's rich men, his
favourite idea was one day to devote these profits to some
work of social value. But he was not spared the fierce,
nerve-racking battles always arising over successful inventions, the period described by Diesel in 1913 as 'the struggle
with stupidity and envy, inertia and malice, secret opposition and open attack by vested interest, the horrible time of
battling with humanity, a martyrdom even in success.'

But Diesel did not want for faithful comrades, helpers,
and friends, and no one was readier than he to admit the
fact. His first thanks were given to the Augsburg engineering firm, and Friedrich Krupp. And if we are here to name
one of his successful supporters, let it be Heinrich von Buz
of Augsburg. His firm grasp of the invention, in face of the
severest disappointments, cannot be too highly estimated in
the history of the Diesel motor. Augsburg was the high
school in Diesel motors for the whole world. Diesel
remained true to the child of his brains in this period of the
design and introduction of marketable engines. He was a
successful representative of the firm at home and abroad,
he saw ever fresh openings for it. He was delighted at its
application to ships and boats. He first got it into submarines in France, for Germany at that time would not hear
of it for the purpose. In 1907 he was working on Diesel
locomotives, and built in 1908 the first Diesel-engined lorry.
He lived to see the complete practical success of the Diesel
engines designed by the world-firms. His journey with the
Director of the Munich Museum to America in 1912, the
reception by the American public, so appreciative of great
engineering achievement, gave him the opportunity of
experiencing the success and recognition accorded to his
great life work. No one could guess that this man would be
snatched from us a year later. Rudolf Diesel left us at the

age of fifty-five, while crossing the Channel to England, a prey to the severest financial worry such as often accompanies the ups and down of great fortunes.

But his work, carried on by a whole generation of first-rate engineers, is flourishing with all the vigour of youth.

His portrait was introduced in 1932 into the Hall of Honour of the Munich Museum, and bears the following inscription:

'He created with the co-operation of the engineers of the Maschinenfabrik Augsburg, and the firm of Fried. Krupp, during the years 1893 to 1897, the internal combustion engine everywhere named after him. The invention of this motor was a great success in machine construction, and increased the reputation of German technical work.'

CHARLES ALGERNON PARSONS
1854–1931

The eighteenth century harnessed the power of steam to the work of humanity. This supreme achievement, for all time inseparably associated with the name of James Watt, was the foundation for the enormous development of trade and transport in the nineteenth century. The steamship and steam locomotive changed the form and face of our lives. The piston engine with its rhythmical rise and fall, first designed for pumping the water out of mines, was soon made to produce a rotary motion by means of the crank and connecting rod, and was then applied to the driving of every imaginable form of machine. The output of engines increased; while at first men were glad to have a 10-h.p. engine to work for them, 20, 50, even 100 h.p. were soon in demand. The revolutions increased from 20 to 50, 80, and people were soon talking of 100, at any rate much sooner than the normal engine builder was able to manage such speeds.

The smoothness of running, necessarily demanded above all by the textile industry if a cloth of even texture was to be woven, was anything but satisfactory. The great coal consumption of the engines was a subject of much complaint. There was an infinite amount of work for engineers before all legitimate demands could be fulfilled. This work was done. Innumerable excellent engineers in Europe and America gave of their best. The great American engineer, George Henry Corliss, designed his much-admired engine, which gave a valuable stimulus to steam engine design all over the world. In Switzerland, at Winterthur, an Englishman, Charles Brown, working with the firm of Gebrüder Sulzer, invented the triple expansion engine, destined to open up a new chapter in steam engine history.

And then in the eighties of last century came electricity, making demands on the steam engine of a sort hitherto unknown. As an important source of orders, electricity became a relentless pacemaker in prime mover development. It was not true, though one may hear it said even to-day, that the age of steam was succeeded by the age of electricity, for at the end of every electric cable there still stands, now as ever, a prime mover, in 90 per cent. of cases a steam engine, generating the power by which the electric current is produced. The possibilities offered by electricity have on the contrary led to undreamed-of progress in steam engine construction. When the most famous steam engine builder had provided the Berlin electricity works with the first 1,000-h.p. engine, a 2,000-h.p. engine was called for; and when a 6,000-h.p. horizontal triple-expansion engine represented a feat which excited the highest admiration, electro-technical circles were enquiring when the first 10,000-h.p. engine would be ready. At this point the limit was reached in the development of the giant slow-speed piston engine, with its excessive demand for space.

WE

Was it a fixed law of Nature that a reciprocating motion had always first to be created, when rapid uniform rotation was the desired effect ? This question was put by many engineers after Watt's time, but they sought for a solution without finding one. It was at this point that the man of whom we are now to tell began his great and successful life work.

Charles Algernon Parsons was born on June 13th, 1854, in London, the youngest of six sons. His father, William Parsons, third Earl of Rosse, was a famous astronomer and a very skilful mechanic, who had built with his own hands his great telescope, the admiration of all professional astronomers. The family lived at their country seat in Birr Castle (Parsonstown) in Ireland. The great engineer passed the first eighteen years of his life there. His mother, a highly educated woman with an especial interest in scientific questions, and herself very skilful with her hands, exerted a great influence on her son's development, as did his father also, who, however, died when the boy was thirteen. Of no less importance for him was the stimulus of contact with the many visitors of scientific eminence who came to his father's house. Parsons did not go to a public school; he was taught by tutors with a mathematical and scientific training. Among them was a man who later became the famous astronomer Sir Robert Ball. Birr possessed a large mechanical workshop, and even an iron and bronze foundry, and these places formed young Parsons' playrooms. He learned to handle tools at as early an age as his famous predecessor in the same line of work, James Watt. The summer months were mostly spent at sea. His father's yacht taught young Parsons everything connected with ships and navigation, and the knowledge thus acquired was of great value to him later in his profession. The children's education was not interrupted while at sea, the tutors forming part of the family.

His favourite occupation was tinkering in the workshops.

Among the products was an air-gun, a sounding machine that was tested in summer on the yacht, even a 4-h.p. steam engine; while in 1868 he built a steam motor car with universal joint, angular drive and differential. Apart from all this, Parsons very early began to amuse himself and others with all sorts of mechanical toys which he invented and constructed. Inherited wealth and environment smoothed for Parsons his road to greatness as an engineer. The friends of his father very early gave him many a word of praise, but as was also the case later in his professional life, he himself was the person whom he found hardest to please. In 1872 Parsons went to Dublin University, where his father also had laid the foundation of his knowledge. A year later we find him at Cambridge where he studied till 1877, chiefly mathematics and science, there being at that time no engineering school there. But that did not hinder our student from concerning himself with important technical problems. He made an engine with radial rotating cylinders, such as is to-day used in aeroplanes.

In 1877 it seemed to him time to acquire a practical training as machine engineer. The Armstrong works in Elswick offered him a good opportunity for this. Here he considerably improved his manual skill, and acquired the art of dealing with workmen and of getting the best out of them, an art for which he was celebrated later on. It was said of him in Elswick at the time that he was the most industrious apprentice that the firm had ever had. Here also he attempted to construct his rotary steam engine. But he also had other ideas to try out. He began by attempting to propel torpedoes by means of rockets. In the meantime his brother had entered a Leeds firm, and in this way Parsons found there the opportunity to experiment for about two years in the direction which most interested him. But he had no success with his rocket torpedoes. He succeeded, it is true, in getting speeds up to 20 knots, but the rockets were not reliable.

In the meantime he had married, and desired to make for himself a permanent position in industry. He entered the firm of Clarke, Chapman & Co., Gateshead, as partner. He had abandoned his rotary steam engine, with its reciprocating parts. His plan was now to bring the steam turbine into being. On April 23rd, 1884, he obtained his first steam turbine patent. Parsons of course was not the first to have such intentions. The aeolipile, a reaction turbine of the simplest sort, was described by Hero of Alexandria at the beginning of our era, nearly 2,000 years ago. The idea of blowing steam against vanes on a wheel had been thought of before Newcomen and Watt. Giovanni Bianca had described and pictured such steam windmills in his book on machines, dated 1629. A small stamp mill was to be driven in this way. But the idea was never carried out, for otherwise it would have appeared that the problem could not be solved in this simple way. New inventors attempted again and again to solve the problem, and again and again they failed. It was impossible at that time to carry out the idea. Also, there was no scientific understanding whatever of the question. Engineers finally ceased to believe that this inventive idea could be realized, and many no doubt put the steam turbine in the same category as perpetual motion. Anyhow, Parsons had to fight as much with these prejudices of the profession, as with material and method of manufacture.

When people spoke of the impossibility of the steam turbine, they forgot that Parsons in the eighties was armed with much wider scientific knowledge; furthermore, methods of construction had improved considerably. Then we have the fact that electrical engineering held out strong inducements for the construction of engines with high speeds of revolution. The success of his steam turbine arose out of his recognition of the fact, stated in his first patent, that the action of the steam must be distributed over a considerable number of stages, if the peripheral speed is to be kept within the limits possible in practice. Parsons thus arrived, on the basis of a variety of carefully designed experiments, at a construction embodying a number of stages of expansion combined with high blade speeds. He succeeded in giving his first turbine the hitherto unheard-of peripheral speed of 220 ft. per second.

He went to Gateshead with his turbine. The firm, which built marine engines, was ready to take over the manufacture of steam turbines, which they wished to use for generating the electric current used for lighting the ship. These first turbines gave 10 h.p. and ran at 18,000 r.p.m. But more was necessary than the provision of a satisfactory turbine. Parsons was successful in making fundamental advances in dynamo design, with the result that he was able to couple his dynamo directly to the turbine running at incredible speed. The idea of the Parsons steam turbine was the simplest imaginable, but a great amount of engineering work was necessary to carry it into effect, and in this work it was a great advantage to Parsons to be able to prove to such of his assistants as came to him with the word 'impossible' on their lips, that he could himself do the job, thanks to his thorough workshop training. And here the question of mastering practical difficulties arose again and again, as turbines became larger and larger, and fresh demands were made on their reliability and fuel economy.

The first small turbines built in Gateshead were called steam-eaters. Coal had to be cheap for them to be economical. Parsons was aware that the efficiency of large units would be higher. At the very start of his work on the turbine, he had foreseen its development a long way ahead. His master patent of 1884 already refers to the possibilities of radial flow and axial flow. He talks of driving ships' screws by the turbine, and even knows that a turbine may by reversal act as a compressor. He began his work with a series of fundamental experiments which lasted for years. Parsons was an experimenter of the first rank, who could never be deterred from pursuing his purpose by any kind of failure, which everyone doing work of this sort must meet with from time to time. If it didn't go one way, he tried another.

Parsons found development going too slowly for him in the firm. The firm proposed to make only small turbines suitable for auxiliary engines on ships. Experiments necessary as a preliminary to building larger units were thought to be too costly. Hence he parted from the firm and started building turbines and dynamos in a works of his own, which he set up in 1889, at Heaton, Newcastle-on-Tyne. He had had to give up, under the terms of his agreement, his patents to the Gateshead firm. The amount required to buy them out was more than he could and would pay. Parsons was for many years in the curious position of having the road to further developments blocked by his own patents. So having hitherto worked with steam flowing parallel to the axis of the turbine, he now turned his attention to radial flow. But after some years, the people in Gateshead realized that they could not do much without Parsons, and an agreement was come to. Parsons was now able to pursue his original line of invention. He gave up the radial-flow turbine and continued to develop his original axial-flow system. Some of the important experiments of those years finally led Parsons to the solution of the turbine problem which, in the form of the impulse turbine and velocity distribution, was developed simultaneously with Parsons by the great Swedish engineer de Laval, the Swiss Heinrich Zoelly, the Frenchman Auguste Rateau, and the American Curtis.

Further progress depended upon the introduction by Parsons of the condenser. He had surmised that this would increase the efficiency of the turbine even more than that of the reciprocating engine. He also decided early on in favour of high steam pressures and superheats. In 1900, Parsons supplied the Elberfeld generating station with two steam turbines each of 1,000 kw. and 1,500 r.p.m. At that time the courage of those who placed this order was much admired, but no less also the success of the machines, which used only

8·5 kilograms of steam per kilowatt-hour. These machines, one of which is now preserved in the Munich Museum as representing a milestone in a great development, ushered in the steam turbine age. To-day no large electricity works, dependent upon coal for power, is without gigantic turbines. Parsons in his lifetime led the way in this development. His last great turbine, supplied to an English central station, generated 40,000 kilowatts on one shaft turning at 3,000 r.p.m., that is to say, 10,000 times the power of his first turbine. To-day steam turbines of 210,000 h.p. on one shaft are already running, and development is not yet at an end.

While Parsons began his work by suiting the construction of his machines to the generation of electric power, he did not confine himself to this line of work. He had as we have seen already mentioned ship propulsion in his first patent. In 1894 he entered upon a series of decisive experiments in this field. In 1897 a little 44-ton steamer, the *Turbinia*, was launched. The turbines ran at 8,000 r.p.m. but the results were disappointing. Parsons came up against the phenomenon of cavitation. When a screw is revolving too fast in water, vacuous spaces are formed which greatly diminish the efficiency. Parsons tried all forms of screw, but could not improve matters. In 1896 he put in three screws, each driven by an axial flow turbine, the three turbines being high-, middle-, and low-pressure respectively, and connected in series. In April, 1897, a speed of 34 knots was attained. This performance excited great attention. Parsons had now recognized that the most effective arrangement was a compromise between the velocity of the turbine and that of the screw. He investigated the phenomenon of cavitation in a large glass tank, so that he could study what occurred with screws of different speeds, forms, and dimensions.

He attempted to introduce the turbine for marine propulsion, and attracted the closest attention of the English Admiralty. A trial with a cruiser gave such good results that it was decided in 1905 to fit turbines to the new battleship *Dreadnought*. As regards merchant shipping, a small steamer was already running with a turbine in 1901, and this proved to have 15 per cent. less coal consumption than a sister ship fitted with triple-expansion reciprocating engines. At first it was thought desirable to couple the turbine direct to the screw, but that confined the use of the turbine to fast ships. Parsons thus came to the use of gearing in order to make the turbine available for slow cargo vessels. Here also the first task was to produce suitable gear wheels, but Parsons' long machine-shop experience again enabled him to solve the problem.

But his scientific and inventive activity was not confined to the steam turbine. Again and again, fresh scientific problems attracted his attention. He worked successfully at Heaton, from 1890 onwards, at parabolic reflectors for searchlights. After the war he devoted himself to further optical problems. He acquired concerns working in this field. He manufactured optical glass and began building telescopes of all sizes. When he died, this department especially was developing rapidly. His interest in this work may have arisen from the recollection of his father, and of his happy youth.

As a physicist, he became interested in the conditions under which carbon may be produced in crystalline form. He set to work with all the appliances of engineering. In 1888 he was already making experiments on the behaviour of carbon at high temperatures and pressures. He was dealing in the first instance with the practical problem of producing arc-lamp carbons. He discovered in the course of the work small particles which he took to be diamonds, and set about the attempt to produce artificial diamonds. This was one of the pieces of work which cost him much trouble, time, and money, without leading to success. He had a brilliant gift for experimenting, but he came upon no solution of the problem he was tackling. He admitted openly that he had made a mistake in looking upon the minute particles seen in his early experiments as diamonds. His friend Alfred Ewing tells us that Parsons, before going away on his last long journey, from which he was never to return, showed him a handful of wonderful diamonds which he had just purchased, and said: 'Nature did that without human help.' But Ewing felt at the moment that Parsons had not yet given up meditating upon the possibility of competing with Nature in this field.

In connection with these experiments, Parsons suggested in 1904 to a large assembly of engineers that the earth's crust should be investigated by a very deep borehole. He described the way in which he imagined the proposal could be carried out, and gave an estimate of the cost. In 1919 he returned to the idea. He pointed out that the cost was in his opinion inconsiderable compared with the knowledge that would certainly be gained by penetrating into the unknown depths of the earth. Quite new information about the internal structure of the earth would be acquired. In Italy there were already boreholes which delivered steam in great quantities at high pressure, driving turbines of over 10,000 h.p. Parsons thought that in volcanic districts great quantities of energy would in the future be gained, directly or indirectly, if the boreholes were carried deep enough. In any case, he thought that this problem should be studied most carefully.

We could tell of many other less important pieces of work which he did, all testifying to the versatility of his technical powers. Alfred Ewing, the friend and collaborator of Parsons, tells us that near the end of his life he frequently discussed the question whether his want of a technical scientific education in his early years had done him harm or not. But Ewing, himself an eminent representative of science and technology, answers in the negative. He thinks that different paths are possible, and that genius such as Parsons possessed may develop its valuable gifts most successfully by going its own way unburdened by opinions acquired at school. He acquired the power of doing scientific work. There were still no teachers in the new field which he opened up. Ewing tells us how surprisingly small was the use made by Parsons of mathematical calculation. His assistants worked out problems which he set them, but he simply thought about them, and had more faith in his intuition than in mathematics. But here the scientific training acquired at the University was of great help to him.

Parsons was a man of unusual modesty, but everyone who came in contact with him was conscious of his worth. His last appearance before an international audience was probably at the Second World Power Conference at Berlin. Here he gave an address on the co-operation of engineers of all nations, and its effect in promoting understanding between them.

Parsons, who died on February 11th, 1931, while on a holiday cruise with his wife to the West Indies, was one of the great engineers who lived long enough to receive full recognition, and to see the success of their creative work. The Verein deutscher Ingenieure conferred on him as early as 1904 its highest distinction, the Grashof Medal.

THOMAS ALVA EDISON

1847–1931

Who has not heard of Thomas Alva Edison? His American admirers called him the 'Wizard of Menlo Park.' Henry Ford has raised a monument to him in Dearborn, his Museum town. With the greatest care, Edison's laboratory and workshop were rebuilt there, and form a wonderful monument to technical history, with much to tell to every visitor. Edison's American biographers state that if all that has been printed about this great engineer were collected together, 1,000 volumes each of 100,000 words would scarcely suffice to contain it, and they add that scarcely one-third of it would be true.

40.   CHARLES ALGERNON PARSONS (1854–1931)

41. THOMAS ALVA EDISON, about 1880 (1847–1931)
Original in the Deutsche Museum, Munich

42. GEORGE WESTINGHOUSE (1846–1914)

Edison certainly did not fail to have notice taken of him during his lifetime. Sometimes perhaps he stood a little too much in the glare of public interest, a fact often made use of by ingenious reporters at the expense of truth. This excessive propaganda, which was none of his doing, injured his scientific reputation as a great pioneer in many fields. But the wonderful fruits of his work have put that right. Let us try to select from the mass of material what seems to us most significant in forming an estimate of Edison.

His ancestors came from Holland. The Edisons were millers on the shores of the Zuyder Zee, and without doubt were also merchants. In 1730 one of these ancestors emigrated to America. The family got along well there, and then came the War of Independence. John Edison took the British side and fought the rebels. After the war was over, he may have considered himself fortunate to escape with his life. He was banished to Canada, and there, in the little town of Vienna on Lake Erie, John Edison became a prosperous and respected man, and a large landed proprietor. John Edison and his sons are described to us as over six feet in height and possessed of iron constitutions. They were marked by long straight noses, strong chins, and piercing blue-grey eyes. Some of these ancestors lived to be over one hundred years of age.

A grandson of this John Edison, Samuel, born in 1804, departed somewhat from the family type. He had little taste either for the strict religious views of the Quakers, or for agriculture. The business enterprise of his ancestors came out again in him. He was successful in all sorts of callings. He married the pretty young school-teacher of the town, a pastor's daughter, who brought neither money nor a knowledge of farming into the marriage as the parents wished, but only a great number of books. Those were exciting times in Canada. Here also there was a struggle to get free from England, and Samuel Edison became a dashing rebel leader, who fought against the English in just the same way as his grandfather, decades before, had fought for them. But the rebellion collapsed, and Edison had to flee. In 1842 he settled in the State of Ohio, in the little town of Milan, and his son Thomas Alva Edison was born there on February 11th, 1847.

As a child, he was distinguished by an unusually large head, which gave his father little hope that he would turn into a clever man. The teacher shared this view, and only his mother took the opposite one. She early recognized her boy's unusual talents, although he made no progress at all at school, to which he went for three months only. His highly intelligent mother took the place of teacher and school. She gained great influence over his early intellectual development; with her he was the keenest of scholars. His father did not worry much about him, being extremely active in all sorts of undertakings. He was also a successful man, so that all the stories of Edison as a poor boy, suffering every hardship, belong to the two-thirds which are not true. Edison's father could not see much chance of getting on in Milan in the way he wanted, so the family migrated to the State of Michigan, to Port Huron, north of Detroit.

Edison was seven years old when the family moved into the new home. Four years later we find him in business on his own. He obtained land from his father, grew vegetables, and sold them. He even, at this early age, became an employer of other boys. In this way he earned his first money, not from the necessity of earning his own living, but because his pocket money did not suffice to buy new books and to satisfy his passion, very early awakened, for experimenting in all sorts of ways. He soon discovered that it was more profitable to buy fruit and vegetables in Detroit and to sell them in the small town; hence he gave up gardening. In order to save the cost of railway fares and carriage, he applied to the railway company for permission to sell papers in the train. This was granted, and he was also given a place in a goods wagon for his fruit and vegetable baskets. He actually managed to equip a corner of the wagon as an experimental laboratory, in which he played about with all sorts of chemicals bought in Detroit, some of them inflammable. But he was not satisfied with selling his newspapers in Detroit.

In the time between arrival and departure of the train he learned, with his uncommon quickness of mind, something of typesetting and printing. He bought all the necessary apparatus, set up a little printing-press in his goods truck, and produced a newspaper of his own, in which he dealt at length with local news from small places, not given much space in the Detroit paper. Even the London *Times* took notice of this first newspaper ever printed in a train in motion. And then came a piece of bad luck. The train, travelling at high speed on a bad track, shook his chemicals up so violently that a stick of phosphorus caught fire. The whole truck caught fire, the guard of the train found the culprit and turned him and all his goods off the train out of hand. The boxes on the ear which, in his very natural indignation, he gave the boy, were the cause of Edison's life-long deafness. It speaks well for the tenacity of the youth that, so far from giving up his plans, he now fixed up his laboratory and printing-press at home.

His close connection with the railway also drew his attention to telegraphy, in which he took so great an interest that he begged an experienced railway telegraphist to introduce him into its secrets. This was his first connection with electric current, and the first decisive step in his career. He was then fifteen years old. He now set out on his travels, which lasted five years and took him all over America.

The terrible war between North and South had broken out, and the whole country was shaken to its foundations. The telegraph came to have a great political importance. But in those exciting times there was neither time nor money to build the systems properly or even keep them in order.

Hence it was left to the ingenuity of the telegraphist to get along as best he could. In those five years, young Edison acquired an immense amount of knowledge. He got to know the country and the people; modest and obliging, he made friends everywhere, the more so as he was always willing to take on duty for a friend who wanted a day off. In this his unexampled power of work, based on excellent health, was already apparent. But he finally became sick of this everlasting moving around. He was able to get a job in Boston, with a view to becoming a first-class press telegraphist. Not much confidence was placed in the unimpressive and slovenly young man, with his long hair falling over his forehead, but a trial of him exceeded all expectations. His salary was raised, and he now began to work out new ideas.

In 1868, at the age of twenty-one, his first patent was granted to him. He had invented a machine for recording parliamentary votes. But one of the members, who belonged to the minority, explained that all of them would be violently opposed to such an apparatus, for it was for the minority a wonderful tactical stroke to be able to raise a doubt every time about the result of a vote, since that wasted time, which was very inconvenient for the majority. So this invention had no success, and Edison later always considered first of all whether there would be a demand for a projected invention.

After the Civil War, economic conditions by no means settled down again to order immediately. Wild speculation in gold started, and everyone who hoped to get rich quickly in this way wanted to be informed continually concerning the rapidly varying stock exchange prices. This had given rise to the production of tape machines on which the prices were registered.

Edison had in the meantime decided that there were more chances of getting on in New York than in Boston, and so he decided out of hand to go there without money and without introductions. He was able, thanks to his abilities, to get a position there at a salary of 300 dollars a month. He then succeeded in making considerable improvements in tape machines, and people were prepared to buy his patents. Edison thought that he deserved to be paid 5,000 dollars considering the time and trouble they had cost him. But he would have been ready to take 3,000 dollars. He was offered 40,000 dollars, and that was the first large sum of money which he received for his work. But it did the young man no harm, for he had no desires except for strong coffee and strong cigars, and he continued to devote himself to his plans with incredible industry and great initiative. He continued to work on the improvement of the telegraph. This brought him in a further 30,000 dollars, but not yet the success he was looking for. This money Edison used, at the age of twenty-three, to found his first workshop on October 1st, 1869. In Newark (N.J.) he was soon able to keep fifty workmen busy with profitable orders, particularly in connection with the tape machine which he had now so essentially improved, and which was called a 'ticker' on account of the noise it made. Siegmund Bergmann and Siegmund Schuckert from Germany helped him in his workshop as trained mechanics and they became valuable assistants to him. Their American experience helped them later to found in Berlin and Nürnberg the industrial undertakings associated with their names.

At that time a self-acting telegraphic apparatus was being introduced. A skilful operator could send up to forty words a minute by hand on a Morse transmitter. If the Morse signs were put in the form of perforations in a paper strip, this could be run through an automatic transmitter, giving a hundred times the speed of hand transmission. But in practice, the self-induction of the wire nullified the advantage. Edison was applied to. He had learned in his long telegraphic experience something of the effects of self-induction. He succeeded, by using a coil of wire with a soft iron core, in separating the individual current impulses. The automatic telegraph thus became, as it were to order, an uncommonly useful instrument, which revolutionized telegraphic working.

Edison continued to work in telegraphy. He produced a printing telegraph, which rendered unnecessary a translation of the messages into writing. He further succeeded in considerably increasing the capacity of the lines, so that first two, and finally four, messages could be sent over one line at the same time. This invention of quadruplex telegraphy was the end of Edison's work in this field. He hoped for a corresponding financial success. He had so far taken out sixty-three patents, which had cost him a large sum of money, quite apart from the years of intensive labour. But now he was caught in the net of the speculator Jay Gould, whose aim was to attain to unlimited power in the world of telegraphy. He bought Edison's rights by a payment of 30,000 dollars as a first instalment, and promised that the 15 million dollar Company which he was going to found would do him justice. But the promise was not kept, and the 30,000 dollars in cash received were not enough to pay debts. In his difficulties, Edison turned to the Western Telegraph Company, which gave him the job of making the long-distance telephone practicable.

Experiments with a view to the transmission of speech by electric current go back to an early date. In Germany in 1861, the school-teacher Philipp Reis made the first telephone and transmitted sounds by means of it. The apparatus was shown in America in 1868. A young Scotsman, Alexander Graham Bell undertook the task of developing this device, noteworthy only as a scientific curiosity, into a practical means of communication. A vibrating metal plate or membrane situated in front of an electro magnet could be set in motion by the human voice in such a way as to set in motion at the other end of the line a similar membrane near a similar electromagnet, so reproducing the words. Bell received a patent in America for his apparatus in March, 1876.

The fact that the human voice could now be transmitted from house to house, and even from one part of a town to another, aroused the greatest astonishment all over the world. But when this great success was not enough, when the attempt was actually made to telephone from New York to Washington, only unintelligible noises came from the receiver. Edison was again called upon to help. The solution was the carbon granule microphone. Edison replaced the transmitting electromagnet by a little box of carbon granules. The electric current sent through these by a battery was changed in strength by every change in the pressure produced by the sound waves on the carbon granules. Edison in this case was led to the solution of the problem by observations made years before. As is almost always the case with inventions of great importance, others were working independently of him in the same direction. It was Edison's invention that made Bell's telephone applicable to long distances. Hence it was only just that for a long time afterwards every telephone bore the name Edison along with that of Bell.

The Western Union Co., which was well aware of the value of the new telephone, was ready to pay 100,000 dollars for it; a very modest reward, but Edison was satisfied, and asked the Company to pay it out to him in yearly instalments of 6,000 dollars. He wanted to be secure for seventeen years from actual want. Edison had now to provide for a family. Scarcely twenty-five years old, he had married at Christmas, 1871, a beautiful sixteen-year-old blonde, Mary Stilwell, who presented him with two sons and a daughter, but was taken from him all too soon, when he was twenty-nine years of age, by typhoid fever. Edison wanted to provide for his family a beautiful home in healthy surroundings, and for himself a quieter place of work than was offered by Newark. He found what he sought not far from New York, in a little place, Menlo Park, where there were only seven houses, and which afterwards became famous

Xᴇ

through his association with it. He built there early in 1876 a house closely connected with his laboratory and workshop, and it was there that the long-distance telephone and the phonograph were produced, the latter being the invention of his of which he thought most highly, and the one which was most completely a new departure. Here also the incandescent lamp was born, and the first form of our present electric central stations, with all the organs connected with it.

The invention of the talking machine—in his first patent specification the inventor calls it a 'speaking machine'—was also connected with his work of making telegraph and telephone more practically valuable. Edison had worked out in the winter of 1876 an apparatus which recorded automatically incoming Morse telegrams, so that they could be transmitted later at high speed. The apparatus was similar to the present-day gramophone. An electromagnet imprinted by means of a needle on a rotating circular disc of paper the Morse signs of the incoming telegram. In order to retransmit the telegram thus mechanically recorded, it was only necessary to reverse the process in a similar apparatus. A needle running over the pits made by the recording needle in the paper, repeated the telegram. A little toy by which Edison had transformed the power of the human voice into visible movement of a little figure cut out of paper, led him to his epoch-making invention. If it were possible to cause the spoken word to make impressions corresponding to the force of the sound, would it not be possible, by running again over such a record, to cause it to set a membrane in vibration in such a way as to reproduce the same sounds ?

Edison was extremely fascinated by this idea, and went to work at once. In place of paper he took tin foil, a much more suitable material. In order to make the external arrangement of the apparatus different from that of the telegraph apparatus, he used a cylinder in place of the disc of paper. He straight away sketched the first form of the phonograph and had it made without saying what it was for. Everyone was surprised that the new apparatus had nothing to do with electricity, having no wires or magnets about it. What was Edison after with this curious little apparatus ? His assistant Kruesi, a Swiss, made it to Edison's sketch, and finally asked the inventor what its purpose was. Edison answered that he wanted to store up speech in order to be able to repeat it at any time. One can imagine the incredulous and pitying astonishment aroused by this statement. A dead machine was to talk like a living person ! Bets were laid that it was impossible. Edison tells us himself of his excitement over the first experiment. The inventor turned the drum covered with tin foil and spoke the old nursery rhyme 'Mary had a little lamb' into the horn. The apparatus, set for reproduction, then gave back the words excellently. Edison himself, who had had enough experience of the length of time needed to realize in practice an inventive idea, was astonished beyond measure. Never in his whole life, as he said later, had he been so full of excitement as over this first attempt to make a machine talk like a human being.

The amazement of the public was limitless when news of the talking machine began to spread beyond Menlo Park. Everyone wanted to see and hear and understand, but not believe. Was not the whole thing near to magic ? Or to clever conjuring ? Even the President in Washington wanted to know how much truth there was in the news. Edison demonstrated the apparatus to him. Every scientific society wanted to hear the machine. People streamed out to Menlo Park, everyone wanted to assure themselves whether the papers were lying or not. At that time the custom arose of talking of Edison as the 'Wizard of Menlo Park.' Business people smelt profits; the enormous public curiosity had to be turned into money. A company was formed, and the invention was pressed to such an extent that he allowed the apparatus to go out long before it had been properly worked out. The phonograph became a novelty exhibited at all sorts of places of amusement. He wanted to abolish shorthand; he was thinking of the dictating machine. Anyone could speak letters and speeches into the machine as fast as he liked, and a secretary could then write them out by listening to the apparatus set to run as slowly as necessary. On February 19th, 1878, he was granted, no longer than fifty days after application, the memorable patent for the phonograph, giving him for seventeen years the sole right to record the human voice by the motion of a membrane on a body. Here a completely new road had been opened up. But Edison wanted to be free for other work. He was satisfied with 10,000 dollars; he never received the share promised him in the receipts from demonstrations of the apparatus. The demonstrator frequently disappeared with the apparatus and the box office receipts. Edison realized that he would have himself to see to the further development of his favourite invention, but he determined to postpone this task, for he saw himself confronted by a great new problem, which he afterwards called the greatest adventure of his life. He wanted to popularize electric light. Everyone was to be able in future to buy current like water, gas, or coal.

The arc-lamp was known. Its great power, and its effect in streets and open spaces were regarded with amazement. The lamps were dear and not easy to keep in order. It was practically necessary to have a dynamo for every lamp, and this again had to be driven by an engine. There was no possibility of the electric light coming into universal use in this form. At that time people talked of dividing the electric light as the great problem to be solved. Everywhere attempts were made at a solution. Edison had a vision of the future. He sensed that here lay the greatest deed he could accomplish. He wanted to compete with gas. Just as gas was sent in pipes all over a town, so that everyone could buy as much as he needed for his purpose, at a fixed price, so now was

electricity to be distributed. The current was to be generated in great stations, placed in the centre of an area over
which current could be sent to any consumer who was
willing to purchase it. The electric current, transformed into
light, was in future to illuminate rooms, halls, and streets.
Edison in 1878 set himself this task in all its magnitude.
He went to work with the tenacity characteristic of him.

The first business was to make a suitable lamp. Edison
thought of the incandescent lamp. Others before him had
also worked at it, and here and there attained a certain
success. The history of the invention of the incandescent
lamp was investigated very thoroughly at the time when
Edison's success had aroused the strongest desire to upset his
patents. We know that Heinrich Goebel, a German, had
already in 1854 used an incandescent lamp made by himself
to attract attention in the streets of New York to a telescope
which one could pay to look through. The inventor and
his lamp were soon forgotten. No practical result of importance was attained. Experiments along these lines may be
followed further. At about the same time as Edison, Swan,
an Englishman, was working on the incandescent lamp.
But the great practical success fell to Edison.

He first tried thin carbon rods in exhausted glass vessels.
But their life was much too short. Then the rarer metals
were tried; platinum and iridium could be had commercially,
but who would be willing to pay the high prices demanded
for them ? Also, their life was too short. Edison improved
the vacuum by means of his own new type air pumps. An
important point was that he gave up a metal seal and sealed
the platinum wires through the walls of the pear-shaped
glass vessel which he designed. Edison made no progress
with the metallic filament lamp, and returned to carbon. The
filament had to be thin, in order to give a high electric
resistance; for only in this way could one use a high voltage
and low current, and therefore thin and not too expensive
copper cables.

After innumerable experiments with all kinds of materials, he at last succeeded on October 21st, 1879, in making a carbon filament lamp which burned for forty hours. With this, the problem was solved. An electric lamp independent of every other was produced, giving a candle power of sixteen, the amount usual in the gas industry. This success was much admired, the rapid extinction of gas lighting was prophesied, and some very clever business men succeeded in producing so great a fall in gas shares on the Stock Exchange, that they made more money by their speculation than the inventor by all his work. The next thing was to manufacture the lamps industrially. Edison left this to a company which he founded for the purpose, and turned to other problems.

He needed dynamos, and he had to build the ones he wanted. Here again he was successful after long effort. These Edison dynamos were to be driven directly by high-speed steam engines of over 200 h.p. This set the engine builders of the day a new and big problem. But even when the engines were there, the end of the matter was not yet. The streets of New York were spanned by an overhead network of electric conductors which we can hardly imagine to-day. True, Edison had obtained permission to add his conductors to the rest, and then to branch off to every story. But that could only be bearable as a temporary measure. He wanted to make a thorough job of it, and so he decided to put down his conductors in the ground alongside the gas pipes. Here also, he had no experience whatever to guide him. Wherever he looked, he was on new territory. If he was to sell his current, he had to measure it. He invented an electro-chemical electricity meter. In order to protect his conductors against short-circuit, which might easily be the cause of fires, he devised lead fuses. Thus one thing was added to another, and it was finally possible to put down in Menlo Park an electric central station where all experiments still necessary could be carried out.

On the basis of the improvements made, it was now decided to put down the first large electric central station. That was a daring enterprise for which much money was necessary. The Company founded by Edison wanted to sell his patents but not to take on so great a risk. So Edison tried to help himself. He had 78,000 dollars at his disposal, and could raise a further 200,000 out of his interests in telegraphic and telephonic undertakings. An Edison electric lighting company was formed with a capital of a million dollars, only half of which, however, was paid up. This was little as compared with the magnitude of the undertaking, but Edison stormed onwards. He bought land in New York and moved there with his workshops from Menlo Park. This was made easy for him by the death of his beloved wife, for there was now nothing to hold him to Menlo Park.

In New York they now set to work to make everything needed for the new Central Station, but their money soon came to an end, and Edison did not know how to pay his workmen. He was so depressed that at times he thought that he would have to go back to earning his living as a telegraphist; there seemed no prospect whatever of getting any more money. The financiers had no longer much interest in Edison. New incandescent lamps had appeared on the scene; the quotations for Edison shares kept on falling. Then the first International Electrical Exhibition at Paris in 1881 came to his aid. Edison had sent to it his incandescent lamps, and his first large dynamo, by which he was able to light a thousand lamps. A great sensation was caused in Paris. Pictures of the Exhibition show us people standing in queues, in order to be able to try for themselves how an Edison glow-lamp could be lit and put out by the turn of a little switch. Everywhere the rights of manufacture of the Edison inventions were taken up. They were acquired for Germany by Emil Rathenau. Young Oskar von Miller also found in Paris his faith in the great future of the incandescent electric lamp, and of electricity works. Rathenau founded on this basis the Allegemeine Elektrizitäts-Gesellschaft and the Berlin Electricity Works, which were destined to do great pioneer work.

Everywhere the conviction became general that Edison had solved magnificently the problem of 'dividing the electric light.' A brilliant future was predicted for his work. This news travelled quickly to the New York Stock Exchange, and the prices of Edison shares were multiplied by ten. All purses were now opened to him. He was offered millions of dollars, but he, wise from bitter experience, determined to be master in his own house, and took only the most necessary funds. But he was now able to make his great work in New York a reality. In the spring of 1882, the whole network of cables had been put underground, and the central station, prototype of those to come, had been built in Pearl Street. Here Edison proved his great powers as a machine designer. On September 4th, 1882, this first great central station was got running; 2,300 lamps in eighty-five buildings were connected to it.

Edison also paid attention, as the result of suggestions coming from outside, to the electric locomotive; this was in 1880, a year after Siemens. And now the time had come to turn again to the phonograph, the favourite child of his brain. He now drove the apparatus with a little electric motor, but did not succeed in creating the dictating machine which he had in mind. Here also, Edison lost money in the end. A new Company now attempted to offer to the public musical records; and we are aware to-day of the enormous economic success later attained by the gramophone, especially in connection with radio. At that time, Edison was also busy with the cinematograph, introducing the perforated film used to-day.

As an example of his versatility we may recall a field of work of enormous industrial importance. Edison's attention had been drawn to sand containing a proportion of iron ore. He invented magnetic separators for these ores, at a time when he was right in the throes of his central station work. Later on, he took up this work again on a large scale, having learned that these mineral-bearing materials existed in enormous deposits. Again he became a machine designer, and erected a vast plant in a most desolate region, for he could only keep the price down to the necessary level by working on a large scale. Technically, he made a great success of the undertaking. But new and rich ore deposits were then discovered in Minnesota, of a sort able to be smelted directly. The price fell to half of the lowest which Edison could sell at. From the economic point of view, the whole enterprise, on which he had worked unceasingly for five years, was a great failure.

He not only lost all his savings, amounting to about two million dollars, but was again completely without means, since he wanted to pay the debts of the Company which bore his name. But all these heavy blows of fate were borne with an equanimity for which his friends could not find high enough praise. He maintained that one must not worry, but go on working, for worrying consumes much more nervous energy than the hardest work. He had put all his shares in the General Electric Company, which had taken over his Companies, with the undertakings, and his friends could easily prove to him that he had to add to his losses over four million dollars which would have been his profit on these.

He had to begin again from the beginning. Edison wanted to make use at least of some of his experiences, and he determined to make Portland cement. Experts laughed at his idea that he could produce something new in a field so far removed from his previous experience. But once more he was successful, for he succeeded in multiplying by five the output of the rotating roaster. He was soon regarded as an expert in cement. He looked for new outlets for his cement. He had no luck with his suggestion of replacing wood by cement for furniture. He determined to cast cement houses on a large scale in an extremely ingenious manner: these, constructed in the shortest possible time complete with all pipes and wiring, were to afford the poorest a home of their own in the smallest space. But here again, he could not at first compete quickly enough with the wooden houses so much beloved in America. He turned the work over to others; again he acted as the great pioneer along new lines. He then took up yet another great problem. He wanted to produce a lighter accumulator, secure against mechanical damage and vibrations. Once more he went to work with the tenacity characteristic of him. It is said that he made over 50,000 experiments, the result of which was the nickel-iron accumulator. Edison thought that this appliance would bring the electrically driven motor car into being, but the internal combustion motor upset his calculations. Henry Ford relates how he asked Edison's advice as to whether he should go ahead with his motor car. Edison advised him to do so, for he saw that the future belonged to the petrol-driven car. This advice from the man whose genius he so much admired gave Ford courage to devote himself on a large scale to his task.

Edison's personal life had in the meantime undergone some changes. In 1886, he found a second wife in Mina Miller. He wanted to make a beautiful new home for himself and her, and found what he was seeking in West Orange, in a country house built completely in the English style, and situated in a large park. He bought it with all its furnishings, and quickly put up near it his laboratories and workshops; soon there were not less than fifty such buildings, housing the work which he had to do apart from the company he had founded. His second marriage brought him two sons and a daughter, and in his new home Edison, who avoided large social gatherings whenever he could, found in the circle of his family, friends, and collaborators the kind of recreation after work which he desired. For the winter, he had acquired for his family a second home on the West Coast of Florida. But here he did not forget his work, which was always his best recreation. He wanted to die in harness, and even at the age of eighty he was at work on new problems which he still hoped to solve.

Though Edison has at times been referred to as a dreamer out of touch with the real world, no estimate could be farther from the truth. He possessed an unusual power of quick decision, and all his energies were devoted completely to real life at every stage of his career. True, he had never been attracted to money-making. What he earned he again and again, as we have seen, spent on new work and experiments, often without consideration for the consequences. His deafness was noticeable in personal intercourse, but he made light of it and often jokingly referred to it as an advantage, which made concentration on his work easier. He also used to tell his friends how fortunate it was that he was not forced to hear everything that was said.

Edison kept right into his old age his kindly, child-like, and modest nature. Those in contact with him were repeatedly astonished at the multiplicity of his interests, and at the extent of his knowledge in the most varied fields. His scientific library in Orange contained many thousands of works. He was not the sort of experimenter who goes looking for a needle in a haystack. He had a very high opinion of scientific work, and well knew how to make use of the powers of one of his chief assistants, who was especially versed in mathematics and a pupil of Helmholtz in Berlin.

Edison's work also bore new and valuable fruits in science. He discovered the passage of electric current from the glowing filament of a lamp to a positive electrode plate introduced into the bulb. This phenomenon is known in science by the name of the Edison effect. It formed the base for the rectifying two-electrode valves introduced into wireless as a receiver by John A. Fleming, an Englishman. An American, De Forest, introduced a grating between the filament and the plate, and so produced the first amplifying valve. So Edison's work led to very important developments in wireless. Here he lived to see the great developments of it, and ever ready to acknowledge the achievements of others, he paid tribute to Guglielmo Marconi as the creator of practical wireless, and gave him some of his own patents which were of value to Marconi.

The overwhelming abundance of Edison's work could only have been performed on the basis of an iron physical constitution inherited from his forefathers, which enabled him to support the greatest exertions. He well knew the decisive value of tenacious and incessant work. His saying that 'successful invention is one per cent. inspiration and ninety-nine per cent. perspiration,' is well known. He was famed for his enviable power of quickly recovering his energies. He was able to do with a minimum of sleep. He was a very moderate eater, and it was his opinion that many people kill themselves by overeating. He indulged in no games or sports, but he looked upon intensive work as health-giving, and he was never at a loss for it. His recreation consisted in reading exciting books—none could be too exciting for him—and in music. He played the violin as a boy, but he gave it up later as costing him too much time; but the piano, and his much beloved organ, which stood in the middle of his laboratory in Menlo Park, afforded him diversion and refreshment. He was especially fond of Beethoven.

He never had a day's illness in his whole life. Only at the end of his life did he become tired. Faithfully tended by his family, he passed away in his sleep on October 18th, 1931.

The Hall of Honour in the Munich Museum has a bust of him presented by the American Institute of Electrical Engineers and Edison Pioneers of New York. It bears the inscription:

'Thomas Alva Edison, the great inventor, to whom the world owes pioneer advances made in the most varied fields of science and technology.'

GEORGE WESTINGHOUSE
1846–1914

George Westinghouse is one of the great engineers of our time whose activity has had a very direct effect on our present-day technical methods. As an engineer, he is to be counted among the first in the profession, a man known far beyond the confines of America. The range of his technical and industrial activity is strikingly evidenced by the manufacturing concerns founded by him, spread over the world from San Francisco to St. Petersburg, and domiciled in many countries. Only a few months older than Edison, he was lost to us too soon, in 1914.

While Edison's forefathers came from Holland, Westinghouse's were Westphalians. His great-grandfather, Johann Heinrich von Wistinghausen, came to America at the age of fifteen with his mother, who was a widow. She settled down in the State of Vermont, north-east of Boston, in the green mountains. She changed her name to Westinghouse and dropped her noble rank, which had no significance in her new country. They cleared the forest, and rejoiced in a large family, for children were great wealth to the settlers in these sparsely inhabited parts. All we know of the son of this first settler, Johann Ferdinand, is that he had twelve children. The fifth of these was George Westinghouse the elder, who lived from 1809 to 1884. He married Emaline Vedder. They were the parents of George Westinghouse, the eighth of ten children, and born on October 6th, 1846, in the village of Central Bridge in the State of New York. His mother was of Dutch and English extraction. Her forefathers were farmers, neither rich nor poor, and a few craftsmen were among them. The Wistinghausens in Westphalia were strong and powerful men of extraordinary bravery, who had several times distinguished themselves in the service of foreign princes. The traits inherited by the young George

Westinghouse were of the highest importance for his career.

The father moved in 1856 to Schenectady where he founded a factory for agricultural machines. He also built small steam engines, and young George spent with him industrious and happy years. The little factory, in which, at ten years of age, he was already becoming familiar with all types of work, was his real technical school in which he acquired abilities and knowledge of the greatest value in his later career. He only spent a short time in a technical college. He thought he could learn what he wanted better and faster in his father's works.

The terrible civil war broke out, and George and his brother could not be held back; they fought for the Northern States, regarding it as self-evident that they should fight for their country. The training in self-control and discipline, in obeying orders, in carrying out with unconditional reliability a command given by a superior, was regarded by Westinghouse as especially important for his education, together with his practical work in the factory. He had a great belief in discipline. One must first learn to obey, he thought, before one is able to command. This reminds me of a remarkable personal experience which I had of George Westinghouse. In 1912, on the occasion of my first visit to America, I was privileged to discuss with him the history of technology. But the first shots had been fired in the Balkans and the discussion came round to the war in Europe, so unusual in those peaceful times. Westinghouse surprised me by asking me when I believed the Great War would break out, which he regarded inevitable in view of the great industrial progress of Germany as compared with England, a fact of which he had been able to convince himself again and again on his visits to the two countries. He would have nothing to do with the idea that such a war was impossible. He maintained that the World War would break out in two years at the most, and he was right. The second question discussed was the reason for the unexampled industrial progress of Germany. I felt it incumbent upon me to point to the great achievements of our technical high schools. Whereupon he gave it as his opinion that the learned professors had no doubt made their contribution, but—and here was the second surprise for me—the decisive factor was our military service, by which every German was taught the discipline without which a great industry could neither be built up nor permanently maintained. He was delighted again and again, when passing through the streets of Essen or Berlin, to see the disciplined demeanour of the young men, and he tried to guess whether or no everyone he met had served his time as a soldier.

Young Westinghouse was already occupied at the age of fifteen in attempting to make a rotary steam engine; his work in his father's factory, and the father himself, stimulated him to start inventing, for his father regarded it as part of his work as an engineer to continually improve his machines. The rotary engine was a failure as a steam engine, but he succeeded in making a very useful water-meter out of it.

He soon came in contact with railway work, to which his own contribution was to be of so great value. In 1865, after the Civil War, he built an appliance for getting derailed railway cars back on to the lines. His experience in a railway accident began to excite his technical activity very strongly. Such accidents could be avoided if an effective brake could be invented, which at that time did not exist. Speed of travelling is like fire. It is only beneficial to man when he is able to tame and control it. If we are to travel fast, we must be able to brake effectively. The efficiency of the railway depends largely on brakes, and a good brake is naturally one of the most important safety devices for traffic. This fact was well known before George Westinghouse's time. Many engineers of the Old and New Worlds had paid the greatest attention to improvement of the brake.

In America the hand-brake, jokingly called the 'Armstrong' brake by railway men, was still commonly used for both passenger and goods traffic. The brakes were first put on the locomotive, and the brakeman then ran back over the roofs of the cars to the last carriage in order to work the hand-brake. Accidents in this operation were of regular occurrence, quite apart from the fact that this brake could do little to avert the sort of accidents which may happen on railways. Westinghouse saw here a great field of work for himself. He first made a braking device in which he put under the car a steam cylinder with a long stroke, acting by a rod on the brakes. He then went on to use winches and chains, only to return to the steam cylinder under each car as the solution. But the steam condensed much too quickly in the long steam pipes and cylinders. No success could be obtained in this way.

And then by chance a journal came his way from which he learned that in driving the Mont Cenis tunnel, compressed air had been used on a large scale in pipes over 3,000 ft. long. From that day his mind was made up that compressed air was most suitable for railway brakes. His first patent for a compressed-air brake was taken out in 1867. He then built with his own hands, working at the lathe, the vice, and the forge, his first air brake, and applied it practically. He was successful, and the Pennsylvania Railroad allowed him to build one for an experimental train of ten cars at his own cost. Westinghouse now determined to found the Airbrake Company in Pittsburg, an undertaking which was to attain a size and importance undreamed of even by the engineer himself. From it, the Westinghouse brake set out on its victorious career on all railway systems of the world.

The first compressed-air brake consisted of the compressor and air reservoir taking a pressure of four or five atmospheres, the compressed air line running under the cars, and connected by flexible pipes, and a brake cylinder under every car. But it worked much too slowly, and when the train broke in two and the danger was specially great, it could not act at all. Westinghouse continually introduced very important improvements. In 1872 he was able to demonstrate his first automatic brake to the railway. Improvement after improvement led to the rapid brake, whih is now universal in railway work. It has been pointed out in America, as illustrating the importance of his work, that in 1869, when his work began, goods trains were made up of about thirty trucks. In 1886 fifty trucks could already be taken, and to-day in America we have gigantic trains with 150 of the long American trucks. While the trains of 1869 travelled at a rate of 15 m.p.h., they now do 50. The importance of this for the economy of the railway system may be readily calculated. Present-day railway traffic is unthinkable without the quick-acting compressed-air brake. As we have already said, Westinghouse was not the inventor of the railway brake. Indeed, it has been shown that at the time he started work, 600 patents for railway brakes were already in existence. Westinghouse alone took out over 100 and this is perhaps the best proof of the fact that there was no question here of the lightning-flash idea, but of arriving step-by-step at the solution by laborious detail work.

Westinghouse had never been satisfied, in this field or in any other of his engineering interests, with simply settling the constructive idea. He was at the same time the great industrialist, who set the greatest value on regular workshop manufacture. He knew that the success of his brake was dependent upon very accurate mass-manufacture of its parts. This led to his putting before the rising American machine tool industry new and great problems. But above all, he recognized the great value of standarization, most especially in this field. What unnecessary expense would not the American railways have finally incurred, if he had given way to the desire of every company to have him make a special brake for it alone ? He regarded the standard-ization of every part as of prime importance, and in this way effected great economies. In the course of improving his

Ye

brake time after time, he insisted that the new constructions
should be designed so as to work together with the old.
This again saved large costs in installation, and enabled the
improvements to be introduced more easily and quickly by
the railways. The history of the Westinghouse brake shows
clearly how highly important these single improvements are,
for without any of them being startling, they add up finally
to make the invention a success.

Westinghouse also used compressed air for signals and
other railway purposes. He made an automatic coupling
worked by compressed air, and this has been introduced in
America in increasing numbers.

Though this field of work was of enormous size and
importance, it did not suffice him. The electric current
began early on to attract him. As early as 1886 he founded
a factory for work in connection with electric light, in
particular the manufacture of lamps. He was also building
small dynamos. Westinghouse studied the development,
and believed in the great future of electric current, foreseeing
that it would be distributed over the country. This would
have been impossible with the direct current at 110 volts
then in use. Even when Edison's three-wire system was
in use, it was not possible to distribute over a greater radius
than a few thousand yards. But Westinghouse looked into
the future and saw a high-tension network of electric conductors covering whole countries and even continents. He
became the pioneer of high-tension alternating current in
America, and so came into conflict with Edison and his
friends, who at first would have nothing to do with high
tension on account of its danger, and would have preferred
to see it forbidden by law.

The fight between direct and alternating current, conducted by passionate and temperamental people, took on, in
the Old and New Worlds, forms hardly conceivable to us
to-day. Instead of saying 'this as well as that' and helping
one another, people went out to fight furiously for one

or the other. When at the time the plan of executing condemned criminals by electricity was put forward in America, the direct-current party was delighted that a Westinghouse alternating current machine was chosen for the purpose. Could there be a better proof of their assertion that alternating current is a killer ? But these years of warfare came to an end, and among the honours conferred on Westinghouse, the Edison gold medal of the American Society of Electrical Engineers must have especially pleased him, for it was presented to him for his courageous advocacy of high-tension alternating current. It would be a good thing if we all now and then looked away from the struggles of the day into the distant future.

Westinghouse acquired for America the alternating current patents of the English engineers Gaulard and Gibbs. Their transformer was further developed in America. The transformer, by which the voltage given by the dynamo may be changed, as required, by an apparatus without moving parts, rendered it possible to send high tension alternating current overland. It was now possible to think of using locally limited sources of energy to supply power at points far distant from them. Nikola Tesla, the great inventor and engineer in the field of alternating current, was called by Westinghouse to Pittsburg. Westinghouse gave him all financial and material help needed for the development of his alternating current motor. In 1887 he acquired the patents granted to Tesla for his work, and he and his company could now set about building great electricity works of a new kind. He built the first ten great 2-phase generators for the Niagara water-power station; these attracted the interest of the whole technical world, for they had been built in fiercest possible competition with the rest of the electrical industry.

The competition for the lighting of the World Exhibition at Chicago in 1893 was also very keen. Westinghouse had need of unusual courage to fight his way in the fullest publicity into a field in which he had only the smallest experience. He put in ten 1,000-h.p. alternating current machines, a size regarded as amazing at the time. His competitors, secure in their monopoly of the Edison patents, had not imagined it possible that Westinghouse would get the order. But the difference between the two tenders was too attractive for the Exhibition Committee. Westinghouse did the business at a loss, but the brilliance of his lighting installation, together with the very high attendance at the Exhibition, repaid his losses many times over. He had introduced himself to the world as the pioneer of high tension electric current. The difficulties which he had to overcome were very great, for he was unable to use Edison's very practical incandescent lamps. He had to make other lamps which did not infringe Edison's patents. He used a 105 volt glow-lamp, the filament of which was enclosed in a glass bulb filled with nitrogen. This was sealed by a stopper, so that burnt-out filaments could be replaced. Hundreds of thousands of lamps had to be manufactured as quickly as possible, and a multiple of this number had to be provided for replacements, since these lamps burned out very quickly. The responsible work of replacing at night the burnt-out lamps must certainly have been rather nerve-racking, but success fell to the man of enterprise. Westinghouse was also able to acquire the services of other first-rate engineers for his undertakings. Here we will only name O. B. Schallenberger, C. F. Scott, and Peter Cooper-Hewitt. These and other colleagues of his have again and again testified with the greatest readiness to the pleasure they found in working with Westinghouse who, always full of new ideas, roused their enthusiasm to the point at which they gave of their best in carrying out his plans. Westinghouse then proceeded to use high-tension electric current on a large scale for electric railways. The great generators needed efficient prime movers to drive them. The attempt was made to use high-speed piston engines for the purpose, but this was not the solution. Then he became aware of Parsons' work in England on the steam turbine. He sent one of his staff there to study the position with instructions that if the turbine was all that it was reported to be in the technical journals, he was to buy the American patent rights at any price. The rights were acquired, and Westinghouse then played his own part in developing Parsons' turbine further in America.

He also took an early interest in the utilization of the natural gas so common in America, and this work with gas finally led him to gas engines; here again he was able to score a respectable success. We see how great was the amount of work accomplished by Westinghouse the engineer in the fields to which we have shortly referred, supported as he was by highly capable assistants whom he always succeeded in finding and retaining.

His creative work in industry is not less extensive. He founded almost a hundred companies in and out of America for the accomplishment of his engineering plans. He was an industrialist in the grand style. But his aim was not the acquisition of wealth. It was said of him that he never speculated on the Stock Exchange, and that he never bought any industrial shares but those of his own companies. Constructive work was the one need and joy of his life. To this was added the pride in the fact that he was finding work and food for a great number of persons, and giving them a secure livelihood. The great works in Pittsburg became even greater. Over 50,000 persons were working day after day at the carrying out of George Westinghouse's plans.

What enabled this man to accomplish a life-work so vast that we have been able to give only the barest outlines of it ? One factor was the characteristics he inherited from his ancestors. This powerful upstanding man, a head taller than those round him, had an iron constitution. Change of work was his best recreation. His temperament forbade him to take the advice of his friends, and allow himself some leisure. He was a constructive worker, who brought a strong common sense to bear upon the very concrete things with which he was concerned, and took little interest in abstract matters. He possessed a great power of concentration, which he regarded as essential to the mastery of the enormous multiplicity of problems which continually confronted him. His manner was short and definite, and his decisions were made quickly.

Another characteristic was his love of a fight, when it was for a real cause, and not for mere personal vanity. Great constructors are always optimists, and Westinghouse himself had this positive attitude towards life. Whenever his best collaborators could no longer see a way out, Westinghouse never gave up things for lost. When one road was blocked, another had to be driven. He was a man of great daring, who pursued his aims without allowing anything to turn him aside. Even he did not have unbroken success; in the industrial side of his work in particular, the great crisis of 1907 brought him bitter disappointment, and the question has been whether, in spite of all his achievements as an engineer, he was not a failure as an industrialist. But these critics are silenced; we now recognize that he had a great and true grasp of developments which he already foresaw far ahead of the times. Those who stood nearest to him all tell us of his fairness of character, his personal kindness, and his sympathetic understanding of his workmen and employees. He neither developed nor followed any system of social measures, but he saw the human being and the fellow worker in the humblest of his employees, and endeavoured to help him as far as lay in his power. Westinghouse suffered from no lack of recognition in the form of honours such as are conferred in our times. The German engineers gave him, a year before his death, their highest distinction, the Grashof medal; he was designated as 'the pioneer inventor of the automatic brake, the successful protagonist of alternating current in the United States, the meritorious designer of high-speed engines.'

Westinghouse died in his sixty-eighth year, on March 12th, 1914, of heart disease. His faithful lifelong companion in a happy marriage which had begun in his twenty-first year, died only a year afterwards. In 1936 the American Engineers celebrated his ninetieth birthday, in full session, by addresses on his work, by recollections of his great personality, thus testifying that the engineer George Westinghouse and his work are living realities for the present generation.

CARL VON LINDE

1842–1934

Among the great engineers whose creative work passed the limit of the nineteenth century and reached to our own day was the *doyen* of refrigerating technology, Carl von Linde. In the address presented to him by the Munich Science Museum on his ninetieth birthday, June 11th, 1932, it is said: 'Your life was marked by success after success, your inventions opened up new fields in physics and technology. You were honoured by everyone who came in contact with you.'

Linde's grandfather was a Berlin shoemaker, Ludwig Linde, who came in the course of his wanderings to Regensburg, and settled there after marrying the daughter of a Regensburg tradesman. In 1811, his only son, Friedrich, was born. The father died when the son was seven years old, and the mother had to bring up the son, whose outstanding intellectual gifts were early recognized, in the greatest poverty. Young Linde was assisted to study theology. In 1838 he married the daughter of a Neuwied merchant. On June 11th, 1842, his third child, Carl, was born in Bernsdorf in Oberfranken; six more children were to follow. The father had an iron sense of duty, and was completely regardless of his own comfort. He was an excellent and conscientious shepherd of souls, trustworthy and faithful. The son claimed for his mother 'a devotion to truth, pure and candid in a rare degree, and a power of devotion to personal ideals, views, and aims combined with a contempt for material obstacles and opinions opposed to her.' The parents endured deprivation and anxiety as a natural duty, in order to equip their numerous children as well as possible for their work in life.

This home, spiritually and physically healthy, and fundamentally religious, gave Carl Linde the roots of his power. At six years of age he went to school in Kempten, where the father had moved to for the sake of the children's upbringing. He did not particularly care for the dead languages, his abilities being rather in mathematics and history. In these years at school, Linde did not neglect his body. Great exertions in long walks, long runs to the sea, bathing, rowing, and sailing always renewed his strength for mental labour.

Linde was in his youth a great lover of literature, even to the extent of at one time seriously thinking of becoming a writer. But his first contact with the technical world, afforded by a cotton mill in Kempten, gave him impressions which were stronger still. The steam engines which he saw there for the first time aroused his enthusiasm and had a decisive effect on his choice of a career. The father, who had at one time hoped to see all his sons pastors some day, did not oppose the desire of the son to become a machine engineer. He even made it possible for him to attend the Polytechnic in Zürich, which at that time was specially famed for its teaching staff. From 1861 to 1864, Linde studied there under Anton Zeuner and Franz Reuleaux, young professors who were able to arouse the enthusiasm of their students, and later did so much in Dresden and Berlin for the training of engineers. Physics was represented by Clausius, whose lectures on heat greatly impressed Linde. They determined the nature of the great work he was afterwards to do. 'No other section of my studies was and has remained of so much importance to me as applied thermodynamics.'

But Linde did not bury himself in the special branches of his own course of reading. He attended the lectures of Fr. Th. Vischer, and every one of his lectures on Goethe and Shakespeare was a festival for him. He also enjoyed the lectures on the general history of art. He found refreshment in the cheerful company of the Swiss families of good standing which he visited. Music played a large part in this side of his life.

In 1864 his studies came to an end. Linde sought a post after a short spell of practical work. But it was hard to find one. Again and again he had to take no for an answer. Personal introductions in Augsburg and Munich failed to help him to what he wanted. He next went to Berlin, but there again he got nothing but refusals. Then his teacher Reuleaux, now Director of the *Gewerbeakademie* (Trade Academy) in Berlin, got him an unpaid post in Borsig's locomotive factory. He was soon able to earn his first money, sixteen thalers a month. He now had to manage to live chiefly on tea, bread, and a little butter. Linde in his reminiscences looks back with especial thankfulness upon the Sundays spent in the Grimm family, the head of which was Attorney General (*Generalstaatsanwalt*). Frau Grimm was his aunt, and Linde in 1866 made the daughter his wife, and lived with her for fifty-three years filled with work and happiness.

The desire to found a family forced him to improve his position. 'Serving Borsig in the hope of advancement' did not seem to offer much hope. Then he heard that the machine engineer Georg Krauss was proposing to found a new works in Munich. Linde applied for the post of head designer. He was then only twenty-three years of age, but he was liked for his steady open nature, and in March, 1866, he began to help in the construction of the new works. Linde was thankful to be allowed to develop as 'apprentice in the school of a distinguished master.' In March, 1867, he was able to drive the first locomotive to Strasbourg, spending twenty hours on the footplate, and thence, in forty hours more, to the World Exhibition in Paris. The machine won the great gold medal. This engine was working in Oldenburg till 1900; to-day, it stands in the Munich Museum as a masterpiece of German technical work.

Linde was well satisfied with his work with Krauss. He complained of only one thing: that he had hardly any time for scientific work, which he had always desired to do. However, he succeeded, at the age of twenty-six, in becoming assistant professor of machine design at the newly erected Polytechnic in Munich, with a yearly salary of 1,000 gulden. But to keep a family on a salary of 1,000 gulden, it was necessary to discover side-lines by which he could add to his income. Linde wrote for journals and taught privately. His very valuable account of experiments done on one of the first great Sulzer engines made him known in the technical world. It led to his often being called in as an expert. His life-work was decided by a scientific paper which appeared in 1870, and had to do with 'the withdrawal of heat at low temperatures by mechanical means.' In 1871 he published a paper on 'Improved ice- and refrigerating-machines.' The brewers now began to take notice. Gabriel Sedlmayr in Munich was ready to have the first machine made at his own expense and to carry out the experiments in his own brewery at Munich. The way was now open for Linde to enter constructive technical work. But it is characteristic of him that right from the start he was not satisfied simply to build better refrigerating machinery, but regarded it as equally important to find suitable means for applying and transmitting cold. In 1873 he developed his programme at the International Brewing Congress during the Vienna Exhibition. The refrigerating machine was to be introduced as a substitute into the already highly organized natural ice technology, but it was not necessary to stop there. The next step was to cool liquids and rooms directly instead of by using artificial ice. If that were properly carried out, the cost of cooling could be lowered to such an extent that natural ice could no longer compete, even at its most favourable price. This created great interest among the brewers. In Munich, Vienna, Copenhagen, Rotterdam, and Strasbourg, to name only a few towns, the desire arose to attain this end with the help of the young professor.

The Maschinenfabrik Augsburg built in the meantime the first Linde refrigerating machine with a very high efficiency as compared with the existing machines. Linde had at first used methyl ether as his liquid: he now went over to ammonia.

Augsburg was to build a second machine. But who was to pay for it? Linde took the course of handing over to those who financed him a share in his patent. Krauss, Sedlmayr, and Heinrich Buz, who was later to exert so decisive an influence on the development of the Diesel engine, were prepared to help. The second Linde refrigerator then worked from 1877 to 1908 in Dreher's brewery in Trieste. It is now in the Technical Museum in Vienna.

A third construction followed in which the same effect was gained by considerably simpler means. This form has been retained in all its essentials in Europe until to-day.

Following out his original aim, Linde now proceeded to apply cold in the most efficient way. The experiments and experimental plants made to this end were an entire success, and absorbed Linde's working powers more and more completely.

Linde might naturally have decided at this point to put up his own works. But he had no intention of making everything himself so long as existing undertakings were able to execute his designs for him in a first-rate way. The Maschinenfabrik Augsburg took over the construction of Linde's plants in Germany, Gebrüder Sulzer of Winterthur in Switzerland, Italy, and Spain; and in France, Holland, Belgium, and

England he also found excellent firms very willing to co-operate with him. These widespread connections are the most striking proof of the success of his fundamental work.

Linde himself was now to receive the fruits of his great success. He founded in Wiesbaden the *Gesellschaft für Lindes Eismaschinen*, at the start a very modest undertaking consisting of one room with a draughtsman working in it. He determined in 1879 to act as manager of this company for ten years. The history of this undertaking is one of great and rapid advance in the introduction and utilization of Linde's inventions, thanks to his brilliant and unceasing labour. The first important field was that of breweries. Here Linde redesigned the whole process of production so as to make use of the new technique. He then proceeded to build ice factories on his own account, and developed the whole field of refrigerating and freezing plants. The company thus became a great designing and drawing office without any manufacturing plant of its own, but having connections with every country in the world. Linde in this way found work for thousands of his fellow Germans. When he left Wiesbaden in 1891, over 1,200 of his refrigerating plants were running, 747 of them in breweries.

Linde was forty-nine years of age when he believed that his position was secure. The financial returns of his work had made him independent. He then set up in Munich an experimental laboratory for research into the lowest temperatures. Here he wanted to devote himself to investigation and to a limited amount of teaching at the technical high school. He was naturally unable to get completely free of the great undertakings which he had created. He was always available to give advice, which was highly valued on the commercial side as well as by those in charge of the business side.

In his low temperature research station in Munich, he was chiefly concerned with recent discoveries. Very low temperatures are necessary to liquefy the 'permanent' gases.

Characteristic of his manner of working is the fact that he first worked carefully through all that had been published in recent years bearing on this theme. Physicists had then only succeeded in producing quite small quantities of liquid oxygen, nitrogen, and carbon monoxide. That was hardly enough for scientific work. There could be no question of any technical application, and it was here that Linde's happy union in one person of the scientific investigator and the experienced engineer and industrialist found a field of action. Linde proposed to sum up the effects of successive coolings by expansion of a gas, by letting the gas so cooled flow in countercurrent to that about to expand. It was only later that Linde learned that William Siemens had already suggested this idea in 1857, and that Ernest Solvay had described it in a patent specification in 1885 and had also attempted to make it work.

William Thomson and James Prescott Joule had shown in 1862 that when a gas expands from a nozzle, it suffers a lowering of temperature of about $\frac{1}{4}°$ C. for every atmosphere decrease in pressure. This fall in temperature is very small. Linde now succeeded in arranging matters in such a way that sufficient cooling was produced in this manner, and had thus found a way of making this source of cold, hitherto disregarded because so small, form the basis of a process of an extremely simple sort. Linde began his work with initial pressures of some 20 atmospheres, and with compressions of some 60 atmospheres. The experiments were started in May, 1895. Linde writes in his reminiscences: 'With great joy and excitement we saw the temperature fall in the regular manner given by Thomson and Joule, even after the limits within which they had worked were long passed.' But it was only on the third day that a liquefaction of the air might be hoped for. 'We continued to work the machine until a certain amount of liquid air might be presumed to have collected. We then allowed the beautiful blue liquid to escape into a large metal pail amid clouds.

About three litres were produced per hour. It was the first time that air had been liquefied on such a scale, and that, too, by means which, as compared with those hitherto used, were of staggering simplicity.' This success aroused the greatest astonishment far beyond the limits of technical circles. Linde was everywhere asked to lecture. Only at the beginning did he decide to lecture himself, and demonstrate his liquid air, to the Physikalisch-Technische Reichsanstalt (the National Physical Laboratory of Germany), the Verein deutscher Ingenieure, and the German Emperor.

What was to be done with this new technical advance in liquefying air ? That was the question which Linde, as an engineer, soon put to himself. His results were seized upon by people who based the wildest speculations on them. He was never tired of rejecting such crazy exaggeration, and of pointing out the limits of applicability of the new discovery and summed up the results as follows. Firstly, laboratories could be supplied with small liquid air machines, and so be enabled to conduct experiments at temperatures down to −200° C. Secondly, mixtures of gases could be separated into their constituents by liquefaction and re-evaporation. Thirdly, liquid air mixed with oxidizable substances might be used as an explosive.

Linde's invention formed the starting-point for remarkable and far-reaching researches in the physics of the lowest temperatures, and also in the investigation of very high vacua. Even to-day, development in this field is still going on.

The technical and industrial development of his invention was carried out by Linde in close collaboration with his company in Wiesbaden. He succeeded in producing, on a technical scale, pure oxygen, which was of the greatest use, for just at that time a rapid development was occurring in welding and cutting metals by oxy-gas flames. For this again, extensive experiments were necessary, and for these Linde, in 1901, provided himself with new facilities in Höllsiegelskreuth

near Munich.   Here also the first oxygen factory, together
with the necessary workshops, was put up in 1902.

At first, the separation of air into its constituents was
carried out for the sake of the oxygen only, but the
nitrogen also soon became of importance.   Linde had to
accomplish a great work of organization in addition to his
engineering labours.   Agreements had to be made with all
sorts of countries spread over the whole earth.   A large
amount of not very agreeable labour was also called for in
defending the patents against infringement, which experience shows always occurs when success is obtained.   Linde
conquered for himself as engineer and scientist two large
provinces of work.

Work and struggle, hope and disappointment, were necessary features of such a life.   But his great success, and the
loyalty of his collaborators, made life pleasant for him.

He had the good fortune to live to a great age, full of
vigour for work, and in close touch with his six children
and their families; he was thus able to witness the further
consequences of his great work.   He was able to have the
fullest confidence in the continuation of his work by his
two sons and his son-in-law, together with other collaborators
of whom he had a high opinion.

Linde, apart from his own life's work, gave his services,
as he had already done when a student in Munich, on behalf
of a great variety of movements.   He did important work
in the technical societies, above all in the Verein deutscher
Ingenieure, which had conferred on him in 1897 its
highest distinction, the Grashof Medal.   He was continually
fertile in new suggestions.   He took part with especial joy
and energy in the foundation of the Munich Museum, the
plan of which he supported with enthusiasm.   The high
esteem in which his person and his work were held was
clearly expressed by the number of honours conferred upon
him.

As the senior of the German engineers, he was able to

follow technical development and retain his mental vigour until he passed away on November 16th, 1934, at the age of ninety-two.

OSKAR VON MILLER

1855–1934

The great Hall of Fame celebrating the engineering achievements of all the world through many thousands of years of history, is in Munich. We will conclude our journey from the times of the Pharaohs to the twentieth century by giving an account of the creator of the 'German Museum of Masterpieces of Science and Technology,' known in English-speaking countries chiefly by its German name the *Deutsche Museum*, or as the Munich Science Museum.

Oskar von Miller was born in the famous Royal Bronze Foundry in Munich, the tenth son, one of fourteen children, of the bronze-founder Ferdinand von Miller, a man who loved his work. He grew up amid the busy activities of the foundry, and in later years he spoke again and again with enthusiasm of that time, when apprentices, journeymen and master, animated by a delight in their work, shared their joys and sorrows in common. Here young Miller experienced the greatness of technical team work, in which the achievement of each is dependent on the work of the others, and great work can only be accomplished by co-operation. His father, the great bronze-founder whose works went all over the world, whose skill is attested by great bronze monuments, set up even in America, was for him the high exemplar of love for one's work and for art, and of a strong sense of the greatness of Germany, arising out of love for his native province.

The question of the choice of a career now came up. Oskar von Miller wished to become an engineer. He thought of one day building roads and canals, regulating rivers. The

43.   CARL VON LINDE (1842–1934)

44.   Oskar von Miller (1855–1934)

Photograph in possession of the Deutsche Museum, Munich

first step was to gain practical experience. In 1878 he was able to take part in building, from the beautiful mediaeval town of Dinkelsbühl, a railway to Dombühl. But Miller's ambition reached far beyond Dinkelsbühl. He saved up with great energy the money to go to London, where he wanted to study the railways. There he also became acquainted with the famous Science Museum in South Kensington. He saw the first locomotives, and wondered at the poor way in which, at that time, these famous monuments of technical culture were housed. They were in a wooden shed in the yard, without one word of explanation, or any reference to their great history.

He then went as a working student to Switzerland, and got to know the St. Gotthard railway, then being built, and other great engineering feats. His next stay was in Neuburg on the Danube, where he was employed on road and river works. A tireless worker, he gained the respect of his superiors everywhere he went. After passing his State examination, he was given a position in the Road and River Office in Munich, and later one with the Government of Upper Bavaria. But this work for the authorities was far from satisfying the young and ambitious engineer. He pressed to be given independent work, but got little attention. At that time Oskar von Miller had already become a photographer. The art was one very little practised, and very difficult as compared with what it is to-day. The young engineer attempted to illustrate by photographs his reports to the authorities on the progress of work; but he received a sharp reprimand. Photography was officially rejected.

And then, in the spring of 1881, came the news that an international electrical exhibition was to take place in Paris in the autumn. The man under whom he was working at the time said jokingly that there was something for Oskar Miller. But he took the matter very seriously, and succeeded in getting sent as Bavarian delegate to Paris, to study the question whether electricity could be generated by Bavarian

water power. This was the task which he himself had
chosen. The visit to Paris and study of the exhibition
determined his future career. Even at a great age he could
still describe his experiences in a way that gripped one.
'The impression produced by the exhibition was overwhelming. The lighting exceeded all one had imagined.
The Edison glow-lamps, set as stars in the dome and on the
staircase, the arc-lamps of Brush and Siemens, which diffused
a light hitherto unknown, the Jablochoff candles, Clerk's
Soleil lamp, which lit up a picture gallery by means of a
glowing block of marble—all this was marvellous. The
greatest excitement of all was one of Edison's glow-lamps,
which one could turn on and off by means of a switch.
People stood in queues of hundreds, in order to be able to
turn the switch themselves. . . . General astonishment was
excited by the telephonic transmission of opera; and people
who have been accustomed to the telephone from early
youth can have no conception of the eerie astonishment
produced by hearing in the telephone singers and instruments
and the applause of the public.'

But that was not all that he found unforgettable. The
great dynamos of Siemens, Gramme, and Edison were standing there, and he studied them with success. Above all, he
wanted to know in what form, and how far, electrical energy
could be transmitted. That would be decisive as an answer
to his question of the utilization of Bavarian water power.
In this connection he came in contact with Marcel Deprez,
who was paying special attention to this matter.

In Paris, he also examined carefully the great technical
museum, the 'Conservatoire National des Arts et Métiers';
not only in order to become acquainted with the technical
arrangements, but also with the object of learning in the
most direct way the French technical expressions in his own
line of work, water engineering.

His visit to the Paris Exhibition was followed by long
journeys through the whole of France for the purpose of

study; these greatly developed his powers. He then returned to Munich, full of the strongest new impressions. He described them in enthusiastic lectures to technical societies. He wanted to have the wonders seen in Paris also exhibited on a great scale in Munich. In this way arose the idea of an electrical exhibition there. A great task was proposed. The father spurred his son on to produce a really good show on a large scale. No one was readier to accept such advice than Oskar von Miller. In spite of the gravest doubts expressed on all sides, he believed that the Glass Palace at Munich would be only just large enough for his exhibition. But it was now a question of going ahead quickly, for the Imperial City of Vienna was sending out invitations for a great international electrotechnical exhibition in 1883. Oskar von Miller wanted to anticipate this, and in the shortest imaginable time, invitations were sent out from Munich for the exhibition of 1882.

The Glass Palace was soon filled with electrical machines, conductors, accumulators and examples of all the electrical apparatus being produced at that time. The detailed report of the exhibition gives us a striking picture of this infant electrotechnical industry. But the centre of interest was electric incandescent lighting. For the first time in Germany Edison's lamps were to be seen on a large scale. The intention was not, however, merely to show the lamp, but to demonstrate its effect in living-rooms; and some of the first artists of the day were called in to produce artistically decorated rooms of the most varied description, illuminated by the new light. So the Bavarian furniture and interior decoration of the period were represented at this technical exhibition. In those days of great theatre fires, the news that dangerous open gas flames could now be replaced by closed electric bulbs was a pleasant surprise for all theatre directors. A theatre was built in the exhibition, and ballets were given in it, all electrically lit. Everyone could now convince himself of the new technical advance, and the theatres became important customers in the early days of the infant industry.

Oskar von Miller had more in view with his exhibition than simply giving visitors an impression of what had been already achieved; his further aim was to raise new problems and to work at their solution; and of these none seemed more important than the question of the transmission of power. He arranged for the exhibition committee to send a very complimentary letter to Marcel Deprez, as member of the French Academy of Sciences, asking him to carry out in Munich the experiments which he had described on the electric transmission of power. The Bavarian Minister of State was willing to put at his disposal a telegraph line, 25 to 50 kilometres long. Even if no machines should be available having all the properties called for by Marcel Deprez, it would still be of great importance to know that power could be transmitted over such great distances.

The French engineer willingly agreed. The line between Miesbach and Munich was chosen, because there was a little 2 h.p. steam engine available to drive the dynamo. The transmission voltage was 1,500 to 2,000 volts. In the Glass Palace in Munich a motor was installed taking the current from Miesbach, and driving a centrifugal pump supplying a waterfall. This is an example of Miller's talent for demonstrating strikingly and effectively to the public the working of the arrangement. The experiment was a success. 'The surprise, joy, and enthusiasm,' writes Oskar von Miller, 'were extraordinarily great, for proof was thus given that it was technically possible to transmit natural power from a long distance to towns.' It was not forgotten to telegraph to the Academy of Sciences in Paris to inform it that one of its members had succeeded for the first time in transmitting power over a distance of 57 kilometres through an ordinary telegraph wire, and that this would be of far-reaching importance for the development of electrotechnics and the utilization of natural sources of power.

Oskar von Miller brought into being another arrangement on the occasion of this exhibition. He did not want to distribute medals, but instead to have an independent commission to test the properties and effectiveness of the objects exhibited, and set these down in a document to be handed to the exhibitor. The idea was more easily stated than carried out. It was first necessary to learn to measure and judge. Here a young assistant, Erasmus Kittler, who later became a distinguished German professor of electrical engineering, played a prominent part; later on, while at Darmstadt, his efforts were very fruitful in promoting the development of the new branch of technology.

The exhibition, and the many-sided work connected with it, had greatly enlarged Miller's knowledge and powers in the field of electrical engineering. But his desire now was to go to America and learn what was being done there. Eminent industrialists commissioned Miller in 1883 to go to France, England, and America, in order to discover personally the latest advances in electrical engineering. In his recollections of London, he specially mentions the great technical museum with its rich treasures. In America he made the acquaintance of Edison. He visited the first electric central station in Pearl Street; he went to Boston, Chicago, and further West. Full of enthusiasm for all that he had been able to see, he returned to Germany. He then went to Vienna to the electrical exhibition already opened there. Here he met Emil Rathenau, who had acquired the rights of Edison's patents for Germany. Rathenau asked Oskar von Miller whether he would come as technical director to the Allgemeine Elektrizitäts-Gesellschaft which was about to be founded in Berlin. He offered him about fourteen times as much as the very modest salary he was receiving as a Bavarian official. Miller asked for time to consider the matter, and it is characteristic of him that he then, instead of asking for an increase in his present salary, put forward to the Bavarian Government the request that he should be put in charge of an office where he could devote himself to the exploitation of Bavarian water power. Thirty years later, the Government created the 'Bureau for Utilization of Water Power and Supply of Electricity.' But at that time no one would hear of the idea. The problem seemed too far outside the sphere of the State.

Miller then determined to go to Berlin, and for seven years he devoted his whole time to Rathenau's new undertaking. Here he had the possibility of greatly increasing his knowledge. He has given us in his reminiscences an exciting description of the difficulties which had to be overcome. But he felt drawn back to his home, Bavaria. He wanted to attempt to establish himself there, however modestly, as an independent engineer. He opened in Munich an office as consulting engineer under his own name. He had troubles and cares to fight, but his love of work, his enthusiastic and yet well-judged activity never flagged. His work was interrupted for a short time by a new and important task, when he was asked to take over the technical direction of the great 1891 Electricity Exhibition in Frankfort. He wanted the programme there to be wider than that of the Munich and Vienna exhibitions. Whereas it had been the chief purpose of the latter to bring before visitors the advantages of electric light, the new exhibition was to demonstrate the electrical distribution and transmission of power in every possible form. In Frankfort workshops were to be exhibited, in order to show hand workers and small traders what a wonderful aid was now at their disposal.

But chiefly, he wanted there to demonstrate the transmission of electric power to great distances, as he had already attempted in Munich with the help of Deprez. At that time no one believed that this could be done remuneratively. In the meantime, a great advance had been made by the invention of the transformer. He proposed to transmit power from Lauffen to Frankfort-on-Main, a distance of 110 miles, at 25,000 volts. Miller succeeded in interesting the firm of Oerlikon, with the great engineer Charles Brown, and also the A.E.G., with Dolivro-Dobrowolsky, the inventor of polyphase current, for this plan. Considerable funds were necessary. No experience as yet existed upon which to draw. And with 8 o'clock in the evening of August 28th, 1891, the hour came at which current could be sent for the first time from Lauffen to Frankfort. The Testing Commission certified that over 75 per cent. of the energy generated in Lauffen was received in Frankfort. At that time the *Times* reporter cabled his paper to the effect that this transmission was the most remarkable and important experiment in technical electricity since this power had been harnessed to the service of man.

From everywhere where large water power existed, there came delegates to study this installation. It aroused particular attention in America where they were in the midst of preparations for the Universal Exhibition at Chicago. The director of this came personally to Frankfort and announced that they proposed to transmit the energy of Niagara Falls to Chicago. Oskar von Miller pointed out to him that that would now be nothing new, and advised the construction of a high-speed electric railway between Chicago and St. Louis. Electrical engineering, he said, would be greatly advanced by the carrying out of such a plan. The idea found favour, but was not realized. The financial difficulties were too great.

After Frankfort, Oskar von Miller devoted himself with great energy to his own consulting practice. He designed and built central stations, for whole communities had to be supplied with electricity, also outside Germany; particularly in Tirol he was responsible for a number of systems. Again and again he became interested in new applications of electric current. For him it was never a luxury article. He wanted the whole people to have this natural force at their disposal to an ever-increasing degree. Hence he was finally very active in promoting the use of the current for heating and cooking.

But again and again, the utilization of the great Bavarian water powers arose before him as the great task of his life. In addition to purely technical questions there arose the economic problem of distributing the power in the most effective way. He did not want to deal with problems of the moment; and private interests also had to give way. This natural force of the land of Bavaria was to be made available to the country as a whole, according to a far-reaching plan. The State as trustee for the community was to manage this property in the common interest. It is natural that this view of his met with great opposition in those days. But his energy succeeded in overcoming this opposition. The works built according to his plan in Upper Bavaria are able to supply Germany with over 250,000 h.p. to-day.

The characteristics of his manner of work are seen by following out this development. First of all he attempted to get an approximate idea of the available water power capable of being utilized. Then he advocated a methodical development of the whole river system. He wished to avoid the selection of only the most favourable parts of it, which would have meant blocking the way to complete development. Bavaria thus became possessed of a general plan, which later served as a model for other countries. He called this plan, in order to emphasize its importance for Bavaria, *Bayernwerk* (Bavarian Power Scheme). The first suggestion of it goes back to 1911. At that time the development of the water power of the Walchensee was under consideration. Miller proposed to direct this energy to the Bavarian scheme, as being a most valuable source of power. The War then interfered with his plans. In 1918 he delivered an impressive address in support of the Bavarian scheme. The carrying out of this scheme was decided upon, as also the development of the Walchensee power. Then came the unhappy end of the War, and the revolution. People were ready to despair of getting on with the work, but Miller pointed out that it was the very moment to supply the demobilized soldiers with work which would be their only salvation. He was appointed Commissioner of State for this purpose, and was able to start at the end of 1918 on the Walchensee scheme.

During the revolution, labour conditions were as difficult as could be imagined. Then came inflation; but once again the work was not stopped, for Miller had been far-sighted enough not to put fixed prices into his contracts with firms, but to base them on a system of calculation depending on wage rates and prices of materials. On January 20th, 1924, the Walchensee works began supplying electrical energy to the Bavarian network.

Soon, however, Miller's plans began to extend far beyond Bavaria. The various German States were all considering the question of uniform supply of electrical energy over large areas. The next step was from the States to the whole *Reich*, and here again Oskar von Miller took a principal part in the debates and plans which finally led to the Reich system of electrical supply.

These comprehensive labours in the service of electrical engineering and electric supply fully occupied a great and active life, but they were overshadowed from 1903 onward by a new and mighty task which Miller set himself, and which he carried through with the greatest energy and enthusiasm, limiting for this purpose as far as possible his work in his own professional field. Oskar von Miller became the creator of the Munich Science Museum. This course was decided by an event which took place in the spring of 1903. Miller who was always willing to give his services in support of the common interests of his profession, was at that time President of the Bavarian local section of the Verein deutscher Ingenieure. He invited the Verein to hold its annual general meeting in Munich. But he also wanted to offer German engineers coming from other places to Munich a very special pleasure. There came to his mind the strong impressions received, many years previously, during his visits to the technical museums in Paris and London. When a young engineer, he was painfully impressed by the fact that no such educative institution existed in the whole of Germany, and he proposed now to create one. He went to work with great energy to carry out this plan. The museum was to demonstrate the development of science and technology. It was to exhibit, in forty great divisions, all the chief fields of technical development. He went into details, and showed how this could be done.

Even his best friends were alarmed when they heard him put forward such plans with the greatest enthusiasm. If only a small part of them could be carried out, they thought, it would be as much as one could hope for Germany. For where was the money to come from, and who was to do the work? Doubt after doubt arose. But Oskar von Miller stuck to his plan, and was able to inspire the men with the desire to help. The locomotive builder Georg Krauss, Carl von Linde, Rudolf Diesel, were among the first to give material aid. The Bavarian Government and King were won over, and work could be started. On May 5th, 1903, he first described his plans to a small circle of specially invited guests, and on June 28th, 1903, he was able to found the Society which was to be responsible for the Museum. Prince Ludwig became Honorary President; the Reich, Bavaria, the town of Munich and German industry ensured the accomplishment of the plan by large grants.

But this enthusiasm for the Museum was not limited to single classes of persons; the whole nation, with rare unanimity, was ready to make sacrifices according to its power. Foremen, workmen, and apprentices gave their services free, so that on Saturday afternoons and Sundays numerous voluntary workers were busy in the Museum building. Just as once the citizens of German towns gave proof of their civic pride by wholehearted co-operation in building the great cathedrals and town halls, so now did German technicians and industrial workers create, on their own account, this unique temple of fame dedicated to technical and scientific progress. Not only large sums, but above all vast quantities of valuable materials, and important parts of the internal structure were sent from all parts of Germany carriage free to Munich.

On November 21st, 1906, the provisional collection in the old National Museum in the Maximilianstrasse astonished all visitors. But at the same time Miller set to work to carry out his scheme of giving the Museum a worthy house of its own. This was to be opened in 1915. Then came the War, with revolution and collapse; enormous depreciation of currency values took place, and it seemed as if forces too strong for the individual man were to prevent the execution of the plan. Even strong characters began to despair about carrying out this great cultural development in our impoverished country. Oskar von Miller's view was: 'Now more than ever.' If anything could save us, and prepare the way for our recovery, it would be intensive scientific work with a technical aim. Now, he thought, the Museum was confronted with its greatest task. When inflation turned the millions into fractions of pence, when all the money so joyfully given melted away, even his best friends advised him, if not to give up the plan, at least to pursue it, but slowly. Miller took the opposite view. He made at that time the strongest impression on the governing body by exclaiming: 'Germany has 30,000 locomotives; we need only the value of a single one of them to carry the work to a point at which it will be of great public value.' Everyone present at that meeting knew that the man behind this work could get over the hill.

Here was an example of the greatness to which a man may attain who has clearly recognized that a work is not accomplished simply by the conception of a brilliant idea, but that a sense of duty and unremitting daily attention to detail are necessary if great things are to be done. Only a few know how Oskar von Miller laboured day by day and year after year in the unpaid service of the Museum, and so in the service of the community. He sacrificed everything to the idea of making for the German nation a centre of scientific and technical progress. When the great Museum building was opened on May 7th, 1925, his seventieth birthday, he regarded the work as only half finished. A building for study must be added, with a library, meeting halls, rooms for research workers; that was his desire. Here again he succeeded, in spite of the hardest of times, in getting the means to carry out his plans. The study building was opened on May 7th, 1932.

To-day, the vast work created by him stands before us as a testimony, admired by all the world, to German cultural work. Millions of visitors receive the impression of the achievements of great men of science and engineers. H. Randall, a young American professor of philosophy, came some years ago to the Museum from Italy, where he had been on a study tour with his pupils; he wrote concerning the Museum in his book *The Transformation of Our Culture*:

'The German Museum may have been started as a collection for the technical expert; but the young students who visit it cannot help reflecting on the whole civilization it represents. Like other institutions of similar origin, it might have been content to bring together a few relics from the outgrown phases of industrialism, mingled with models of recent achievements. But so carefully have the exhibits been ordered, and so completely have they been gathered, that one finds instead the whole panorama of man's advancing conquest of nature. Perhaps as yet only in Germany could the work have been carried through with such a historical sense for the changing stages of industrial growth. . . . No longer can the machine and science build a new world without men marking the process. Such a historical sense, nowhere more vividly illustrated than in the German Museum, means that we shall no longer be swept along blindly. We shall at least see whither we are being led, and, perhaps, we shall be able to avoid the worst obstacles in the path.'

The fundamental idea followed by Miller in all his work for the Museum was to create for all circles of the German nation an educative institution from which everyone according to his powers may receive whatever stimulus will help him along. But in addition he wished, more especially by continued reference to the men whose achievements are there displayed, to awaken that enthusiasm which, as Goethe once said, is the most valuable thing which human history can convey to us.

Again and again Oskar von Miller found time to work in other fields, to advance science and technology. A characteristic of his was his power to absorb new impressions, to make them part of himself. He loved up to the last to learn something new, to be gripped by new ideas. Travelling was for him a great stimulus and recreation. His remarkable vitality enabled him at a great age to make journeys to Mexico, the Far East, and India, and no hardships were too great to ensure his seeing all that the journey had to offer.

This same power to absorb and to inspire enthusiasm, which he exhibited on his travels, was displayed also in connection with new fields of technical work. When young he had performed some remarkable feats in sport. At a time when no one had much faith in the future of the motor car, he made journeys in it and pointed to the great development to come; and when aviation came into being, he was an enthusiastic supporter of Count Zeppelin and also of the aeroplane. As a result of his suggestion, those taking part in the annual general meeting of the V.D.I. were afforded an opportunity to make flights. He allowed Professor Hugo Junkers, whose great technical eminence he recognized unreservedly, to make him President of the Transeuropa-Union and reported to the general meeting of the V.D.I. at Hanover on problems of air transport. He there pointed out the great contributions made by Germans to aviation, mentioned the great French pioneers, and said of Zeppelin that he had given mankind the courage and confidence to conquer the air. He then recalled Otto Lilienthal, who taught mankind to make wings, and called Lilienthal's first glider, preserved in the Munich Science Museum, one of the latter's greatest treasures. He looked far into the future. He believed that all the facts he was able to state in 1924 were only the modest beginnings, and that in a few years things would have gone far ahead of them. Here again, as we know, he was right.

His infectious German idealism opened all hearts to him and made him many friends. His strength lay in the fact that he looked at problems in an unprejudiced, common-sense way, and went straight ahead with an unerring instinct for the right thing to do at the moment. He was no man of learning, attempting to shape things from his writing table; he could and would only work when in contact with active life. He rejoiced in a full life, in cheerful company, in exchange of ideas; and what a talent he had for festive occasions! Honours and distinctions were showered upon the *doyen* of German engineers, and creator of the great centres where the history of science and technology were studied.

As in the home of his childhood, so in later years he looked upon the family as the centre of his being. He and his wife Marie, *née* Seitz, were loyal companions for nearly fifty years. Three sons and two daughters were the offspring of this marriage. He rejoiced in a number of grandchildren.

He suffered much pain. The infirmities of age overtook him. Severe heart trouble was the last phase. For the first time he felt tired, and he therefore believed himself called upon to retire from his office as Director of the Museum, a position in which he had been active for over thirty years. And then came the death of his wife, a few months before their golden wedding. The tirelessly active man began to long for rest, and on April 9th, 1934, fate gave him his desire.

Oskar von Miller was carried to his grave in the Neuhauser cemetery from the Hall of Honour of the Museum on April 12th, on a wonderful day in spring. Once more men who revered him spoke in his honour, from representatives of the President and Government downwards. They celebrated his services to Germany, for he had followed his father's example in always putting the interests of a united Germany before those of his home country. He was devoted with all his heart to the German people, the German Fatherland. Praise was given to the great engineer, to the eminent organizer, but above all, to the kindly man who had been to so many a true friend and helper.

Many millions of persons have visited the great museum he created, and have had their admiration for the great achievements of humanity aroused. Countless millions will in the future go in and out of the collections and the library, and when they ask who it was who brought all this into being, the answer will be: Oskar von Miller and the many thousands who were carried away by his enthusiasm and took part in the work of creation.

SOURCES

This list of books does not attempt to be exhaustive, but only to point the way to wider reading. Many of the books listed provide references to further literature.

Abbreviations: *Abh. u. Ber.* = Deutsches Museum, Abhandlungen und Berichte. *B.G.T.* = Beiträge zur Geschichte der Technik und Industrie. *Z.V.D.I.* = Zeitschrift des Vereines deutscher Ingenieure.

GENERAL

Beck, L., *Geschichte des Eisens*. 5 vols. Braunschweig, 1884–1903.

Beck, Th., *Beiträge zur Geschichte des Maschinenbaues*. 2nd ed. Berlin, 1900.

Beiträge zur Geschichte der Technik und Industrie. *Jahrbuch des Vereins deutscher Ingenieure*, Vol. 1 (1909). Vol. 22 (1933) onwards: Technikgeschichte.

Briggs, M. S., *The Architect in History*. Oxford, 1928.

Daub, H., *Die Vergangenheit des Hochbaues*. Vienna, Stuttgart, Leipzig, 1911.

Deutsches Museum, *Abhandlungen und Berichte*. From Vol. 1 (1929) to end of 1938, 58 numbers have been published.

Goddard, D., *Eminent Engineers*. New York, 1906.

Jähns, M., *Handbuch einer Geschichte des Kriegswesens von der Urzeit bis zur Renaissance*. Technischer Theil. Leipzig, 1880.

Johannsen, O., *Geschichte des Eisens*, 2nd ed. Düsseldorf, 1925.

Matschoss, C., *Geschichte der Dampfmaschine*. Berlin, 1901.

Matschoss, C., *Entwicklung der Dampfmaschine*. 2 vols. Berlin, 1908.

Matschoss, C., *Männer der Technik*. Ein biographisches Handbuch. Berlin, 1925.

Rheinisch-Westfälische Wirtschaftsbiographien. Edited by the Historical Commission of the Provinzialinstitut and others. Vol. 1 (Münster, 1931) onwards.

Smiles, S., *Lives of the Engineers, with an Account of their Principal Works*. 4 vols. London, 1861–5.

GREAT ENGINEERS OF ANTIQUITY

Beck, Th., 'Herons Mechanik,' *B.G.T.* **1** (1909), pp. 84–107.

Beck, Th., 'Der altgriechische und altrömische Geschützbau nach Heron, Philon, Vitruv und Ammianus Marcellinus,' *B.G.T.*, **3** (1911), pp. 163–184.

Breasted, J. H., *The Conquest of Civilization.* New York and London, 1926.

Clarke, S., and Engelbach, R., *Ancient Egyptian Masonry. The Building Craft.* London, 1930.

Diels, H., *Antike Technik.* 3rd ed. Leipzig, 1924.

Ebhardt, B., *Die zehn Bücher der Architektur des Vitruv und ihre Herausgeber seit* 1484. Berlin, 1919.

Engelbach, R., *The Problem of the Obelisks.* London, 1922.

Erman, Ad., *Aegypten und ägyptisches Leben im Altertum.* Tübingen, 1885. Revised by H. Ranke. Tübingen, 1923.

Heiberg, E. L., *Geschichte der Mathematik und Naturwissenschaften im Altertum.* Munich, 1925.

Heronis Opera Omnia (mit Übersetzung). Edited by W. Schmidt. 5 vols. Leipzig, 1899–1914.

Merckel, R., *Ingenieurtechnik im Altertum.* Berlin, 1899.

Niemann, W. B., 'Von altägyptischer Technik,' *B.G.T.*, **20** (1930), pp. 99–103.

Reil, Th., *Beiträge zur Kenntnis des Gewerbes im hellenistischen Aegypten.* Leipzig, 1913.

Sackur, W., *Vitruv und die Poliorketiker.* Berlin, 1925.

FROM THE FALL OF THE ROMAN EMPIRE TO THE EIGHTEENTH CENTURY

Agricola, Georg, *De Re Metallica.* Basel, 1556. New edition, Berlin, 1928.

Cabanes, Ch., *Denys Papin, inventeur et philosophe cosmopolite.* Paris, 1935.

Darmstädter, E., *Georg Agricola. Leben und Werk,* 1494–1555. Munich, 1926.

Dehio, G., *Das Strassburger Münster.* Munich, 1922. (For Erwin von Steinbach.)

Dickinson, H. W. and Jenkins, R., *James Watt and the Steam Engine.* Oxford, 1927.

Dickinson, H. W., 'Thomas Newcomen und seine Dampfmaschine,' *B.G.T.*, **19** (1929), pp. 139–43.

Domel, G., *Gutenberg, die Erfindung des Typengusses und seine Frühdrucke.* Cologne, 1919.

Dyck, W. v., *Georg Reichenbach* (Deutsches Museum. Lebensbeschreibungen und Urkunden). Munich, 1912.

For A. F. W. Holtzhausen: Matschoss, C., 'Die Einführung der Dampfmaschine in Deutschland,' *Z.V.D.I.*, **49** (1905), pp. 901–7, 1002–6; **51** (1907), pp. 1673–6.

Gerland, E., *Leibnizens und Huygens' Briefwechsel mit Papin.* Berlin, 1881. Supplementary volume, Stuttgart, 1903.

Guericke, Otto von, *Experimenta nova (ut vocantur) Magdeburgica de vacuo spatio.* Amsterdam, 1672. The first German edition will appear shortly in V.D.I. Verlag, Berlin.

Haebler, R., *Die Erfindung der Druckkunst und ihre erste Ausbreitung in den Ländern Europas.* Mainz, 1930.

Hart, J. B., *The Mechanical Investigations of Leonardo da Vinci.* London, 1925.

Hoffman, F. W., *Otto v. Guericke.* Magdeburg, 1874.

Hoffmann, R., *Dr. Georg Agricola. Ein Gelehrtenleben aus dem Zeitaltar der Reformation.* Gotha, 1905.

Jenkins, R., 'Savery, Newcomen, and the Early History of the Steam Engine,' *Transactions of the Newcomen Society*, **3** (1922–3), pp. 96–118; **4** (1923–4), pp. 113–30.

Kletzl, O., *Titel und Namen von Baumeistern deutscher Gotik* (*Schriften der Deutschen Akademie*, No. 26). Munich, 1935.

Kohler, E., *Georg v. Reichenbach. Das Leben eines deutschen Erfinders.* Munich, 1933.

Lieb, J. W., 'Leonardo da Vinci, Natural Philosopher and Engineer,' *Journal of the Franklin Institute.* Philadelphia, 1921, pp. 47–68, 767–806.

Matschoss, C., 'Hochleistung und Weltgeltung deutscher Technik vor dem Dreissigjährigen Kriege,' *Deutsche Rundschau*, **240** (1934), pp. 135–42.

Matschoss, C., 'Franz Dinnendahl, ein hundertjähriges Dampfmaschinen-Jubiläum,' *Z.V.D.I.*, **47** (1903), pp. 585–92.

Matschoss, C., 'Franz Dinnendahl,' *Rhein.-Westf. Wirtschaftsbiogr.*, Vol. 1 (1932), pp. 357–72.

Matschoss, C., 'James Watt,' *Z.V.D.I.*, **80** (1936), pp. 73–4.

(Maximilian I), *Der Weiss-Kunig.* 1514. 2 vols. Printed in Vienna, 1775.

Müller-Walde, P., *Leonardo da Vinci.* Munich, 1889.

Muirhead, J. P., *The Life of James Watt. With Selections from his Correspondence.* London, 1858.

Pohl, R. W., 'Otto v. Guericke als Physiker,' *Abh. u. Ber.*, **8** (1936), No. 4.

Rathgen, B., *Das Geschütz im Mittelalter*. Quellenkritische Untersuchungen. Berlin, 1928.

Ruppel, A., 'Gutenberg.' In *Die grossen Deutschen*. Vol. 1, pp. 284–97. Berlin, 1935.

Schimank, H., 'Otto von Guericke. Leben und Werk eines Ingenieurs,' *B.G.T.*, **19** (1929), pp. 13–30.

Schimank, H., 'Otto von Guericke, Bürgermeister von Magdeburg.' A German statesman, thinker, and investigator. From the series *Magdeburgs Kultur- und Wirtschaftsleben*, Vol. 6. Magdeburg, 1936.

Schimank, H., 'Otto von Guericke,' *Z.V.D.I.*, **80** (1936), pp. 557–62.

Seidlitz, W. von, *Leonardo da Vinci. Der Wendepunkt der Renaissance*. Vienna, 1935.

GREAT MODERN ENGINEERS

Benz, Carl, *Lebensfahrt eines deutschen Erfinders*. Leipzig, 1936.

Berdrow, W., *Alfred Krupp*. 2 vols. Berlin, 1926.

Berdrow, W., *Alfred Krupps Briefe, 1826–1887*. Berlin, 1928.

Berdrow, W., *Alfred Krupp und sein Geschlecht*. Berlin, 1937.

Bessemer, Henry, *An Autobiography*. London, 1905.

Bryan, G. S., *Edison. Der Mann und sein Werk*. Leipzig, 1937.

Burnie, R. W., *Memoir and Letters of Sidney Gilchrist Thomas*. London, 1891.

Church, W. C., *The Life of John Ericsson*. 2 vols. London, 1891.

Colburn, L., *Locomotive Engineering*. Glasgow, 1864–6. Pp. 9–104.

Dickinson, H. W., *Robert Fulton, Engineer and Artist*. London, 1913.

Dickinson, H. W., and Titley, A., *Richard Trevithick, the Engineer and the Man*. Cambridge, 1934.

Diesel, E., *Diesel. Der Mensch—Das Werk—Das Schicksal*. Hamburg, 1937.

Diesel, Rudolf, *Die Entstehung des Dieselmotors*. Berlin, 1913.

Dyer, F. L., Martin, T. C., and Meadowcroft, W. H., *Edison, His Life and Inventions*. New York, 1929.

'Engineering Achievements of George Westinghouse,' *Mechanical Engineering*, **59** (1937), pp. 263–79; **60**, pp. 156–8, 159–62.

Ericsson, J., *Contributions of the Centennial Exhibition*. New York, 1876.

Ewing, Sir A., *An Engineer's Outlook*. London, 1933. Pp. 195–229.

Fodor, St. v., *Edison. Der Lebensweg eines Erfinders*. Berlin, 1927.

Kraft, E. A., 'Ch. A. Parsons†,' *Z.V.D.I.*, **75** (1931), pp. 409–11.

Langen, A., 'Die Erfindung des Verbrennungsmotors,' *Z.V.D.I.*, **80** (1936), pp. 1258–88.

Linde, Carl v., *Aus meinem Leben und von meiner Arbeit: Aufzeichnungen für meine Kinder und meine Mitarbeiter*. Munich, 1916.

Linde, Carl v., 'zum 90 Geburtstag.' *Abh. u. Ber.*, **4** (1932), No. 3.

Lindwall, G., *Ingeniören vid Beach Street. John Ericssons liv i ny belysning*. Stockholm, 1937.

Matschoss, C., 'Carl v. Linde,' *Z.V.D.I.*, **78** (1934), pp. 1417–20.

Matschoss, C., *Geschichte der Gasmotorenfabrik Deutz*. Berlin, 1921.

Matschoss, C., 'Krupp, 1812–1912,' *Z.V.D.I.*, **56** (1912), pp. 1261–81.

Matschoss, C., *Werner v. Siemens*. Ein kurzgefasstes Lebensbild nebst einer Auswahl seiner Briefe. 2 vols. Berlin, 1916.

Matschoss, C., 'Oskar v. Miller†,' *Z.V.D.I.*, **78** (1934), pp. 483–5.

Matschoss, C., 'Gottlieb Daimler in der Geschichte des Kraftwagens,' *Abh. u. Ber.*, **6** (1934), No. 1.

Miller, W. v., *Oskar v. Miller*. Nach eigenen Aufzeichnungen, Reden und Briefen. Munich, 1932.

Nägel, A., 'Die Bedeutung Ottos und Langens für die Entwicklung des Verbrennungsmotors,' *Z.V.D.I.*, **75** (1931), pp. 827–9; **80** (1936), p. 1289.

Nasmyth, James, *An Autobiography*. Edited by S. Smiles. London, 1883.

N. A. Otto and Eugen Langen zum Gedächtnis. Privately printed, Cologne, 1933.

Parsons, W. B., *Robert Fulton and the Submarine*. New York, 1922.

Pole, W., *The Life of Robert Stephenson*. 2 vols. London, 1864

Prout, H. G., *A Life of George Westinghouse*. New York, 1921.

Richardson, A., *The Evolution of the Parsons Steam Turbine*. London, 1911.

Scientific Papers and Addresses of the Hon. Sir Charles A. Parsons, with a Memoir by Lord Rayleigh. Cambridge, 1934.

Siemens, Werner von, *Lebenserinnerungen*. Berlin, 1889.

Simonds, W. A., *Edison, his Life, his Work, his Genius*. New York, 1934.

Slaby, A., 'J. Ericssohn und G. A. Hirn Gedächtnisrede,' *Verh. d. Vereins z. Beforderung d. Gewerbefleisses*, **69** (1890), pp. 229–44.

Smiles, S., *Lives of the Engineers*. Vol. III. *George and Robert Stephenson*. London, 1868.

Trevithick, F., *Life of Richard Trevithick, with an Account of his Inventions*. 2 vols. London, 1872.

Wilhelm Maybach, *Z.V.D.I.*, **74** (1930), pp. 457–8.

Zenneck, J., 'Werner v. Siemens und die Gründung der Phys.-Techn. Reichsanstalt,' *Abh. u. Ber.*, **3** (1931), No. 1.

Zenneck, J., 'Oskar v. Miller†,' *Abh. u. Ber.*, **6** (1934), No. 2.

INDEX

375

★ Some BELL Science Books

THE MECHANISM OF NATURE
Prof. E. N. da C. Andrade, D SC, F R S   *Revised Edition*

'It is about as right as it is possible to be for the class of readers it is intended to interest: those who hate text-books but want to be informed about physics with the greatest precision.' *The Listener*
5th Printing Illustrated **6s net**

THE NEW CHEMISTRY
Prof. E. N. da C. Andrade, D SC, F R S

A short explanation of the recent work on the transmutation of matter. 'A first-rate exposition.' *Sunday Times*   Illustrated **3s 6d net**

HEARING IN MAN AND ANIMALS
R. T. Beatty, M A, D SC

'This account of the development and structure of the hearing organs of the various types of living beings, from the fishes, where they may be said to begin among the vertebrates, upward to man, is singularly complete as a gathering up of our rather scattered knowledge of the subject. What is almost better, it is remarkably good scientific reading.' *Manchester Guardian*
Illustrated **5s net**

THE AIR AND ITS MYSTERIES
C. M. Botley, F R MET SOC

'A very clear and simple explanation of the work and importance of the modern science of meteorology, written in an easy and attractive style.' *Country Life*
'Packed with interest, scientifically accurate, and up-to-date.' *Belfast News Letter*   Illustrated **8s 6d net**

THE UNIVERSE OF LIGHT
Sir William Bragg, O M, P R S

'As a popular exponent of physical science, Sir William Bragg is unrivalled . . . he has again laid under obligation the great lay public.' *The Times* Illustrated
3rd Printing **12s 6d net**

ELECTRICITY
Prof. W. L. Bragg, D SC, F R S

'An admirable and lucidly arranged introduction to the study of electricity.' *Scotsman*
Illustrated **8s 6d net**

THE NEW CONCEPTIONS OF MATTER
Prof. C. G. Darwin, M A, F R S

'It is by far and away the best account of wave mechanics for non-specialists that I have ever read.' PROFESSOR J. B. S. HALDANE
2nd Printing **10s 6d net**

EVERYDAY SCIENCE
A. W. Haslett

A very readable book. . . The author's shrewd and thoughtful comments on the various aspects and implications of modern science as they affect our everyday life, make the book one of exceptional interest.' *Times Literary Supplement*   **7s 6d net**

UNSOLVED PROBLEMS OF SCIENCE
A. W. Haslett

'Learned and illuminating . . . this book is more thrilling than any dozen dramas of detection. It discusses the most abstruse matters in language which any non-scientific person can understand.' *Morning Post*
4th Printing **7s 6d net**